C000129361

Terms and conditions

IMPORTANT – PERMITTED USE AND WARNINGS – READ CAREFULLY BEFORE USING

Copyright in the software contained in this CD-ROM and in its accompanying material belongs to Scholastic Limited. All rights reserved. © 2014 Scholastic Ltd.

Save for these purposes, or as expressly authorised in the accompanying materials, the software may not be copied, reproduced, used, sold, licensed, transferred, exchanged, hired, or exported in whole or in part or in any manner or form without the prior written consent of Scholastic Ltd. Any such unauthorised use or activities are prohibited and may give rise to civil liabilities and criminal prosecutions.

The material contained on this CD-ROM may only be used in the context for which it was intended in *100 Maths Lessons for the 2014 Curriculum*, and is for use only by the purchaser or purchasing institution that has purchased the book and CD-ROM. Permission to download images is given for purchasers only and not for users from any lending service. Any further use of the material contravenes Scholastic Ltd's copyright and that of other rights holders.

This CD-ROM has been tested for viruses at all stages of its production. However, we recommend that you run virus-checking software on your computer systems at all times. Scholastic Ltd cannot accept any responsibility for any loss, disruption or damage to your data or your computer system that may occur as a result of using either the CD-ROM or the data held on it.

IF YOU ACCEPT THE ABOVE CONDITIONS YOU MAY PROCEED TO USE THE CD-ROM.

Recommended system requirements:

- Windows: XP (Service Pack 3), Vista (Service Pack 2), Windows 7 or Windows 8 with 2.33GHz processor
- Mac: OS 10.6 to 10.8 with Intel Core™ Duo processor
- 1GB RAM (recommended)
- 1024 x 768 Screen resolution
- CD-ROM drive (24x speed recommended)
- 16-bit sound card
- Adobe Reader (version 9 recommended for Mac users)
- Broadband internet connections (for installation and updates)

For all technical support queries, please phone Scholastic Customer Services on 0845 6039091.

Book End, Range Road, Witney, Oxfordshire, OX29 0YD
www.scholastic.co.uk

© 2014, Scholastic Ltd

1 2 3 4 5 6 7 8 9   4 5 6 7 8 9 0 1 2 3

British Library Cataloguing-in-Publication Data
A catalogue record for this book is available from the
British Library.

ISBN 978-1407-12774-3
Printed by Bell & Bain Ltd, Glasgow

Due to the nature of the web we cannot guarantee the
content or links of any site mentioned. We strongly
recommend that teachers check websites before using
them in the classroom.

Extracts from *The National Curriculum in Maths, Maths
Programme of Study* © Crown Copyright. Reproduced
under the terms of the Open Government Licence
(OGL). http://www.nationalarchives.gov.uk/doc/open-
government-licence/open-government-licence.htm

Author
Hilary Koll and Steve Mills

Series Editor
Ann Montague-Smith

Editorial team
Emily Jefferson, Jenny Wilcox, Margaret Eaton
and Mary Nathan

Cover Design
Andrea Lewis

Design Team
Sarah Garbett, Shelley Best and Andrea Lewis

CD-ROM development
Hannah Barnett, Phil Crothers, MWA Technologies
Private Ltd

Typesetting and illustrations
Ricky Capanni, International Book Management

Contents

Introduction

About the series

The *100 Maths Lessons* series is designed to meet the requirements of the 2014 National Curriculum, Mathematics Programme of Study. There are six books in the series for Years 1–6, and each book contains lesson plans, resources and ideas matched to the new curriculum. These six titles – along with the accompanying *100 Maths Planning Guide* – have been carefully structured to ensure that a progressive and appropriate school curriculum can be planned and taught throughout the primary years.

About the 2014 Curriculum

The curriculum documentation for Mathematics provides a yearly programme for Years 1 to 6 (ages 5 to 11).

The new curriculum goes further than the previous version with times tables to 12 x 12 by Year 4, an early introduction to long division and an increasingly complex understanding of fractions and decimals. The new curriculum also has a strong focus on varied and frequent practice of the fundamentals of maths – mastery of number facts and times tables should be developed throughout the primary phase.

There is a renewed emphasis on reasoning mathematically and solving problems with particular emphasis on multi-step problems and problems in the context of measurement, money and time. The main coverage of the use and application of mathematics however can be found in the aims of the curriculum:

> *The National Curriculum for Mathematics aims to ensure that all pupils:*
> - *become fluent in the fundamentals of mathematics, including through varied and frequent practice with increasingly complex problems over time, so that pupils have conceptual understanding and are able to recall and apply their knowledge rapidly and accurately to problems*
> - *reason mathematically by following a line of enquiry, conjecturing relationships and generalisations, and developing an argument, justification or proof using mathematical language*
> - *can solve problems by applying their mathematics to a variety of routine and non-routine problems with increasing sophistication, including breaking down problems into a series of simpler steps and persevering in seeking solutions.*

Terminology

The curriculum terminology has changed; the main terms used are:

- **Domains:** The main areas of mathematical study, such as Number and Geometry.
- **Topics:** These are identified in each weekly planning grid and drill the domains down into 'Place value', 'Addition and subtraction' and so on.
- **Curriculum objectives:** These are the statutory programme of study statements or objectives.
- **Appendix:** Any reference to an appendix refers to the Mathematics Apendix 1 'Examples of formal written methods for addition, subtraction, multiplication and division.'

■ SCHOLASTIC

About the book

This book is divided by term and week with a summary heading giving an indication of the week's work. Each week follows the same structure:

Weekly overview

At the start of each week you will find a summary of what is covered, which includes:

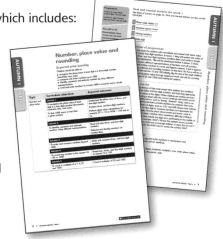

- **Expected prior learning:** What the children are expected to know before starting the work in the chapter.
- **Weekly planning grid:** A lesson-by-lesson breakdown of the coverage of each week – by 'topic', 'curriculum objectives' and 'expected outcomes'.
- **Oral and mental starters:** Suggested activities that might be used from the bank of starters that follow each half-term's lessons.
- **Overview of progression:** A brief explanation of the expected progress that children should make through each week's work.
- **Watch out for:** Possible mathematical misconceptions with ideas for addressing them.
- **Creative context:** How the week's work could link to other 2014 curriculum areas.
- **Vocabulary:** Key vocabulary to introduce or consolidate. (Words in bold also appear in the glossary, see CD-ROM notes on page 7.)
- **Preparation/You will need:** A full list of resources required from book and CD, as well as any general class resources requiring preparation. (A full equipment list is given on page 255.)
- **Further practice:** Ideas for consolidating learning using additional resources or practical activities.

Lessons

Each half term contains six weeks' work. Each week contains five lessons. Each lesson includes the following:

- **Curriculum objectives:** A list of the relevant objectives from the Programme of Study.
- **Success criteria:** Expected outcomes for the lesson written as 'can do' statements.
- **You will need:** List of required resources.
- **Whole-class work:** Ideas for working together as a class.
- **Group/Paired/Independent work:** Teaching notes for paired, groups or independent work.
- **Differentiation:** Ideas to support children who are not sufficiently fluent with concepts or to challenge children to apply their understanding (see 2014 National Curriculum aims for further information on the approach to differentiation).
- **Progress check:** 'Mini-plenaries' to enable teachers to check progress throughout the lesson.
- **Review:** Opportunity to reflect on children's learning, and address any misconceptions.

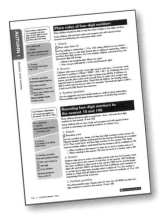

Assess and review

At the end of each half term are activities designed to assess children's understanding or mastery of key curriculum objectives. These can be conducted during the half-term's lessons or at the end, in an 'assess and review week'.

There are four curriculum objectives covered in each half–term. Each section includes ideas to:

- Check progress using appropriate starter activities.
- Assess children's learning using a mix of activities, problems and puzzles.
- Provide further practice activities to consolidate their understanding.

Oral and mental starter activities

In each half term a bank of oral and mental starters is provided. These can be used flexibly to address particular requirements, though suggestions are made within each weekly overview as to which starters might be used across a week's lessons. Each starter includes modelled teacher questions to probe children's ability to recall facts, rehearse strategies or apply learning.

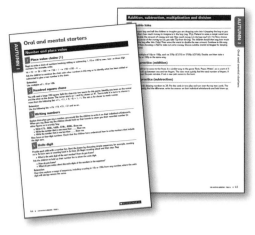

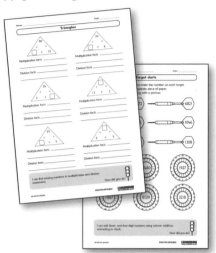

Photocopiable pages

At the end of each chapter, you will find a bank of photocopiable pages linked to the 'Assess and review' section. These sheets offer an 'I can...' statement at the bottom to allow self-assessment of pupil progress towards a particular curriculum objective. Ask the children to colour in the traffic lights next to each statement green, amber or red to reflect their confidence with the objective. There is also space for comments. Additional sheets, linked to the lessons, can be found on the CD-ROM (see page 7 for further information).

Equipment list

This provides an overview of all of the classroom resources required to teach each year's lessons. The resources are broken down by mathematics topic.

Vocabulary list

This provides a list of all key vocabulary to introduce or consolidate over the course of the year. Words appearing in bold type also appear in the glossary and can be found on the CD-ROM (see page 7 for further information).

SCHOLASTIC

About the CD-ROM

The CD-ROM contains:

- Printable versions of the photocopiable sheets from the book and additional photocopiable sheets as referenced in the lesson plans.
- Interactive activities for children to complete or to use on the whiteboard.
- Interactive teaching resources such as 'Number grids' and 'Pattern squares', designed to support whole–class teaching.
- Printable versions of the lesson plans and the oral and mental starters.
- Digital versions of the lesson plans with the relevant resources linked to them.

Getting started

- Put the CD-ROM into your CD-ROM drive.
  - For Windows users, the install wizard should autorun, if it fails to do so then navigate to your CD-ROM drive. Then follow the installation process.
  - For Mac users, copy the disk image file to your hard drive. After it has finished copying, double-click it to mount the disk image. Navigate to the mounted disk image and run the installer. After installation the disk image can be unmounted and the DMG can be deleted from the hard drive.
- To complete the installation of the program, you need to open the program and click 'Update' in the pop-up. **NB** This CD-ROM is web-enabled and the content needs to be downloaded from the internet to your hard-drive to populate the CD-ROM with the relevant resources. A web connection is only required on first use, after which you will be able to use the CD–ROM without any connection. If at any point any content is updated you will receive a pop-up message upon start–up when you are next connected to the web. You will then have the option to update the content as required.

Navigating the CD-ROM

There are two options to navigate the CD-ROM, either as a Child or as a Teacher.

Child

- Click on the 'Child' button on the first menu screen. In the second menu click on the relevant year group (please note only the books installed on the machine or network will be accessible. You can also rename year groups to match your school's naming conventions via Teacher > Settings > Rename Books area.)
- A list of interactive activities will be displayed; children need to locate the correct class or year group and click 'Go' to launch.
- There is the opportunity to print or save a PDF of the results of each activity on completion.

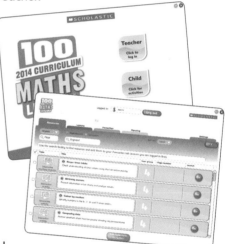

Teacher

- Click on the 'Teacher' button on the first menu screen and you will be taken to a menu showing which of the *100 Maths Lessons* titles you have purchased. From here, you can also access the credits and 'Getting started' information
- To enter the product, click 'Next' in the bottom right of the screen.
- You can then enter a password (the password is: login).
- On first use:
  - Enter as a Guest by clicking on the 'Guest' button.
  - If desired, create a profile for yourself by adding your name to the list of users. Profiles allow you to save favourites and to specify which year group(s) you wish to be able to view.
  - Go to 'Settings' to create a profile for yourself – click 'Add user' and enter your name. Then choose the year groups you wish to have access to (you can return to this screen to change this at any time). Click on 'Login' at the top of the screen to re-enter the CD-ROM with your new profile.
- On subsequent uses you can then select your name from the drop-down list.
- The 'Guest' option will always be available if you, or a colleague, prefer to use this.
- When you have set up your profile, you can then save activities or lessons in 'Favourites'.

For more information about how to use the CD-ROM, please refer to the 'Help' file which can be found in the teacher area of the CD-ROM. It is displayed as a red button with a question mark inside, on the right-hand side of the screen just underneath the 'Settings' tab.

Number, place value and rounding

Expected prior learning

Children should be able to:

- recognise the place value of each digit in a three-digit number (hundreds, tens, ones)
- compare and order numbers up to 1000
- identify, represent and estimate numbers by using different representations
- read and write numbers to at least 1000 in numerals and in words.

Topic	Curriculum objectives	Expected outcomes
Number and place value	**Lesson 1**	
	To recognise the place value of each digit in a four-digit number (thousands, hundreds, tens, and ones). To find 1000 more or less than a given number.	Understand the place value of three- and four-digit numbers. Partition three- and four-digit numbers. Perform place value calculations, for example 375 + 10 or 4836 − 100 and so on.
	Lesson 2	
	To identify, represent and estimate numbers using different representations.	Read and write three- and four-digit numbers. Estimate and identify numbers on number lines.
	Lesson 3	
	To order and compare numbers beyond 1000.	Order and compare three- and four-digit numbers.
	Lesson 4	
	To round any number to the nearest 10, 100 or 1000.	Round two-, three- and four-digit numbers to nearest 10 or 100.
	Lesson 5	
	To count in multiples of 6, 7, 9, 25 and 1000.	Count in multiples of 25 and 1000.

See bank of starters on page 44.

Preparation

Lesson 2: copy 'Blank number lines', one per child

Lesson 4: copy 'Oceans, seas and rivers', one per child

You will need

Photocopiable sheet

'Oceans, seas and rivers'

General resources

'Blank number lines'; interactive teaching resource 'Number line'; interactive activity 'Four-digit numbers'

Equipment

Individual whiteboards; place value arrow cards; 0–9 number cards (or a dice); coloured pencils

Further practice

Photocopiable sheets

'Partition party'

Oral and mental starters for week 1

See bank of starters on page 44. Oral and mental starters are also on the CD-ROM.

1 Place value chains (1)

2 Hundred square chase

3 Writing numbers

4 Units digit

Overview of progression

During this week the children will consolidate and extend their place value ideas to include four-digit numbers. In lesson 1 they will explore the value of digits in three- and four-digit numbers, partition them and perform simple place value calculations. This will be developed further in lesson 2 where they will explore different representations of numbers and will practise reading and writing numbers in words and figures. Lessons 3 and 4 explore comparing, ordering and rounding numbers. In this term, the focus will be on rounding to the nearest 10 and 100 initially. By the end of the week children will be exploring place value through sequences work and will be counting on in multiples of 25 and 1000 and looking for pattern.

Watch out for

In the early lessons of this week ensure that children are confident with the place value of three-digit numbers and that they appreciate the different values of the digits. When children are writing numbers in words, display a sheet with the correct spellings and watch out for common spelling errors, such as 'fourty', 'fiveteen', 'ninty', and so on. When comparing numbers, provide numbers to compare that have different numbers of digits, such as 3101 and 899. Ensure that children don't just use the first digit to compare numbers, but appreciate the value of the digits. Provide place value boards and arrow cards to exemplify these ideas. Children often experience difficulty writing in words numbers that include the digit zero, particularly in the middle of the number (for example, 6047). Where this mistake occurs, provide place value arrow cards and encourage children to place the 40 and 7 cards correctly onto the 6000 card to create the number 6047.

Creative context

Encourage children to say and write numbers in newspapers and magazines in words, using correct spellings.

Vocabulary

compare, digit, estimate, figure, hundreds, multiples, ones, order, **place value**, rounding, sequences, tens, thousands, units

Curriculum objectives

● To recognise the place value of each digit in a four-digit number (thousands, hundreds, tens, and ones).
● To find 1000 more or less than a given number.

Success criteria

● I can give the value of each digit in a four-digit number and can partition the number.
● I can find 1000 more or less than a number.

You will need

Equipment

Place value arrow cards (four-digit numbers); 0–9 number cards (or a dice each); coloured pencils

Differentiation

Less confident learners

Provide these children with their own set of place value arrow cards.

More confident learners

Encourage children to create and partition five-digit numbers if appropriate.

Lesson 1

Oral and mental starter 1

Main teaching activities

Whole-class work: Explain that today's lesson will involve saying what each digit in a number stands for and partitioning them. Write a three-digit number on the board (say, 674) and write H T U above the digits. Ask a range of questions: *What do these letters stand for? Which digit is the tens digit? What is the digit 6 worth?* Invite a child to come to the front and write the number in partitioned form – for example, 674 = 600 + 70 + 4. Demonstrate this with place value arrow cards. Now write the digit 1 in front of the three-digit number (1674). Ask: *What is the value of the digit 1?* Discuss that the digit represents thousands and write Th above the digit 1. Explain that you want to add 1000 to this number and ask children to talk in pairs about what the answer would look like (2674). Draw attention to the fact that, when adding a thousand here, the hundreds, tens and units digits remain unchanged. Invite a child to partition this four-digit number: 2674 = 2000 + 600 + 70 + 4. Again, demonstrate using place value arrow cards.

Create a chain of four-digit numbers on the board that involve adding or subtracting 1000 or 2000, in the same way as the activity. For example:

4378 $\boxed{+1000}$ → 5378 $\boxed{-2000}$ → 3378 $\boxed{-1000}$ → 2378 $\boxed{+2000}$ →

As children complete each step, partition the numbers on the board to reinforce the place value ideas.

Independent work: Provide each child with a dice or a set of 0–9 number cards. Ask them to roll the dice (or pick cards) to create four-digit numbers. Invite them to write each number down and partition it. They should do this eight times. When they have done this, they should use coloured pencils to underline the hundreds digit of each number in one colour and the thousands digit in another colour. If time, ask them to write several four-digit numbers with a given digit in a given column. For example: *Write five numbers that have the tens digit 6... the hundreds digit 8...* (and so on).

Progress check: Ask: *Which digit has the largest value in the number 1234?* Watch out for children who incorrectly say 4 as this can indicate that they have failed to grasp how position affects the values of the digits. Invite them to partition the number and ask the question again.

Review

Play a 'space invader' game. Write a four-digit number on the board and ask children to shoot down each digit by subtracting each to 0. For example, for 5738, to shoot down the digit 7 you subtract 700, to shoot the digit 5 you would subtract 5000 and so on. Ask: *What do you need to subtract to remove the digit 3?* After several games, change the rules and ask the children to change the digits by adding to turn the number into 9999 – for example, for 5738, you add 4000, 200, 60 and 1.

Curriculum objectives
- To identify, represent and estimate numbers using different representations.

Success criteria
- I can read and write three- and four-digit numbers.
- I can identify, position and estimate numbers on number lines.

You will need
General resources
'Blank number lines'; interactive teaching resource 'Number line'

Equipment
Individual whiteboard

Differentiation
Less confident learners
Focus initially on three-digit numbers, marking 0 and 1000 at the ends of the line.

More confident learners
Write adjacent four-digit multiples of 100 at the ends of the line – for example, 6400 and 6500.

Lesson 2
Oral and mental starter 2

Main teaching activities
Whole-class work: Write three- and four-digit numbers on the board, such as 5647, 456, 1448, 573, 1569. Point to each in turn and ask: *Is this less than 1000?* Children do 'thumbs up' or 'thumbs down' to show if each is or not. They should say the names of three-digit numbers and write them in words on their whiteboards. Now draw a number line with 0 at the left-hand end and 1000 at the right. Ask the children where on the line each three-digit number goes. *How can you be sure?* Split the line into equal parts to help them estimate and check.

Next explore four-digit numbers. *Which are between 1000 and 2000? How do you know?* (They will have the thousands digit 1.) Display interactive teaching resource 'Number line' and, using the tools, mark a point and ask children to estimate the number. Continue for other numbers on the line, inviting children to say and write the names of each and to mark it on a number line.

Independent work: Provide each child with photocopiable page 'Blank number lines' from the CD-ROM. Ask them to write adjacent multiples of 1000 at each end of the number line (say, 4000 on the left and 5000 on the right). They then write three four-digit numbers that lie between the two multiples, write the numbers in words and mark their approximate position on the line.

Progress check: Ask: *Where will 4647 go on this number line? How can you be sure?*

Review
Take feedback on the number lines work. Children can copy one of their lines onto the board and mark a point for the others to estimate. If time, use the interactive teaching resource 'Number line' on the CD-ROM to explore other numbers that lie between multiples of 1000.

Curriculum objectives
- To order and compare numbers beyond 1000.

Success criteria
- I can order and compare three- and four-digit numbers.

You will need
General resources
Interactive activity 'Four-digit numbers'

Equipment
0–9 number cards

Differentiation
Less confident learners
Ask pairs of children to choose three cards to make three-digit numbers, and then order them.

More confident learners
Ask pairs to choose five cards to make five-digit numbers, and then order them.

Lesson 3
Oral and mental starter 3

Main teaching activities
Whole-class work: Open the interactive activity 'Four-digit numbers' on the CD-ROM. Ask the children to read the numbers and drag them into the correct order. Discuss that the thousands digit is the most significant and is the one they should compare first. Provide further sets of numbers to order on the board, including a mix of three- and four-digit numbers.

Paired work: Give each pair a set of 0–9 number cards. Each child chooses four cards and writes down the four-digit numbers that they can make. Then they each write their numbers in order of size, explaining their reasoning to their partner. Ask the children to say the highest/lowest number they can make, and explain how they know.

Progress check: During the paired work, ask children to hold up what they have done so far. *How did you decide which was the largest/smallest number? Which digits did you compare first?*

Review
Play a secret number game. Give clues as to where in a list of numbers the secret number would come and ask children to make guesses. For example: *It is larger than 2885 and smaller than 3506. It has two digits that are 6.* Ask children to work out which digits cannot be the digit 6, and continue to provide sufficient clues to identify the number, such as: *Its hundreds digit is 7 more than its thousands digit.* (2966)

Curriculum objectives
• To round any number to the nearest 10 or 100.

Success criteria
• I can round two-, three- and four-digit numbers to the nearest 10 or 100.

You will need
Photocopiable sheets
'Oceans, seas and rivers'

Differentiation
Less confident learners
Let these children focus on rounding only to the nearest 10m or 10km.

More confident learners
Ask children to round to the nearest 1000 as well.

Lesson 4   Oral and mental starter 3

Main teaching activities

Whole-class work: Draw several number lines with multiples of 10 evenly spaced along the line, for example:

50	60	70	80	90

280	290	300	310	320

2520	2530	2540	2550	2560

Ask: *What is special about all these numbers?* (They are multiples of 10.) Call out numbers within the ranges on the lines and ask children to mark the positions (for example, 72, 284, 2549). *Which multiple of 10 is each closest to?* Record these using arrows (72 ⟶ 70, 2549 ⟶ 2550). Remind children that this is rounding to the nearest 10 and that numbers ending in 5 round up. Repeat for rounding to 100 by drawing two more lines, one with three-digit multiples of 100 (400, 500, 600...), and the other with four-digit multiples of 100 (5600, 5700, 5800...). Remind children that numbers ending in 50 round up.

Independent work: Give each child photocopiable page 'Oceans, seas and rivers' from the CD-ROM to complete.

Progress check: Select a measurement from the photocopiable sheet and ask children: *What is this to the nearest 10 or 100? How do you know?*

Review

Call out a four-digit multiple of 10 or 100 and ask children to say numbers that would round to it. For example: *What numbers when rounded to the nearest 100 round to 5400? Which would be the highest/lowest number?*

Curriculum objectives
• To count in multiples of 25 and 1000.

Success criteria
• I can count in multiples of 25 and 1000.

Differentiation
Less confident learners
Invite children to sketch a quick picture or diagram to help them decide which operation(s) to use when solving each problem. They could also be provided with one-step problems initially.

More confident learners
Encourage children to create their own one- and two-step problems for other children to solve.

Lesson 5   Oral and mental starter 4

Main teaching activities

Whole-class work: Introduce this real-life context to explore sequences. *A factory makes pencil sharpeners. The sharpeners come along the conveyor belt in batches of 1000. 2000 have already been made.* Ask children to count in 1000s as batches come along the belt (3000, 4000, 5000...). Change the start number to 5000, then 2700, then 4650, asking children to count on in 1000s each time. Point out that the hundreds, tens and units digits don't change. Repeat for batches being removed from the factory in batches of 1000.

Similarly, explore counting in 25s from a multiple of 25: *A factory makes mugs. The mugs come along the conveyor belt in batches of 25. They have 75 mugs already.* Count in 25s as new batches come along the belt (75, 100, 125...). Gradually explore harder start numbers (say, near-multiples of 25, such as 26 or 74). Record sequences on the board and encourage children to look for patterns.

Paired work: List on the board: 175, 950, 2000, 1625, 301, 449. Ask children to count on in 25s, writing at least eight numbers in each sequence.

Progress check: Take feedback. Encourage children to look for patterns in each sequence. *What is special about each fourth number? Which of the numbers are multiples of 100?*

Review

Ask problems that involve counting in 1000s or 25s, such as: *A farmer buys some sheep at market. He already has 474 sheep. He brings home the new sheep in five lorries, each containing 25 sheep. How many sheep has he now?*

Mental addition and subtraction

Expected prior learning

Children should be able to:

- rapidly recall and use addition and subtraction facts to 20
- recognise the place value of each digit in two- and three-digit numbers
- accurately add and subtract numbers mentally including one- and two-digit numbers.

Topic	Curriculum objectives	Expected outcomes
Addition and subtraction	**Lesson 1**	
	To add and subtract numbers with up to 4-digits using the formal written methods of columnar addition and subtraction where appropriate.	Mentally add pairs of two-digit numbers using partitioning and counting-on methods.
		Mentally add pairs of multiples of 10, 100 and 1000 and doubles of 2-digit numbers and multiples of 10, 100 and 1000.
	Lesson 2	
	To add and subtract numbers with up to 4-digits using the formal written methods of columnar addition and subtraction where appropriate.	Mentally subtract pairs of two-digit numbers using counting on and back methods.
	Lesson 3	
	To add and subtract numbers with up to 4-digits using the formal written methods of columnar addition and subtraction where appropriate.	Mentally add and subtract pairs of two-digit numbers.
	To estimate and use inverse operations to check answers to a calculation.	Mentally add and subtract pairs of multiples of 10, 100 and 1000 and doubles of 2-digit numbers and multiples of 10, 100 and 1000.
		Estimate answers.
	Lesson 4	
	To add and subtract numbers with up to 4-digits using the formal written methods of columnar addition and subtraction where appropriate.	Mentally add and subtract pairs of two-digit numbers.
	To estimate and use inverse operations to check answers to a calculation.	Check using inverses.
	Lesson 5	
	To solve addition and subtraction two-step problems in contexts, deciding which operations and methods to use and why.	Solve one and two-step problems involving addition and subtraction.

Preparation

Lesson 1: copy 'Grid templates', one per pair

Lesson 2: copy 'How did I subtract?', one per child

Lesson 3: copy 'Target grids (1)', one per pair

Lesson 4: copy 'Check Sam's answers', one per child; enlarge 'Target grids (1)' to A3

Lesson 5: copy 'Fair questions', one per pair

You will need

Photocopiable sheets
'How did I subtract?'; 'Check Sam's answers'; 'Fair questions'

General resources
'Grid templates'; 'Target grids (1)'

Equipment
Number fans; individual whiteboards

Further practice

Photocopiable sheets
'Sums and differences of multiples of ten'

Oral and mental starters for week 2

See bank of starters on pages 44 to 45. Oral and mental starters are also on the CD-ROM.

6 Fact practice (addition)

7 Fact practice (subtraction)

2 Hundred square chase

5 Double-take

1 Place value chains (1)

Overview of progression

During this week the children will consolidate and extend their abilities to mentally add and subtract two-digit numbers and related multiples of 10, 100 and 1000. They will learn to use inverses to check their calculations and to use estimates to check whether answers are sensible. Children will need to be confident in knowing addition and subtraction bonds and less confident children may need revision and reinforcement of the more difficult facts (8 + 7 = 15, 13 − 6 = 7 and so on). Provide cards with the questions on one side and answers on the other and encourage children to take them away to learn at home. Children should be familiar with partitioning and counting on and back strategies for addition and subtraction from Year 3 work and may also be familiar with other adjusting strategies such as adding and subtracting near-multiples. During this week they need to be given opportunities to select which approach is most suitable for particular questions and to check through estimating and inverses. In lesson 5 they will use and apply these calculation strategies in solving one- and two-step problems.

> ### Watch out for
> For those children less confident with addition and subtraction facts to 20, focus on recall in the early lessons of this week. Provide addition and subtraction grids, like those used in lesson 1, but use numbers to 20 rather than larger ones. Encourage the children not to use fingers or objects to find answers but rather use facts that they can recall to deduce unknown ones.

Creative context

Look out for opportunities to perform addition and subtraction in real-life contexts – for example, number of absent children, dinner numbers, cooking situations.

Vocabulary

compare, digit, estimate, figure, hundreds, **inverse**, multiples, ones, order, place value, rounding, sequences, tens, thousands, units

Curriculum objectives
● To add numbers with up to four-digits.
Success criteria
● I can add pairs of two-digit numbers and multiples of 10, 100 and 100.

You will need
General resources
'Grid templates'

Differentiation
Less confident learners
Grids should contain numbers to 20 to provide practice in recall of addition facts.

More confident learners
Ask children to complete grids involving mainly the digits 5, 6, 7, 8 and 9 in the numbers requiring crossing significant boundaries, such as 59,000 + 86,000.

Lesson 1   Oral and mental starter 6

Main teaching activities

Whole-class work: Explain that in this lesson the children will revise some of the addition strategies they already know. On the interactive whiteboard draw this grid:

+	34	47	68
51			
35			
49			

Take each cell at a time and find the sum, asking children to describe the mental strategies they used. For example, 51 + 34: *I counted on 3 tens from 51 and then added 4* or *I added the tens first and then the ones'*. Illustrate counting-on strategies on number lines and for partitioning strategies show how tens and ones are added separately. Encourage children to say which methods seem easier for which questions. Add further rows to the table to provide more practice if necessary.

As they arise, discuss other strategies including: doubling and adjusting (for example, 34 + 35); adding near-multiples of 10 and adjusting (49 + 68); knowing totals to 100 (using 35 + 65 = 100 to answer 35 + 68). Ask: *Which way can you work out this sum in your head? Which addition facts could you use to help you answer this?*

Now put a zero after each number in the grid to make them multiples of 10 (510, 340, 470...). Explain that each number has been multiplied by 10, so the tens digit is now the hundreds digit, the ones digit is now the tens digit and so on. Discuss the effect this has on the sums – for example, instead of (30 + 5) + (40 + 7) it is (300 + 50) + (400 + 70) – and that answers are ten times larger than for the two-digit numbers. Similarly, show addition grids with all multiples of 100 or 1000 by putting zeros after two-digit numbers.

Paired work: Provide each pair with photocopiable page 'Grid templates' from the CD-ROM. On the board, draw grids for children to copy and complete, involving either two-digit numbers or multiples of 10, 100 or 1000 (with two non-zero digits, such as 460, 5200, 86,000). All numbers in a grid must be the same type.

Progress check: Invite children to select several of the questions from their grids. Ask: *Which mental strategy do you think is best for each?*

Review

Provide additions such as 45 + 47, 85 + 24, 78 + 86. *Which mental strategy do you think is best for each?* Focus on using known facts (for example, double 45 is 90), counting on in tens and ones (for example, from 85 counting 2 tens and then 4 ones) and on partitioning approaches (for example, 70 + 80 = 150, 8 + 6 = 14). Similarly, provide multiples of 10, 100 and 1000 (say, 570 + 740, 2500 + 6800 and so on) and ask: *How can you find these sums? How are they related to two-digit numbers?* (Multiplied by 10, 100 or 1000.) *What will be different about the answers?*

Curriculum objectives
● To subtract numbers with up to four-digits.
Success criteria
● I can subtract using a range of mental methods.

You will need
Photocopiable sheets
'How did I subtract?'

Differentiation
Less confident learners
Support these children in saying which have numbers close together, which involve subtracting a small number or near-multiples of 10, and so on.
More confident learners
Ask them to write their own subtractions and say which mental methods are most suitable for each.

Lesson 2   Oral and mental starter 7

Main teaching activities

Whole-class work: Explain that this lesson is about subtracting two-digit numbers and revising subtraction strategies the children already know. List these subtractions on the board: 85 − 21, 75 − 67, 93 − 38, 82 − 49. Ask them in pairs to discuss how they would answer each question mentally. Take feedback and list strategies used, such as:

- finding the difference by counting up (for example, counting up from 67 to 75)
- counting back in tens and then ones (93 − 30 − 8)
- subtracting near-multiples of 10 and adjusting (82 − 50 + 1)
- using partitioning (80 − 20, 5 − 1).

Ask: *Which method do you think is best for each question? Why?*

Draw attention to the fact that finding a difference by counting up from the smaller number is useful when two numbers are close together and that counting back in tens and ones is particularly useful when the number being subtracted is quite small.

Independent work: Ask children to complete photocopiable page 'How did I subtract?' from the CD-ROM.

Progress check: Invite children to discuss the questions on the photocopiable sheet. *Which mental strategy do you think is best for each subtraction?*

Review

Take feedback on the photocopiable sheet. *Which method do you think is most suitable for questions such as 83 − 24? 92 − 85? 177 − 39? 107 − 59?*

Curriculum objectives
● To add and subtract numbers with up to four-digits.
● To estimate to check answers to a calculation.
Success criteria
● I can add and subtract numbers, using estimating to check.

You will need
General resources
'Target grids (1)'

Differentiation
Less confident learners
Use the first grid only on photocopiable page 'Target grids (1)'. Provide a list of number facts to 20 to support calculation.
More confident learners
Use the second grid on the photocopiable sheet. Give targets such as: *Find a pair with a sum of about 17,000 and a difference of about 1000.*

Lesson 3   Oral and mental starter 2

Main teaching activities

Whole-class work: Write two-digit additions and subtractions, such as 47 + 86, 96 − 39, 58 + 69, 94 − 25. *Which has an answer about 130? How could you guess without working out all the answers?* Children approximate, rounding to the nearest 10 (for example, 50 + 90 = 140, 100 − 40 = 60 and so on). Record estimates on the board. Ask children to answer the original questions mentally. *Now use the estimates to check that your answers are about right.*

Paired work: Using the photocopiable page 'Target grids (1)' from the CD-ROM, pairs choose pairs of numbers from either grid and find their sums and differences using mental methods, making an estimate first and using it to check answers. Targets can be given such as: *Find a pair with a sum of about 150 and a difference of about 30* or *Find a pair with a difference of about 2000.*

Progress check: Remind children to use their estimates to check during the paired work. *What estimate did you make for this sum/difference? Was your estimate helpful in highlighting an error?*

Review

Take feedback, asking questions such as: *What addition and subtraction strategies did you use? Did any of you realise you'd made an error when you used your estimate to check?*

SCHOLASTIC

Curriculum objectives
● To add and subtract numbers with up to four-digits.
● To use inverse operations to check answers to a calculation.

Success criteria
● I can check additions by subtracting and subtractions by adding.

You will need

Photocopiable sheets
'Check Sam's answers'

General resources
'Target grids (1)'

Equipment
Number fans

Differentiation

Less confident learners
Provide number lines and lists of number facts to support calculations.

More confident learners
Invite children to check each answer using two different inverse calculations – for example, for 95 + 57 = 152, calculate 152 − 57 and 152 − 95 to check.

Lesson 4 — Oral and mental starter 5

Main teaching activities

Whole-class work: Show the children an A3 copy of photocopiable page 'Target grids (1)' from the CD-ROM. Circle 92 and 38 in the first grid and ask: *What is the sum of these two numbers?* Children show their answers using number fans. *What strategy did you use to find the answer?* Invite children to the front to demonstrate what they did to find the answer (for example: *I counted on 8 first and then 30*). Ask the rest of the class: *Did you use a different strategy?* Encourage discussion of different methods, such as counting on 30 and then 8 or counting on 40 and back 2.

Show each strategy on a number line:

Ask: *How can you be sure that the answer is correct?* Remind children that if an estimate was taken first it could be used to check that the answer is about right. *What else could we do to check that we have the correct answer?* Encourage them to remember that

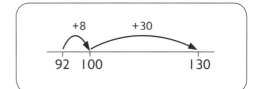

subtraction is the inverse of addition and that subtraction can be used to check additions 92 + 38 = 130, 130 − 38 = ? Invite children to perform this subtraction to check the addition, holding up their number fans to show the answer.

Now provide a new addition fact and explain that you are not sure if the answer is correct (say, 77 + 65 = 132). Write several subtractions on the board, such as 77 − 65, 65 − 132, 132 − 65, and so on. Ask: *Which of these subtractions should you use to check the addition? What answer would you expect to get, if the addition is correct?* Help children to realise that the subtraction 132 − 65 should give you the first number in the addition. Ask children to check and, when they discover the answer is 67, they should realise that the addition is incorrect. Correct the addition and show that 142 is the right answer.

Find the numbers 85 and 58 on the A3 copy of 'Target grids (1)' and ask children to find the difference mentally. Similarly, discuss subtraction strategies and ask children to perform an addition to check the answer (for example, 85 − 58 = 27) by finding 27 + 58.

Independent work: Give each child photocopiable page 'Check Sam's answers' from the CD-ROM. Ask them to use inverses to check each of Sam's calculations in part 1 and then to answer the questions in part 2 and check them in the same way.

Progress check: Invite various children to give answers to the questions in part 2 of the photocopiable sheet and to explain how they calculated each time. Then ask children to say the inverse calculation they used. Ask: *Did any of you realise you'd made an error when you used your inverse calculation to check?*

Review

Now write on the board: 123 − 45 = 87. *Which of these additions could you use to check the subtraction: 123 + 87, 45 + 87, 87 + 123?* Ask children to choose the appropriate addition and use it to check the subtraction.

Curriculum objectives
● To solve addition and subtraction two-step problems in contexts, deciding which operations and methods to use and why.

Success criteria
● I can solve two-step problems.

You will need
Photocopiable sheets
'Fair questions'
Equipment
Individual whiteboards

Differentiation
Less confident learners
Invite children to sketch a quick picture or diagram to help them decide which operation(s) to use when solving each problem. Provide them with one-step problems initially.

More confident learners
Encourage children to create their own one- and two-step problems for other children to solve.

Lesson 5   Oral and mental starter 1

Main teaching activities

Whole-class work: Introduce a general context through which addition and subtraction problems can be explored. Record a two-digit number on the board, such as: *Jane and Wayne collect stickers. Jayne has 68 stickers.*

Then ask questions such as: *How many stickers could Wayne have:*
- *if he has 47 more stickers than Jane?*
- *if he has 47 fewer stickers than Jane?*
- *if the difference between the numbers of stickers they have is 43?*
- *if the total number of stickers they have is 82/150/118?*

Working in pairs, ask the children to solve these problems, showing their working on their individual whiteboards. Discuss together the strategies used and solutions. Invite children to the front to sketch pictures or diagrams to illustrate each question and to make it easier to identify what calculation to do. Encourage them to highlight the important numbers in each problem. Invite them to identify any words used that might indicate which calculation they will make, such as *fewer, more, difference* or *total*.

Remind the children to watch out for false clues by discussing the following problem: *How many stickers would Wayne have if Jayne had 44 fewer stickers than Wayne?* Despite using the word *fewer* this problem involves *adding* 44 to 68. Stress the importance of picturing the situation and reading the problem carefully.

Now introduce several two-step problems about the same theme. For example:
- *Wayne had 67 more stickers than Jayne, but he gave 24 of them to his younger brother. How many has he now?*
- *A third friend, Lorraine, has 12 stickers fewer than Jayne. If Jayne and Wayne have 100 stickers in total, how many do the three children have in total?*

Invite children to the front to sketch pictures or diagrams to illustrate each question and to make it easier to identify the steps required to solve each problem. Again they can use their whiteboards and work in pairs to solve each problem.

Add some irrelevant numerical information into one of the problems, for example: *A third friend, Lorraine, who is nine years-old, has 12 stickers fewer than Jayne. If Jayne and Wayne have 100 stickers in total, how many do the three children have in total?* Remind children to look out for numbers that do not need to be used in the calculations.

Paired work: Provide each pair of children with photocopiable page 'Fair questions' from the CD-ROM. Invite them to work together to solve the problems, using appropriate addition and subtraction strategies, and estimating and checking solutions.

Progress check: Ask children to hold up their whiteboards and show the methods and checking approaches they used to solve each problem. Ask: *How did you decide what to do? Did you estimate first? What checking strategy did you use? How can you check using an inverse strategy?*

Review

Take feedback on the photocopiable sheet that the children completed in the paired work. Ask: *How did you solve each problem? Which methods of addition and subtraction did you use?* Encourage children to summarise the mental addition and subtraction strategies they used this week and to explain how these were used and applied in this problem-solving work.

Multiplication: recall and mental methods

Expected prior learning

Children should be able to:

- recall and use multiplication facts for the 1, 2, 3, 4, 5, 6, 8 and 10 multiplication tables
- write and calculate mathematical statements for multiplication using the multiplication tables that they know, using mental methods.

Topic	Curriculum objectives	Expected outcomes
Multiplication	**Lesson 1**	
	To recall multiplication facts for multiplication tables up to 12 × 12.	Recall facts from the 7- and 9-times tables.
	Lesson 2	
	To recall multiplication facts for multiplication tables up to 12 × 12.	Recall facts from the 11- and 12-times tables.
	To use place value, known and derived facts to multiply and divide mentally, including: multiplying by 0 and 1; dividing by 1; multiplying together three numbers.	Multiply multiples of 10 and 100.
	Lesson 3	
	To use place value, known and derived facts to multiply and divide mentally, including: multiplying by 0 and 1; dividing by 1; multiplying together three numbers.	Mentally multiply a range of numbers, including a single digit, by 0 and 1.
	Lesson 4	
	To use place value, known and derived facts to multiply and divide mentally, including: multiplying by 0 and 1; dividing by 1; multiplying together three numbers.	Multiply together three numbers.
	Lesson 5	
	To solve problems involving multiplying and adding, including using the distributive law to multiply two-digit numbers by one digit, integer scaling problems and harder correspondence such as which n objects are connected to m objects.	Solve one- and two-step problems involving multiplication.

Preparation

Lesson 3: copy 'Grid of multiples', one per pair

Lesson 4: copy 'Quick times', one per child

You will need

Photocopiable sheets
'Quick times'

General resources
'Grid of multiples'; interactive teaching resource 'Multiplication square'

Equipment
Coloured pencils; dice; 0–10 number cards; number fans

Further practice

Photocopiable sheets
'Multiples of numbers to 10'

Oral and mental starters for week 3

See bank of starters on pages 85 to 86. Oral and mental starters are also on the CD-ROM.

8 Function machine

10 Multiplication and division facts for 8

12 9-times table

11 Magic square (1)

9 Story time

Overview of progression

During this week the children will consolidate and extend their abilities to recall multiplication facts and mentally multiply numbers. In the early part of the week, they consolidate and revise facts from the 1-, 2-, 3-, 4-, 5-, 8- and 10-times tables and learn facts from the 6-, 7-, 9-, 11- and 12-times tables. They will learn to use known facts to multiply numbers, such as teen numbers, and will multiply by 0 and 1. In lesson 4 they will use and explore ideas of commutativity and associativity in multiplying three numbers together. Lesson 5 gives opportunity for children to use and apply their facts and skills to solve one- and two-step multiplication problems.

Watch out for

For those children who struggle to recall particular times tables facts, provide cards with the questions on one side and answers on the other and encourage children to take them away to learn at home. Ensure that a range of visual, aural and kinaesthetic approaches are used when teaching tables facts to appeal to all learning styles.

Creative context

Look out for opportunities to perform multiplication in real-life contexts, such as getting into teams in PE, sitting on benches in the hall, giving out items such as coloured pencils to children, cooking situations, and so on.

Vocabulary

facts, groups of, lots of, multiply, **product**, tables, times

Curriculum objectives

● To recall multiplication facts for multiplication tables up to 12 × 12 (7 and 9).

Success criteria

● I can recall facts from the 7- and 9-times tables.

You will need

General resources

Interactive teaching resource 'Multiplication square'

Differentiation

Less confident learners

If some children do not know facts from the other times tables write the difficult facts on blank cards for them to take home to memorise.

More confident learners

Rather than listing up to 10 times a number, invite children to list the facts up to 12-times tables.

Lesson 1

Oral and mental starter 8

Main teaching activities

Whole-class work: Write questions from the 2-, 3-, 4-, 5-, 6-, 8- and 10-times tables, inviting children to give the answers (4 × 3 = 12, 7 × 5 = 35...). Then ask the children these questions and get them to state the answers: 3 × 4 = 12, 5 × 7 = 35... Ask: *Can you do this without any working out?* Remind children that the order of multiplication is unimportant. Use the interactive teaching resource 'Multiplication square' on the CD-ROM to show how this can reduce the number of tables facts to be learned by almost a half. Open the resource to show the facts from the tables 1–10. Both vertically and horizontally, highlight the one-times table. *We all know these facts don't we?* Similarly continue to highlight the facts from the 2-, 5-, 10-times tables and then the 3-, 4- and 8-times tables. Point out the four facts unhighlighted for the 6-, 7- and 9-times tables: *7 × 9 and 9 × 7 have the same answer so there are three facts to be learned: 7 × 7 = 49, 7 × 9 or 9 × 7 = 63 and 9 × 9 = 81.* Remind children that ×6 is double the 3-times table.

Draw an image for each of these three facts on the board and ask children to make up a rhyme to help them learn each fact. For example:

● Draw two T-shirts on a washing line with 7 × 7 on one and 49 on the other: *T-shirts on a washing line – seven times seven is forty-nine.*
● Draw a picture of a tree with a monkey at the top, holding the number fact 9 × 7 = 63 on a card: *Monkey sitting in a tree – nine times seven is sixty-three.*
● Draw a picture of the sun and in the centre write the fact 9 × 9 = 81: *Written in the middle of the sun – nine times nine is eighty-one.*

Take each fact in turn and spend time saying the rhyme and repeating the facts. Erase the answer to each fact and continue in the same way. Discuss other ways children can learn them (for example, using their fingers for the 9-times table).

Independent work: Hide any times tables information on display and ask children to write out the 6-, 7- and 9-times tables, listing all the facts from 1× to 10× (at this stage). Ask them to use their knowledge of the other times tables to work out the answers together with the three facts in the pictures and rhymes.

Paired work: Invite the children to test each other on the facts in the 6-, 7- and 9-times tables.

Progress check: As children are writing the facts of the times tables, ask: *Which other fact did you know that helped you with this one? How could you check whether this answer is correct?*

Review

Explore 11 × 7, 11 × 9, 12 × 7 and 12 × 9. *Does anyone know what the answers to these facts are?* Discuss the pattern with multiplying 11 by single-digit numbers, such as 11 × 3 = 33, 11 × 7 = 77. Show that 10 × 7 and 2 × 7 can be added together to get 12 × 7, or that counting on two 7s from 70, gives 12 × 7 = 84. Show 12 × 9 in the same way. Remind children to practise recalling these facts at home.

Curriculum objectives

- To use place value, known and derived facts to multiply mentally.
- To recall multiplication facts for multiplication tables up to 12 × 12.

Success criteria

- I can recall facts from the 11- and 12-times tables.
- I can mentally multiply multiples of 10 and 100.

You will need

General resources

Interactive teaching resource 'Multiplication square'

Differentiation

Less confident learners

Choose a lower times table, such as 3, 4 or 6.

More confident learners

Choose the 11- or 12-times table and multiply numbers by 110, 120, 1100 and 1200.

Lesson 2 — Oral and mental starter 10

Main teaching activities

Whole-class work: Explain that this lesson is about multiplying by 11, 12 and by multiples of 10 and 100. Prepare the interactive teaching resource 'Multiplication square' on the CD-ROM: under 'Options', change the start number to 3 to show tables from 3 to 12. As in lesson 1, highlight both horizontally and vertically the facts that children already know, that is those from the tables 3, 4, 5, 8 and 10 and then the facts from lesson 1. Only a few facts will remain, such as $11 \times 11 = 121$, $11 \times 12 = 132$ and $12 \times 12 = 144$. Discuss patterns in the numbers of the 11- and 12-times tables, drawing attention to the 12-times table answers being even. Invite children to suggest pictures and rhymes that could be made to help them memorise the new facts. Ask them in pairs to write the 4-times table onto their whiteboards. Call out questions involving multiplying by 40. They should use their answers and what they know about multiplying by 10 to answer them, such as $7 \times 40 = 280$. Similarly, call out questions involving multiplying by 400.

Independent work: Ask the children to choose a times table to write out (for example, 6-, 7- or 9-times tables). Then they write related facts involving multiplying by multiples of 10 and 100 (6×70 or 3×90, and so on).

Progress check: Say: *Explain how to multiply by a multiple of 10 or 100, such as by 60 or by 700. Write an explanation or draw a diagram to help a younger child understand what to do.*

Review

Invite children to call out questions they have written for other children to answer. Ask: *What fact did you know already? How do you multiply a number by 10 or 100?*

Curriculum objectives

- To use place value, known and derived facts to multiply mentally, including: multiplying by 0 and 1.

Success criteria

- I can multiply a range of numbers, including a single digit, by 0 and 1.

You will need

General resources

'Grid of multiples'

Equipment

Individual whiteboards; coloured pencils; dice

Differentiation

Less confident learners

Let children focus on the lower numbers on the grid (for example, up to 36 and use two dice to roll instead).

More confident learners

Ask them to list the numbers on the grid that cannot be made and begin to record them as prime numbers.

Lesson 3 — Oral and mental starter 12

Main teaching activities

Whole-class work: Write ten multiplications on the board including those that involve ×1 or ×0. For example:

7 × 7	8 × 12	6 × 3	12 × 0	9 × 9
7 × 8	11 × 12	6 × 11	467 × 1	5673 × 0

In pairs, give children a few minutes to write the answers of as many of the questions as they can on their whiteboards. Go through the answers, discussing facts they should know and the effect of multiplying by 1 or by zero.

Paired work: Give each pair photocopiable page 'Grid of multiples' from the CD-ROM, two different-coloured pencils and a dice. Children take it in turn to choose a number between 1 and 12 and then roll the dice – for example, 11 followed by a dice roll of 5. The child multiplies the two numbers and colours the answer on the sheet in his/her own colour. If a player gets an answer already coloured or not on the board, the other player gets two consecutive turns. The aim is to get the most sections coloured by the end of the game.

Progress check: While children are playing the game ask: *Which numbers are impossible to get and why?* You could introduce the term *prime numbers* for those that are impossible (although be aware that some coloured numbers will also be prime, such as 1, 2, 3 and 5).

Review

Revise the more difficult facts that the children are learning this week and remind them to practise at home.

SCHOLASTIC

Curriculum objectives
● To use place value, known and derived facts to multiply and divide mentally, including multiplying together three numbers.

Success criteria
● I can multiply three numbers together.

You will need
Photocopiable sheets
'Quick times'
Equipment
Dice; 0–10 number cards

Differentiation
Less confident learners
Give the children the number cards 2, 3, 4 and 5. Ask them to pick three of the cards to multiply together, and find as many different answers as they can.

More confident learners
Rather than dice, provide children with a set of 0-10 number cards. Some could also begin to multiply four numbers.

Lesson 4 — Oral and mental starter 11

Main teaching activities

Whole-class work: Explain that this lesson focuses on the order in which we multiply. Write on the board:

$$6 \times 2 \times 5 \qquad 6 \times 2 \times 5$$

Explain that the arc indicates the part of the question to be done first. Ask children to work out both of these. *What do you notice about the answers?* (They are the same.) *Which is the easier way of working out the answer? Why?* Explore $3 \times 6 \times 5$ in the same way. Discuss that multiplying 18 by 5 is more difficult to do than 3×30. The way we choose to group numbers to multiply them doesn't affect the answer.

Paired work: Provide each pair of children with three dice. They take turns to roll the dice, multiply the numbers together and record the question and answer. Score 2 points for an even answer and 1 point for an odd answer.

Independent work: Give each child photocopiable page 'Quick times' from the CD-ROM to complete as quickly as they can. Ask them to draw arcs to show which numbers they multiplied together first.

Progress check: During the paired work ask: *What do you notice about the numbers that give odd answers?* During the independent work ask: *Which numbers did you multiply together first? Why?*

Review

Mark the photocopiable sheet together, discussing children's chosen order of multiplication. *Why did you choose to multiply these two numbers first? Which facts did you use? Why do you think this way is easier?* Provide a question that includes zero. *What will the answer be?*

Curriculum objectives
● To solve problems involving multiplying, including harder correspondence problems.

Success criteria
● I can solve one- and two-step problems involving multiplication.

You will need

Equipment
Number fans

Differentiation

Less confident learners
Support these children in deciding how many times greater one number will be than the other.

More confident learners
Children can make up their own equivalent statements.

Lesson 5   Oral and mental starter 9

Main teaching activities

Whole-class work: Introduce the following theme: *Kim's mum is buying some party bags. Here are the items and their prices:* Write/draw these on the board:

bag 2p

chew 3p

lolly 5p

eraser 7p

pencil 10p

badge 8p

sticker 4p

sharpener 12p

Ask questions such as:

- *How much would she pay for: 7 bags? 8 chews? 11 pencils? 6 badges? 9 sharpeners?*
- *How many of each did she buy if she spent: 35p on lollies? 48p on sharpeners?*

Ask children to show their answers using number fans. Explore questions that involve multiplying the prices by multiples of 10 or 100 (for example, if she bought 40/700 chews?).

Introduce several two-step problems about the same theme, such as:

- *There are five erasers in a pack. How much will it cost for two packs? (5 × 7 × 2)*
- *The stickers double in price. How much for nine stickers now? (4 × 2 × 9)*

Independent work: On the board, write a range of equivalent statements with missing numbers. For example:

[ ] toes on [ ] feet   [ ] legs on [ ] sheep

[ ] legs on [ ] spiders   [ ] sides on [ ] triangles

[ ] days = [ ] weeks   [ ] months = [ ] years

[ ] years = [ ] centuries   [ ] players in [ ] eleven-a-side football teams

Ask children to write each statement at least three times, filling in different numbers to make them true.

Progress check: Ask: *How many times greater is the number of days than the number of weeks? Which tables fact did you use?*

Review

Take feedback on the independent work. Ask children to call out statements they have written, missing out a number each time for others to find.

Multiplication and division

Expected prior learning

Children should be able to:

- recall and use multiplication and division facts for the 3, 4 and 8 multiplication tables
- write and calculate mathematical statements for multiplication and division using the multiplication tables that they know, using mental methods.

Topic	Curriculum objectives	Expected outcomes
Multiplication and division	**Lesson 1**	
	To recall multiplication and division facts for multiplication tables up to 12 × 12.	Know the relationship between multiplication and division.
		Recall division facts for multiplication tables up to 12 × 12.
	Lesson 2	
	To recall multiplication and division facts for multiplication tables up to 12 × 12.	Divide multiples of 10 and 100.
	To use place value, known and derived facts to multiply and divide mentally, including: multiplying by 0 and 1; dividing by 1; multiplying together three numbers.	
	Lesson 3	
	To use place value, known and derived facts to multiply and divide mentally, including: multiplying by 0 and 1; dividing by 1; multiplying together three numbers.	Divide numbers mentally, including remainders.
	Lesson 4	
	To use place value, known and derived facts to multiply and divide mentally, including: multiplying by 0 and 1; dividing by 1; multiplying together three numbers.	Use place value, known and derived facts to divide mentally, including dividing numbers by 1.
		Find missing numbers in multiplication and division statements.
	Lesson 5	
	To solve problems involving multiplying and adding, including using the distributive law to multiply two-digit numbers by one digit, integer scaling problems and harder correspondence problems such as which n objects are connected to m objects.	Solve division problems, including rounding up or down.

Preparation

Lesson 2: copy 'Multiple divisions', one per child

Lesson 4: copy 'Triangles', one per pair, and 'Missing numbers', one per child

Lesson 5: copy 'Division dilemmas', one per child; prepare 'Division examples' for display on the interactive whiteboard

You will need

Photocopiable sheets

'Multiple divisions'; 'Triangles'; 'Missing numbers'; 'Division dilemmas'; 'Division examples'

General resources

Interactive activity 'Multiplication and division facts for 8'; interactive activity 'Multiples'; interactive activity 'Inverse operations'

Equipment

0–9 number cards

Further practice

Photocopiable sheets

'Division dilemmas'; 'Multiples'

Oral and mental starters for week 4

See bank of starters on pages 85 to 86. Oral and mental starters are also on the CD-ROM.

12 9-times table

8 Function machine

11 Magic square (1)

13 Targets

Overview of progression

During this week the children will consolidate and extend their abilities to recall multiplication facts and will use the relationship between multiplication and division to practise recalling and deriving division facts. In the early part of the week, they consolidate and revise facts from the times tables up to 12×12. They will write division facts related to tables facts and will use inverses to divide multiples of 10 and 100. In lesson 3 the idea of remainders will be developed and in lesson 4 the children will find missing numbers in related multiplications and divisions. Lesson 5 provides opportunity for children to use and apply their facts and skills to solve division problems, where rounding is required in the answer.

Watch out for

Some children may struggle to recall particular times tables facts or fail to appreciate the link between division facts and tables facts. Provide cards with the questions on one side and answers on the other and encourage children to take them away to learn at home. Ensure that a range of visual, aural and kinaesthetic approaches are used when teaching tables facts to appeal to all learning styles.

Creative context

Look out for opportunities to perform sharing and grouping division in real-life contexts, such as getting into teams in PE, sitting on benches in the hall, sharing items such as coloured pencils, cooking situations, and so on.

Vocabulary

divide, facts, groups of, lots of, round up, round down, share, tables

Curriculum objectives

● To recall multiplication and division facts for multiplication tables up to 12 × 12 (7 and 9).

Success criteria

● I can use the relationship between multiplication and division to recall division facts for multiplication tables up to 12 × 12.

You will need

General resources

Interactive activity 'Multiplication and division facts for 8'; interactive activity 'Multiples'

Differentiation

Less confident learners

Children can write division facts related to an easier times table, such as 3 or 4. You could also ask them to draw arrays or use dotted paper to help them appreciate how the multiplication and division facts are related.

More confident learners

Children can choose facts from other times tables, including 11 and 12.

Lesson 1   Oral and mental starter 12

Main teaching activities

Whole-class work: Explain that today's lesson is about the relationship between multiplication and division. Following on from the oral and mental starter about the 9-times table or a practice of 9-times table facts, begin to ask questions that involve dividing by 9. For example: *What is 36 divided by 9? Share 54 by 9. How many 9s make 81?* Invite children to explain how they can use their fingers (as they had done for the 9-times table facts) to answer the questions (for example, make 36 on your hand by holding down the fourth finger). *So how many 9s are 36/45/81?* List the division facts on the board (45 ÷ 9 = 5) and discuss the related tables fact (5 × 9 = 45). *What other division and multiplication facts use the same numbers?* List all four related facts (two multiplication and two division). Remind children that knowing one means that you know all four. Draw attention to which is the largest number in the multiplication (the answer) and which is the largest number in the division (the first number). Ensure that children appreciate the nature of how the facts are related using an array. Sketch an array for one of the facts (for example, 4 × 9 = 36) as four rows of nine dots. *How does this relate to the fact?* (There are four rows of 9, making 36 altogether.) *How does this array relate to the other three related facts?* (For example, there are 36 dots that are split into four rows with 9 in each row.)

Using the second screen of the interactive activity 'Multiplication and division facts for 8' on the CD-ROM, go through the division questions related to the 8-times table together, discussing the related tables fact for each. *How do you remember the related tables fact for the question 56 ÷ 8? Tell me a question that matches this division question?* (For example: *How many octopuses have 56 legs altogether?*)

Paired work: Ask children to choose any fact from the 7-times table and to write the related multiplication and division facts as a set. They should then write a word question to match one of the facts from the set. For example, for 63 ÷ 7 = 9, they could ask: *What is the maximum number of £7 DVDs I could buy with £63?* They should do this for as many of the facts from the 7-times table as they can.

Independent work: Children can use the interactive activity 'Multiples' on the CD-ROM to write a multiplication and division fact related to different 6- and 9-times tables.

Progress check: As children are writing the facts, ask: *How do you remember this tables fact? Have you found a fact that only has one multiplication and one related division? Why is this?* (7 × 7 = 49 only has one related division, since it is a squared number.)

Review

Ask children to read out the questions they wrote in the paired activity and for others to give the answers. *Is this question a multiplication or a division? Which tables fact can you use to help you work out this division question? Which is your favourite question?* As a final activity invite children to fill in the missing numbers to make this statement true in as many different ways as they can: [   ] days = [   ] weeks (for example, 56 days = 8 weeks). Draw out any facts that children find difficult to memorise (such as 7 × 8 = 56) and ask them to write the fact on a small piece of card to take home to practise with.

Curriculum objectives
- To recall multiplication and division facts for multiplication tables up to 12 × 12.
- To use place value, known and derived facts to multiply and divide mentally.

Success criteria
- I can divide multiples of 10 and 100.

You will need
Photocopiable sheets
'Multiple divisions'
Equipment
Individual whiteboards

Differentiation
Less confident learners
Provide these children with a copy of the tables facts from the 7- and 9-times tables.
More confident learners
Children can make up their own questions related to multiples of 10 and 100 linked to other times tables.

Curriculum objectives
- To use place value, known and derived facts to multiply and divide mentally.

Success criteria
- I can divide numbers mentally, including finding remainders.

You will need
Equipment
0–9 number cards

Differentiation
Less confident learners
Give groups digit cards with only lower numbers, such as 3–6.
More confident learners
Give groups cards showing 11 and 12 also.

Lesson 2
Oral and mental starter 8

Main teaching activities

Whole-class work: Explain that this lesson is about dividing multiples of 10 and 100. Write ÷ 7 and ÷ 9 on the board. Using their individual whiteboards, children in pairs write any four division facts related to the facts in either the 7- or the 9-times table. Work through the facts they come up with, writing a class list and discussing the related times tables facts.

Now ask questions related to those on the board but involving either a multiple of 10 or a multiple of 100 as the first number. For example, related to 42 ÷ 7 = 6, ask: *What is 420 divided by 7?* For each question, demonstrate that the facts are related in that there are 10 or 100 times more to divide and so the answer will be 10 or 100 times more. Remind children that making a number 10 or 100 times larger involves moving the digits to the left – for example, 12 becomes 120 or 1200.

Independent work: Give each child photocopiable page 'Multiple divisions' from the CD-ROM to complete.

Progress check: Ask children to say how many times larger each number is than the one in the related division fact from the table: *Will the answer be 10 or 100 times larger? How do you make a number 10 or 100 times larger?*

Review

Write four related facts from several of those on the sheet, such as 560 ÷ 7 = 80, 560 ÷ 80 = 7, 7 × 80 = 560 and 80 × 7 = 560. *How many 80s in 560? How do you know?*

Lesson 3
Oral and mental starter 12

Main teaching activities

Whole-class work: Write eight or nine consecutive numbers, such as 26, 27, 28, 29, 30, 31, 32, 33, 34. Ask: *Which are multiples of 3... 4...7...?*. Then select some multiples and ask division questions: *What is 28 divided by 4... by 7...?* Now select a number to divide by (say, 9). Underline a multiple of that number (say, 27) and then choose the next number up (28). Ask: *What is 28 divided by 9?* (3 r 1) Revise remainders and encourage children to notice that if the number being divided isn't a multiple, there will be a remainder. Continue adding one to the number and dividing (29 ÷ 9 = 3 r 2...). Help children to see the pattern in the remainders.

Group work: Arrange the children into groups of four. Place the digit cards 3, 4, 6, 7, 8 and 9 face down. Ask the group to write ten consecutive numbers (say, 30 to 39). Each child takes a category: 'multiple', 'remainder 1', 'remainder 2' or 'remainder 3'. They take turns to choose a number from the list and pick a digit card to divide it by. If the number is a multiple, the player with that category scores a point. If it has a remainder 1, the 'remainder 1' player wins a point. The winner is the first to win five points. Then the players switch categories. Questions and answers should be recorded each time.

Progress check: While children are playing the game ask: *Which category do you think is best? Why?*

Review

Call out divisions used in the game as quick-fire questions. Revise the more difficult division facts and remind children to practise them at home.

■SCHOLASTIC

Curriculum objectives

- To use place value, known and derived facts to multiply and divide mentally, including dividing by 1.

Success criteria

- I can divide mentally, including dividing by 1.
- I can find missing numbers in multiplication and division statements.

You will need

Photocopiable sheets

'Triangles'; 'Missing numbers'

General resources

Interactive activity 'Inverse operations'

Differentiation

Less confident learners

During the paired work, children can choose facts from the 3-, 4-, 6- or 8-times tables.

More confident learners

During paired work, encourage children to choose the most difficult facts from those times tables (7×8, 9×12)

Lesson 4 — Oral and mental starter

Main teaching activities

Whole-class work: Use the interactive activity 'Inverse operations' on the CD-ROM to remind children of the relationship between multiplication and division and to introduce missing numbers in such number sentences. Draw attention to which is the largest number in each multiplication (the answer) and in each division (the first number). Explain that this is true when multiplying and dividing numbers greater than 1. *Which division questions or multiplication questions involve two of the same number?* Help children to realise that multiplying or dividing by 1 leaves the number unchanged – for example, $7 \times 1 = 7$ or $12 \div 1 = 12$.

Paired work: Provide each pair with photocopiable page 'Triangles' from the CD-ROM. Ask them to choose facts from the 7-, 9-, 11- or 12-times tables to write into the boxes, and write the four related multiplication and division statements.

Independent work: Provide each child with photocopiable page 'Missing numbers' from the CD-ROM to complete during the remainder of the lesson or later for homework.

Progress check: During the paired work ask: *Which is the largest number in this multiplication? Which division fact is it related to?* During the independent work ask: *What operation could you use to find this missing number? Which tables fact is it related to?*

Review

Write [ ] $\div$ [ ] = [ ] on the board and ask children to say which number in the division they think would be larger, and why. *What if this was a 'divided by 1' question? What if the first two numbers were the same?* Invite children to explain what they notice.

Curriculum objectives

- To solve two-step problems in contexts, working with increasingly harder numbers.

Success criteria

- I can solve division problems, including rounding up or down.

You will need

Photocopiable sheets

'Division dilemmas'; 'Division examples'

Differentiation

Less confident learners

Support children through peer tutoring, where a more confident child explains their method to a less confident child.

More confident learners

Ask children to make up their own rounding problems.

Lesson 5 — Oral and mental starter 13

Main teaching activities

Whole-class work: Display the photocopiable page 'Division examples' from the CD-ROM, and work through the questions together. Give children time in pairs to discuss how each problem would be solved. Point out that sometimes remainders in an answer don't make sense and so the answer to a division has to be rounded up or down. Write each problem as a division statement first – for example, $37 \div 5 = 7$ r 2 and $35 \div 4 = 8$ r 3. Discuss them in context to show how giving a remainder isn't appropriate in answering the question: *I can only buy seven tickets as I don't have enough money for eight, so I give the answer 7 by rounding down. In question 2, however, I need nine tables to seat all the children, so I rounded up!*

Independent work: Give each child photocopiable page 'Division dilemmas' from the CD-ROM to complete. If time, encourage them to make up more of their own rounding up or down division problems.

Progress check: Ask: *Did you round up or down? Why?*

Review

Give children a few moments to discuss with a partner what all the questions that needed rounding down (or up) had in common. Draw attention to the fact that if you are buying as many things as you can or filling as many things as you can, you usually round down. If you are fitting things into boxes, minibuses, on pages, around tables, you usually need to have an extra box for the remainder so you round up.

Geometry: properties of shapes

Expected prior learning

Children should be able to:

- identify and name shapes according to the numbers of sides
- identify and recognise right angles in shapes
- understand the nature of parallel sides.

Topic	Curriculum objectives	Expected outcomes
Geometry: properties of shapes	**Lesson 1**	
	To compare and classify geometric shapes, including quadrilaterals and triangles, based on their properties and sizes.	Understand and identify regular and irregular 2D shapes.
	Lesson 2	
	To identify lines of symmetry in 2D shapes presented in different orientations.	Identify lines of symmetry.
	Lesson 3	
	To compare and classify geometric shapes, including quadrilaterals and triangles, based on their properties and sizes.	Compare shapes based on properties including symmetry. Classify shapes using geometrical properties.
	Lesson 4	
	To complete a simple symmetric figure with respect to a specific line of symmetry.	Draw reflections and complete symmetrical figures.
	Lesson 5	
	To compare and classify geometric shapes, including quadrilaterals and triangles, based on their properties and sizes.	Solve problems involving 2D shapes.

Preparation

Lesson 1: prepare 'Visualised shapes' for display on interactive whiteboard; copy '2D shapes – polygons', one per child

Lesson 2: prepare 'Visualised shapes' for display on interactive whiteboard; copy '2D shapes – polygons', one per child

Lesson 3: prepare 'Carroll diagrams' for display on interactive whiteboard; copy '2D shapes – polygons', one per pair

Lesson 4: copy 'Reflections', one per child

Lesson 5: copy 'Visualised shapes', one per pair, and prepare the sheet for display on interactive whiteboard

You will need

Photocopiable sheets

'Reflections'

General resources

'Visualised shapes'; '2D shapes – polygons'; 'Carroll diagrams'; interactive activity 'Shape shifting'; interactive teaching resource 'Reflection grid'

Equipment

Individual whiteboards; mirrors or semi-transparent reflective materials; tracing paper; large sheets of paper; scissors; glue; rectangular paper; equilateral triangle

Further practice

Prepare some shapes using the interactive teaching resource 'Reflection grid' to give children further practice of identifying or completing symmetrical shapes

Oral and mental starters for week 5

See bank of starters on pages 45, 86 and 126. Oral and mental starters are also on the CD-ROM.

15 Twenty questions

6 Fact practice (addition)

7 Fact practice (subtraction)

13 Targets

Overview of progression

During this week, the children will consolidate and extend their knowledge of the properties of 2D shapes, including lines of symmetry and regularity. Lesson 1 introduces regular shapes and children are asked to identify which polygons are regular and which are irregular. Lesson 2 explores lines of symmetry of shapes presented in different orientations. These ideas are developed further in the next lesson as children classify shapes according to properties including regularity and symmetry. In lesson 4 children are given opportunities to reflect shapes in a range of mirror lines and to complete symmetrical figures. The final lesson of the week draws together all the properties explored in problem-solving situations.

Watch out for

Some children find spatial topics more difficult than other children, particularly in relation to symmetry. Look out for children who merely want to replicate the same shape on the other side of the mirror line when reflecting, rather than drawing the reflected image. It is vital that children are given suitable reflecting equipment such as mirrors or semi-transparent reflective materials to enable them to check reflections.

Creative context

Link this shape work to art activities, including creating symmetrical patterns using colour and shapes.

Vocabulary

angles, decagon, heptagon, irregular, **line of symmetry**, octagon, pentagon, quadrilateral, rectangle, reflection, **regular polygon**, shape, sides, square, triangle

Curriculum objectives
● To compare and classify geometric shapes based on their properties and sizes.

Success criteria
● I can identify regular and irregular shapes.

You will need

General resources
'Visualised shapes'; '2D shapes – polygons'; interactive activity 'Shape shifting'

Differentiation

Less confident learners
Provide children with a list of the names and numbers of sides of the shapes, including triangles, quadrilaterals, pentagons, hexagons, heptagons and octagons.

More confident learners
Encourage children to write *regular* or *irregular* together with the shape name – for example, *irregular heptagon*.

Lesson 1
Oral and mental starter 15

Main teaching activities

Whole-class work: Explain that today's lesson is about 2D (flat) shapes. Remind the children that the word 'polygon' is used for flat shapes with straight sides. Ask them to close their eyes and imagine the shape you describe to them: *This shape has four sides. Each side is straight. The shape has four corners (vertices). What shape do you imagine?* Ask children to draw the shape they imagined in the air. Now display part 1 of the photocopiable page 'Visualised shapes' from the CD-ROM and ask: *Which of these shapes did you imagine? Which of the shapes fit the description? Which of the shapes do not?* Point out that only the triangle in the centre does not fit the description – all the others have four straight sides and four corners. Ask children to raise their hands to show which shape most closely matched the one they visualised to see which representation most children imagined. *What do you call the polygon I described?* Remind children of the term *quadrilateral* to mean any polygon with four sides. Ensure that they realise that any of the shapes correctly visualised will have been a quadrilateral, but that some of them may have a special name, such as a square or a rectangle. *What is special about rectangles and squares?* (They have four right angles.) *What is particularly special about squares?* (They have four equal sides.) Explain that we call any shape that has equal sides and equal angles *regular*. Write the word on the board and write *equal sides AND equal angles*.

Now show part 2 of the photocopiable page. *Which of these shapes are regular? Which have equal sides and equal angles?* Ask children to identify which are regular. Give particular attention to the hexagon that has equal sides but *not* equal angles. *This is NOT regular.* Explain that shapes that are not regular are called *irregular*. Point to each shape in both parts of the sheet in turn and ask children to say *regular* or *irregular*. Children often want to believe that a non-square rectangle is regular as it is a common representation, but ensure they see that the sides are not equal. (You could explain that a non-square rectangle is sometimes called an oblong.)

Independent work: Give each child photocopiable page '2D shapes – polygons' from the CD-ROM. Ask them to write *regular* or *irregular* next to each shape as appropriate.

Progress check: As children are identifying regular and irregular shapes ask: *Which of the shapes on your sheet is a regular quadrilateral? Octagon? Hexagon? Pentagon? Heptagon? Which is an irregular triangle? Quadrilateral? Pentagon?*

Review

As a whole-class, answer the questions on screens 1 and 2 of the interactive activity 'Shape shifting' on the CD-ROM. Invite children to describe each with a name: *This is an irregular octagon... a regular hexagon* and so on. Explain that the next lesson will continue with looking at the properties of polygons, including sorting shapes according to whether they are regular or irregular.

■SCHOLASTIC

Lesson 2 — Oral and mental starter 6

Main teaching activities

Whole-class work: Explain that this lesson is about finding lines of symmetry. Begin by reminding children that a line of symmetry separates two reflected halves. Invite a child to the front to sketch a shape that is symmetrical and ask the others to say where the lines of symmetry are. Discuss how lines of symmetry can be identified, by using a mirror, just looking or using tracing paper and folding.

Hold up a rectangular (non-square) piece of paper. *Some people sometimes make mistakes about the lines of symmetry of rectangles.* Distinguish between a diagonal and a line of symmetry by folding the shape from corner to corner. Open it out with the crease vertically.

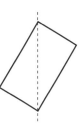

Can you see that this is not a line of symmetry? Invite children to say where the lines of symmetry of a rectangle are (not along a diagonal), for example:

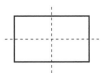

Stress the importance of looking at shapes from all orientations to check how many lines of symmetry they have. Draw or hold up an equilateral triangle and ask children to say how many lines of symmetry it has (three). Rotate the shape as children find it much easier to see vertical or horizontal lines of symmetry rather than diagonal ones.

Look together at and answer the questions on screen 3 of the interactive activity 'Shape shifting' on the CD-ROM. Discuss that a circle has an infinite number of lines of symmetry and complete the activity screen.

Independent work: Give each child the photocopiable page '2D shapes – polygons' from the CD-ROM together with mirrors (or reflective equipment), tracing paper and scissors. Ask them to work out and draw on all the lines of symmetry and use suitable reflective equipment or tracing and folding to check. Children should then write the number of lines of symmetry of each shape next to it.

Progress check: Look out for examples of when a child has marked a diagonal which is not a line of symmetry. Ask: *If you fold the shape along this line, are both sides a reflection of each other?* Remind children to rotate the shape to view it from all sides and if necessary, ask them to cut out the shape and fold it for confirmation.

Review

Show part 1 of the photocopiable page 'Visualised shapes' from the CD-ROM. Look at shape h and draw the diagonal that is not a line of symmetry. *What do you notice about this line? Is it a line of symmetry?* Similarly look at the non-rectangular parallelogram (shape c). Children find it hard to believe that such shapes have no lines of reflective symmetry. If necessary, hold up a paper shape and fold it to prove this to them.

Curriculum objectives
● To identify lines of symmetry in 2D shapes presented in different orientations.

Success criteria
● I can identify lines of symmetry.

You will need

General resources
'Visualised shapes'; '2D shapes – polygons'; interactive activity 'Shape shifting'

Equipment
Mirrors or reflective equipment; tracing paper; scissors; rectangular paper, equilateral triangle

Differentiation

Less confident learners
Let children cut out and fold the shapes to find their lines of symmetry.

More confident learners
Ask children to complete a table, with the headings: *Shape, Regular or irregular?, Number of sides, Number of lines of symmetry.* Encourage them to notice that for regular shapes the number of lines of symmetry is the same as the number of sides.

Curriculum objectives

- To compare and classify geometric shapes based on their properties and sizes.

Success criteria

- I can compare shapes based on properties including symmetry.
- I can classify shapes using geometrical properties.

You will need

General resources

'Carroll diagrams'; '2D shapes – polygons'

Equipment

Large sheets of paper; scissors; glue

Differentiation

Less confident learners

Let children sort the shapes into just two categories such as *Regular/Irregular* or *Has more than five sides* and so on.

More confident learners

Ask children to draw further shapes on each diagram.

Lesson 3   Oral and mental starter 7

Main teaching activities

Whole-class work: Display the photocopiable page 'Carroll diagrams' from the CD-ROM. Write the following headings on the first diagram: *Regular shape, Irregular shape, Is a quadrilateral, Is not a quadrilateral*. Discuss a range of shapes that would go into each section of the diagram, revising what each section of it should contain. For example: *Here you would put regular quadrilaterals. Here you would put irregular shapes that do not have four sides* (and so on).

Paired work: Hand out the photocopiable page '2D shapes – polygons' from the CD-ROM to each pair of children. Ask them to draw Carroll diagrams on large sheets of paper with headings such as those given below. They then sort the shapes from the photocopiable sheet into the diagrams, cutting and sticking shapes into each of the sections.

- Regular shape/Irregular shape
- Has two or fewer lines of symmetry/Has more than two lines of symmetry
- Is a quadrilateral/Is not a quadrilateral
- Has more than five sides/Has five or fewer sides
- Has some parallel sides/Has no parallel sides
- Has no right angles/Has at least one right angle.

Progress check: While children are classifying the shapes ask: *What shape should go in this section of the diagram? Why?*

Review

Choose pairs of children to show their Carroll diagrams and to explain to the class which shapes they put in each section.

Curriculum objectives

- To complete a simple symmetric figure with respect to a specific line of symmetry.

Success criteria

- I can draw reflections and complete symmetrical figures.

You will need

Photocopiable sheets

'Reflections'

General resources

Interactive teaching resource 'Reflection grid'

Equipment

Mirrors

Differentiation

Less confident learners

Provide children with mirrors to use to help them explore reflections.

More confident learners

Ask children to create specific shapes, such as a hexagon with a vertical line of symmetry.

Lesson 4   Oral and mental starter 15

Main teaching activities

Whole-class work: Display the interactive teaching resource 'Reflection grid' on the CD-ROM. Make sure the mirror line is vertical (change using the 'Options' button, if necessary), draw a simple shape from squares on one side of the mirror line. Invite children to visualise where the reflection will be and to draw it in. Click 'Done' and then 'Check' to see whether the answer is correct. Repeat for shapes made from squares in vertical, horizontal and diagonal mirror lines.

Paired work: Invite children to use the interactive teaching resource 'Reflection grid' on the CD-ROM to explore different shapes and their reflections.

Independent work: Give each child photocopiable page 'Reflections' from the CD-ROM to draw their own symmetrical shapes by reflecting them in the mirror lines. This can be completed during the remainder of the lesson.

Progress check: During paired work ask: *What would you call this shape? How many sides does it have? Is it regular or irregular?* During independent work ask: *Can you draw an octagon that has a diagonal mirror line? How many sides of the shape would be on this side of the mirror line?*

Review

Invite children to show symmetrical shapes created in the lesson. *Has anyone drawn a shape with more than one line of symmetry?* Using the interactive teaching resource 'Reflection grid', select 'Vertical and Horizontal' under the 'Options' menu and create a shape with two lines of symmetry.

Curriculum objectives
● To compare and classify geometric shapes based on their properties and sizes.

Success criteria
● I can solve problems involving 2D shapes.

You will need
General resources
'Visualised shapes'

Equipment
Individual whiteboards; mirrors

Differentiation
Less confident learners
Provide children with mirrors or other reflective equipment for checking which shapes are symmetrical.

More confident learners
Encourage children to draw their own extra polygons and matching descriptions.

Lesson 5   Oral and mental starter 13

Main teaching activities

Whole-class work: Show both parts of the photocopiable page 'Visualised shapes' from the CD-ROM on the interactive whiteboard. Explain that you are going to describe one of the shapes on the sheet without using its shape name and that you'd like the children to identify which shape they think it is and to write the letter of the shape on their whiteboards. Read out each of these sets of clues and discuss which shape it is.

- *This polygon does not have any lines of symmetry. (It is not symmetrical). It has two right angles. (m)*
- *This polygon has one mirror line that is vertical. It has no right angles. (k) If children say (h), point out that the angle at the top of the kite is a mirror line.*
- *This polygon is regular. It has six lines of symmetry. (l)*
- *This polygon is irregular. It has two lines of symmetry. It has fewer than five sides. (i)*
- *This polygon is irregular. It has two lines of symmetry. It has more than five sides. (q)*

Spend time discussing cases where children have given wrong answers and encourage them to see why their chosen shape does not match the description. Invite them, in pairs, to make up their own descriptions for the shapes and to read them to the class to guess. Explain that they will continue to do this and write down their descriptions in the next activity.

Paired work: Provide each pair with photocopiable page 'Visualised shapes'. Ask them to choose a shape and write a detailed description of it, making reference to numbers of sides, right angles, whether shapes are regular or symmetrical and the number of lines of symmetry that each has. They should try to write a description that matches only one shape.

Progress check: Ask children to read one of their descriptions. *Does it describe more than one of these shapes? How can you add something to the description so that it only describes this shape? What are the differences between these two shapes?*

Review

Give children a few moments to discuss with their partner which description they think is best. Choose pairs to read their favourite description aloud and ask the others to identify which shape is being described. To finish the lesson read out the following description: *This polygon is irregular. It has no parallel sides. Which of the shapes could it be?*

Ask children in pairs to list on their whiteboards all the shapes that this could be (e, h, j, k n, t). Ask: *What extra piece of information could we add so that it only describes one of the shapes?* For example: *It has three sides* (e), or *It is a quadrilateral with one right angle* (h) or *It is a quadrilateral with no right angles* (j).

Measurement

Expected prior learning

Children should be able to:

- give the common units of measure for length, mass, capacity and time
- give the number of seconds in a minute and the number of days in each month, year and leap year
- measure the perimeters of rectangles
- multiply and divide numbers by 10, 100 and 1000.

Topic	Curriculum objectives	Expected outcomes
Measurement	**Lesson 1**	
	To estimate, compare and calculate different measures, including money in pounds and pence.	Know units of measure, and their abbreviations.
		Know relationships between units.
		Make estimates and compare different measurements.
	Lesson 2	
	To convert between different units of measure [for example kilometre to metre; hour to minute].	Convert between whole number metric units of measure (larger to smaller units).
	Lesson 3	
	To convert between different units of measure [for example kilometre to metre; hour to minute].	Convert pounds to pence and pence to pounds.
	To estimate, compare and calculate different measures, including money in pounds and pence.	Convert decimal measurement from a larger metric unit to a smaller one.
		Estimate, compare and calculate different measures.
	Lesson 4	
	To measure and calculate the perimeter of a rectilinear figure (including squares) in centimetres and metres.	Calculate perimeters of rectilinear shapes, including sides with lengths not given.
	Lesson 5	
	To convert between different units of measure [for example kilometre to metre; hour to minute].	Convert between units of time.
		Solve problems involving measures.
	To solve problems involving converting from hours to minutes; minutes to seconds; years to months; weeks to days.	

Oral and mental starters for week 6

See bank of starters on pages 45, 86 and 126. Oral and mental starters are also on the CD-ROM.

16 Multiply by 10 and 100

6 Fact practice (addition)

14 Measurement facts

Overview of progression

During this week the children will revise, consolidate and extend their knowledge of units of measurement, including their abbreviations and the relationships between them. They will estimate and compare measures and, in lesson 2, will convert from one whole number unit to another in different metric measurement topics. In lesson 3 children will be given opportunities to convert amounts of money from pence to pounds and vice versa, together with decimal measurements. Lesson 4 explores the perimeter of rectilinear shapes and builds on children's previous experiences of finding perimeters of rectangles and simple shapes in Year 3. The final lesson of the week explores measurement problems including those related to time. Children will be given opportunity to convert between units of time and estimate and compare them.

Watch out for

The most common error in measurement topics is that children fail to write a unit at all – for example, 6 rather than 6cm or 6 seconds. Watch out for children doing this (or giving the wrong unit) and draw attention to the fact that we do *not* put an s on the end of the abbreviated unit (as in 5cms).

Creative context

Link this measurement work to science activities, cooking, athletics and other sporting activities.

Vocabulary

capacity, centimetres (cm), century, day, gram (g), hour, kilogram (kg), kilometre (km), length, litre (l), mass, measurement, metre (m), millilitre (ml), millimetre (mm), minute, month, perimeter, second, time, unit, week, year

Curriculum objectives
● To estimate, compare and calculate different measures.

Success criteria
● I can identify units of measure and their abbreviations.
● I know the relationships between units.
● I can make estimates and compare different measurements.

You will need
Photocopiable sheets
'Which is greater?'

Differentiation
Less confident learners

For those children who are uncertain with the relationships between units of measure, ensure that the list of units is provided for them to refer to.

More confident learners

Ask children to choose measurements from the sheet and to suggest something that might have that measurement, such as: *1000m is the distance from my home to school, 45 minutes is the length of time we have for a lunch break, or 300ml is about the capacity of a mug.*

Lesson 1
Oral and mental starter 16

Main teaching activities

Whole-class work: Begin the week with a revision of units of measurements and measuring equipment. Write these measurement topics on the board:

Length   Mass   Capacity   Time

Ask the children to think of other words used to describe length, such as *height, width, perimeter, distance, depth, thickness, breadth,* and discuss the uses of these terms. as a measurement of length.

Now ask: *What instruments do we use to measure length? Mass? Capacity? Time?* Beneath each of the measurement topics listed on the board, write a list of some of the measuring instruments we might use. For example:

Length	Mass	Capacity	Time
ruler, tape measure, metre stick, trundle wheel	bathroom or kitchen scales, balance scales	measuring jug bucket	watch, clock egg timer

Ask: *What is a unit of measurement?* Discuss the word '*unit*' in this context and explain that when we give a measurement we have to say a *number* and then the *unit* we are using. For example, say: *44.* Ask: *44 what? Centimetres? Seconds? Grams? Litres?* Discuss that it would be inappropriate to describe a length as 44 grams, or a capacity as 44 seconds.

Write the appropriate metric units beneath each measurement using words rather than abbreviations. If imperial measures are offered, explain that, the focus is on the most common units (called metric units), although there are others we will come to later.

kilometres, metres, centimetres, millimetres	kilograms, grams	litres, millilitres,	years, days months, weeks, hours minutes, seconds

Read out some measurements such as 14 kilograms, 12 millilitres, 4 centimetres, and invite children to write these measurements in a shortened form – for example, 14kg, 12ml, 4cm.

Invite children to say how many of one unit make up another and build a list on the board. For example: 10mm = 1cm, 100cm = 1m, 1000m = 1km, 1000g = 1kg, 1000ml = 1l, 60 seconds = 1 minute, 60 minutes = 1 hour, 24 hours = 1 day, 7 days = 1 week (and so on). Leave this on the board for reference throughout the lesson.

Independent work: Provide each child with photocopiable page 'Which is greater?' from the CD-ROM. Ask them to use the < or > signs to show which measurement is greater, such as 1000m or half a kilometre.

Progress check: As children are comparing measurements, ask: *How many grams make up a kilogram? What about half/quarter/three quarters of a kilogram?*

Review

Revise the units of length, mass, capacity and time and their abbreviations. Choose some children to make up and call out measurements and invite the rest of the class to say (a) which type of measurement it is, (b) how you would write the abbreviation and (c) what this might be measuring. For example:

1.6 metres: (a) length   (b) 1.6m   (c) the height of teacher

Curriculum objectives

● To convert between different units of measure.

Success criteria

● I can convert between whole-number metric units of measure (larger to smaller units).

You will need

Equipment

Individual whiteboards; number cards

Differentiation

Less confident learners

Give these children number cards and a place value chart showing the column headings TH H T U. They can make each number and then multiply it by 10, 100 or 1000 to convert it from one measurement to another.

More confident learners

Encourage children to convert decimals with one or two decimal places, such as 0.5cm = 5mm, 2.7m = 270cm, 3.75kg = 3750g.

Lesson 2 — Oral and mental starter 16

Main teaching activities

Whole-class work: Tell the children that today they are going to convert units of measurement. Write 2cm on the board and ask: *How could this length be written using millimetres instead?* Explain that we can convert 2cm into 20mm as both measurements are the same length. *As 10mm = 1cm we multiply by 10.* Write the table headings below and fill in measurements in cm to convert to mm, revising multiplying numbers by 10.

cm ⟶ ×10 ⟶ mm

2cm	20mm
7cm	70mm…

Repeat for other measurements, converting from a large unit to a small one, such as 3m to 300cm. Remind children that when multiplying by 10, 100 or 1000 the digits of the number move to the left. Practise a number of conversions together, reinforcing the units and stating each as an equivalence. For example say: *Three metres is the same length as 300cm.*

Paired work: Children draw simple table headings like that above, such as cm ⟶ mm, m ⟶ cm, km ⟶ m, kg ⟶ g and l ⟶ ml. They take it in turns to write a measurement and their partner converts it to the smaller unit.

Progress check: Children read out the numbers from their tables as measurement equivalents: *Two kilograms is the same mass as 2000 grams.* Ask related questions: *How many grams is the same as five kilograms?*

Review

Invite children to call out measurements for others to convert to a smaller unit.

Curriculum objectives

● To convert between different units of measure.
● To estimate, compare and calculate different measures, including money.

Success criteria

● I can convert decimal measurements from a larger unit to a smaller one.
● I can estimate, compare and calculate measures.

You will need

Photocopiable sheets

'Missing measurements and money'

Equipment

Individual whiteboards; place value chart; number cards

Differentiation

Less confident learners

Give children number cards and a place value chart.

More confident learners

Children can write their own equivalence statements involving two related units.

Lesson 3 — Oral and mental starter 16

Main teaching activities

Whole-class work: Write the following headings and explain that we can convert money in the same way as measurements. *What is £2 in pence?* List some amounts in whole pounds and revise converting to pence by multiplying by 100. Remind children that the digits move two places to the left.

pounds ⟶ ×100 ⟶ pence (p)

£2	200p
£13	1300p

Then list amounts in pounds as decimals. Use a place value chart (HTU.th) to show how we can multiply decimals by 100 by moving the digits two places to the left. For example: £4.30 ⟶ 430p, £8.27 ⟶ 827p. Provide a range of decimal amounts in pounds. Ask children to write each in pence on their individual whiteboards and hold up. Similarly, return to the measurement topics explored in the previous lesson. Give decimal measurements, in the larger unit each time, and ask children to convert each to the smaller unit.

Independent work: Give each child photocopiable page 'Missing measurements and money' from the CD-ROM to complete.

Progress check: Ask: *Which numbers do you find most difficult to convert? Why?*

Review

Provide some simple examples of converting a smaller unit to a larger one including amounts of money in pence, such as 800p, 440p, 1275p. *How would you convert each of these to pounds?* Remind children that they should divide by 100 and move the digits two places to the right.

Curriculum objectives
● To measure and calculate the perimeter of a rectilinear figure in centimetres and metres.

Success criteria
● I can calculate perimeters of rectilinear shapes, including sides with lengths not given.

You will need
Photocopiable sheets
'Perimeter puzzles'
Equipment
Rulers; metre stick; string; scissors

Differentiation
Less confident learners
Support children in measuring accurately and provide a range of rectangles (rather than rectilinear shapes) to focus on finding perimeters.
More confident learners
Children could draw their own more complex rectilinear shapes and measure lengths and find perimeters.

Lesson 4

Main teaching activities

Whole-class work: Draw a large rectangle on the board and measure each of the sides using a metre stick or ruler. Label all four sides with the measurements in centimetres (for example, 28cm, 42cm, 28cm, 42cm). *What is special about the opposite sides of a rectangle?* (The lengths are the same.) Now use some string to go around the edge of the rectangle. *This length of string is the distance all around the edge of the shape. What word do we use for this?* (Perimeter) Revise that the perimeter can be found by adding the four dimensions. Discuss that a quicker way of finding the perimeter is by adding the length and the width and then doubling (28 + 42 = 70, 70 × 2 = 140).

Now draw a large copy of the following shape:

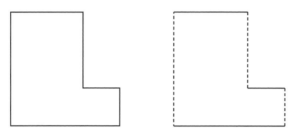

Use the string and scissors to demonstrate that the dotted length on the left is equal to the sum of the dotted lengths on the right. Similarly demonstrate that the longest horizontal line is equal to the two other horizontal lines. Use this information to find the perimeter of the shape. Discuss appropriate mental addition strategies the children could use.

Draw another rectilinear shape and give some but not all of the dimensions. Encourage children to find each missing length using subtraction strategies and then to find the perimeter.

Independent work: Give each child photocopiable pages 'Perimeter puzzles' from the CD-ROM. Explain that some of the shapes require measuring with a ruler and some are sketches of rooms.

Progress check: During independent work ask: *How did you work out the length of this unmarked side? What method of addition did you use to find the total of these numbers?*

Review

Take feedback on the photocopiable page. *How did you work out the perimeter/ length of this side? How much skirting board would be needed for this room?*

Curriculum objectives
● To convert between different units of measure.
● To solve problems involving converting from hours to minutes; minutes to seconds; years to months; weeks to days.

Success criteria
● I can convert between units of time.
● I can solve problems involving measures.

You will need
Photocopiable sheets
'Present problems'

Differentiation
Less confident learners
Let children work in pairs to solve the problems on the photocopiable sheet.
More confident learners
Ask children to make up their own problems of this type.

Main teaching activities

Whole-class work: Explain that in today's lesson the focus will be on solving measurement problems including those involving time. *What units of time do we use? How long can things take?* Invite children to list a range of time units (years, weeks, seconds and so on). Draw the following headings along the top of the board and ask children to say what we would multiply by each time to convert from one unit of time to the next:

years ⟶ × ? ⟶ months   weeks ⟶ × ? ⟶ days   days ⟶ × ? ⟶ hours

hours ⟶ × ? ⟶ minutes   minutes ⟶ × ? ⟶ seconds

Complete each heading with the correct multiplier, that is 12, 7, 24, 60 and 60, and give some simple numbers for the larger unit to convert to the smaller unit (4 years, 5 weeks, 2 days and so on). Discuss appropriate multiplication strategies, including multiplying by units of 10: *If you know that 4 × 6 = 24, then what is 4 × 60?*

Provide some easy lengths of time given in the smaller units, such as 120 seconds or 36 months. *How do I convert this to a larger unit, such as to minutes or years?* Remind children that if converting from a smaller unit to a larger one you would need to *divide* by the number. For example, when converting 36 months into years you would divide 36 by 12 to get the number of years. List examples under the headings and provide practice of this.

Present some problems that require children to use the headings on the board when converting units of time, for example:

- *Ben's plane is due to take off in 50 hours' time. It is now Friday at 9am. When is Ben's flight?*
- *With his mobile phone contract Jake gets the first three hours of calls free. This month he has made 500 minutes of calls. How many minutes will he pay for?*
- *It is eight weeks and four days until Joe goes on holiday. He decides to save £1 each day until then to use as spending money. How much spending money will he end up with?*

Spend time discussing how each problem could be solved and how a conversion is required in order to solve each problem. Demonstrate how the conversion headings for time and for other measurement topics can be written and used to help reach sensible answers.

Independent work: Provide each child with photocopiable page 'Present problems' from the CD-ROM and ask them to solve each problem, converting units as necessary.

Progress check: Ask children to describe how they solved a problem from their photocopiable sheet: *How did you work out this answer? What unit did you convert from/to? What number did you multiply or divide by?*

Review

Give children a few moments to discuss with a partner which problems they found easier and which they found harder. Invite volunteers to come to the front and demonstrate how they solved one of their problems and to show their working on the board.

Curriculum objectives
● To recognise the place value of each digit in a four-digit number (thousands, hundreds, tens and ones).

You will need
1. Check
Oral and mental starter
23 Place value chains (2)

2. Assess
0–9 number cards; place value cards

3. Further practice
Oral and mental starters
3 Writing numbers
16 Multiply by 10 and 100
29 Place value additions and subtractions
Photocopiable sheets
'Partition party'

Place value of four-digit numbers

Most children should be able to say the value of digits in four-digit numbers.

Some children will not have made such progress and will require further practice in partitioning and using place value cards.

1. Check

23 Place value chains (2)

Start by adding or subtracting 1, 10 or 100, asking children to say which is the hundreds, tens or units digit. Extend this to adding or subtracting 1000 to and from four-digit numbers and note whether children understand how the thousands digit will change.

- *Which is the hundreds digit? What is its value?*
- *How can you add/subtract 1 to the tens/thousands digit?*

2. Assess

Children take turns to make a four-digit number with four 1–9 number cards and then to partition it (5362 = 5000 + 300 + 60 + 2). Challenge the more confident to include zero digits in their numbers (say, 8405). If children are unsure, provide place value cards and ask them to make each number and separate them to partition them. Check that all children can identify which digit is which and can say its value. For example: *The hundreds digit in 5385 is 3 and is worth 300.* Record the outcomes.

3. Further practice

Use the suggested oral and mental starter to reinforce place value ideas. Photocopiable page 46 'Partition party' gives further experience of partitioning numbers.

Curriculum objectives
● To round any number to the nearest 10, 100 or 1000.

You will need
1. Check
Oral and mental starter
25 Rounding round

2. Assess
0–9 number cards; 'Blank number lines'

3. Further practice
Oral and mental starters
23 Place value chains (2)
4 Units digit
24 Secret numbers

General resources
'Target grids (2)'

Rounding four-digit numbers to the nearest 10 and 100

Most children should be able to round two-, three- and even four-digit numbers to the nearest 10 and 100.

Some children will not have made such progress and will require further practice in estimating and marking numbers on number lines.

1. Check

25 Rounding round

Start by rounding two-, three- and then four-digit numbers to the nearest 10. Observe whether children understand that the answer will always be a multiple of 10. Then round three- and four-digit numbers to the nearest 100. Again observe whether children understand that the answers will be multiples of 100.

- *When rounding to the nearest 10, what do we do if a number ends in 5?*
- *When rounding to the nearest 100, what do we do if a number ends in 50?*

2. Assess

Children take turns to make a four-digit number with four 0–9 number cards. They round each to the nearest 10 and then to the nearest 100. Challenge the more confident to also round to the nearest 1000 and to use the larger digits (for example, 6987). Let those who lack confidence mark numbers on a number line to help them visualise which multiple of 10/100 the number is closest to. Check that all children give answers that are multiples of 10 or 100 respectively. Record the outcomes.

3. Further practice

The photocopiable page 'Target grids (2)' from the CD-ROM provides four-digit numbers to round to the nearest 10 and 100.

Curriculum objectives
● To recall multiplication facts for multiplication tables up to 12 × 12.

You will need
1. Check

Oral and mental starter

12 9-times table

2. Assess
'Multiple questions'; multiplication square

3. Further practice

Oral and mental starters

8 Function machine

11 Magic square (1)

20 Bingo

Photocopiable sheets
'Multiples grid game'; 'Missing numbers'

9-times table facts

Most children should be able to recall the multiplication facts for the 9-times table.

Some children will not have made such progress and will require further practice in learning the multiples and then recalling the multiplication facts.

1. Check

12 9-times table

Encourage the children to recall the facts quickly by keeping the pace sharp. Observe which children are confident and which need further practice. Extend to division facts for multiples of 9 for the more confident children. Ask:

- *What are eight nines?*
- *Which multiple of 9 is 99?*
- *What is the product of 4 and 9?*

2. Assess

Provide photocopiable page 47 'Multiple questions' with 9 written into the blank space at the top. Observe which children work quickly and accurately. Give children lacking confidence a multiplication square to refer to. For the more confident, when they have finished the activity, ask them to write a word problem which uses multiplying by 9. They can then swap word problems with their partner to find the solution. Record the outcomes.

3. Further practice

The recommended oral and mental starter activities and photocopiable sheets provide further practice in recall of multiplication facts for the 9-times table and other multiplication facts.

Curriculum objectives
● To convert between different units of measure [for example, kilometre to metre; hour to minute].

You will need
1. Check

Oral and mental starter

14 Measurement facts

2. Assess
'Converting units'; place value chart

3. Further practice

Oral and mental starters

35 Mass facts

16 Multiply by 10 and 100

39 Divide by 10 and 100

Photocopiable sheets
'Metric units for length'; 'Missing measurements and money'; 'Which is greater?'

Converting between metric units of measure

Most children should be able to convert from centimetres to millimetres, metres to centimetres, kilometres to metres, kilograms to grams and litres to millilitres.

Some children will not have made such progress and may need to learn the relationships between units or have further practice in multiplying numbers by 10, 100 and 1000.

1. Check

14 Measurement facts

Choose whole-number measurements in metres and the corresponding measures in centimetres to write into the grid. Observe whether children can recognise the relationships between metres and centimetres and can find equivalent pairs. Extend this to including several measures involving decimals (for example, 1.2m). Again observe whether children can convert each measurement to centimetres.

- *How many centimetres in one metre? Millimetres in one centimetre? Metres in one kilometre?*
- *How can you change a whole number or decimal from metres into centimetres?*

2. Assess

Provide photocopiable page 48 'Converting units'. Observe the children at work. Give children lacking confidence a place value grid to refer to when multiplying by 10, 100 and 1000. For the more confident, when they have finished the activity, ask them to write other equivalent pairs of measurements. Record the outcomes.

3. Further practice

The recommended oral and mental starter activities provide further practice in converting between units and multiplying and dividing by 10, 100 and 1000. The photocopiable sheets provide further experience of comparing measurements given in different units.

Oral and mental starters

Number and place value

Place value chains (1)

Begin to write a chain of numbers involving adding or subtracting 1, 10 or 100 to one-, two- or three-digit numbers. For example, write:

46 +10 ⟶ 56 +100 ⟶ 156 − 1 ⟶ 155 +100 ⟶ ....

Ask the children to continue the chain with other numbers in this way or to identify what has been added or subtracted to give a new number in the chain.

Extension
Use multiples of 1, 10 or 100.

Hundred square chase

You will need '100 square' from the CD-ROM. Split the class into two teams for this game. Identify one team as the runner and the other as the chaser. The runner starts on 1 and the chaser on 91. Teams take it in turns to choose a move from the following list: +11, −11, + 9, −9, + 1, −1. The aim is for chaser to reach runner.

Extension
Use the following list: +19, −19, +21, −21 and so on.

Writing numbers

Explain that when you say a number, you would like the children to write it on their individual whiteboards. When you say *Show me*, the children should hold up their boards to show you their recorded number (in either figures or in words). Say:

- *Write 473... 3000... 4600... 5784... 8008... Show me.*
- *Write the number that is one more than _____. Show me.*
- *Write the number that is one less than _____. Show me.*

Now focus on four-digit numbers. Check that the children have understood how to write numbers that include the digit zero.

Units digit

Provide each child with a number fan. Start the lesson by discussing simple sequences, for example, counting on in 5s from zero or counting back in 2s from 20. Begin counting aloud and then stop. Say:

- *What is the units digit of the next number? How do you know?*

Ask the children to hold up their number fan to show the units digit.

- *How do you know?*
- *What do you notice about the units digits of the numbers in the sequence?*

Extension
Over time explore a range of sequences, including counting in 10s or 100s from any number, where the units digit will always remain the same.

Addition, subtraction, multiplication and division

Double-take

Hold up a paper bag and tell the children to imagine you are dropping coins into it (tapping the bag as you do so). Tell them how much money to imagine is in the bag (say, 57p). Pretend to wave a magic wand over the bag to double the amount of money and ask: *How much money is in the bag now?* (£1.14) Now choose a child to give some of the money to: *Lia, you take 72p from the bag.* The children should then say how much money is in the bag after this. (42p) Then wave the wand to double the new amount. Continue in this way, doubling and then choosing a child to take out some money. Discuss suitable mental strategies for keeping the running total.

Extension

Start with a multiple of 10p or 100p, such as 570p (£5.70) or 5700p (£57.00). Double and then take a multiple of 10p or 100p in the same way.

Fact practice (addition)

Choose two children to come to the front. In a similar way to the game 'Rock, Paper, Water', on a count of 3 both children hold up between one and ten fingers. The class must quickly find the total number of fingers. If the answer is even the pair remains, if not a new pair comes to the front.

7 Fact practice (subtraction)

You will need cards showing numbers to 20. Put the cards in two piles and turn over the top two cards. The children must quickly find the difference, write the answer on their individual whiteboards and hold them up.

Partition party

■ Partition these numbers.

2375	→	2000	+	300	+	70	+	5
8245	→		+		+		+	
1529	→		+		+		+	
9618	→		+		+		+	
3528	→		+		+		+	
7812	→		+		+		+	
4619	→		+		+		+	
6279	→		+		+		+	
9009	→		+		+		+	
8080	→		+		+		+	

■ Write five numbers like the ones above on the back of this sheet for your maths partner to partition.

I can partition four-digit numbers.

How did you do?

Multiple questions

- Multiply each of these numbers by [   ].

2   10

6

5   3

4

11

8   9

0

1

7   12

I can multiply.

How did you do?

Converting units

- Fill in the missing numbers.

1. 9m = _____ cm

7. 6.5kg = _____ g

2. 7kg = _____ g

8. 8.3m = _____ cm

3. 12cm = _____ mm

9. 2.1cm = _____ mm

4. 6km = _____ m

10. 0.4m = _____ cm

5. 8l = _____ ml

11. 0.9km = _____ m

6. 32m = _____ cm

12. 0.3l = _____ ml

- Now write some equivalent pairs of measurements using different units.

I can convert units.

How did you do?

Addition and subtraction: mental and written methods

Expected prior learning

Children should be able to:

- rapidly recall and use addition and subtraction facts to 20
- recognise the place value of each digit in three- and four-digit numbers
- accurately add and subtract numbers mentally, including one- and two-digit numbers.

Topic	Curriculum objectives	Expected outcomes
Addition and subtraction	**Lesson 1**	
	To add and subtract numbers with up to 4-digits using the formal methods of columnar addition and subtraction where appropriate.	Add numbers mentally and use place value ideas, for example 238 + 20.
	Lesson 2	
	To add and subtract numbers with up to 4-digits using the formal written methods of columnar addition and subtraction where appropriate. To estimate and use inverse operations to check answers to a calculation.	Add four-digit numbers using column addition, estimating to check.
	Lesson 3	
	To add and subtract numbers with up to 4-digits using the formal written methods of columnar addition and subtraction where appropriate. To estimate and use inverse operations to check answers to a calculation.	Subtract numbers, using mental methods and place value; estimating to check.
	Lesson 4	
	To add and subtract numbers with up to 4-digits using the formal written methods of columnar addition and subtraction where appropriate. To estimate and use inverse operations to check answers to a calculation.	Use a written column method of subtraction and check by adding.
	Lesson 5	
	To solve addition and subtraction two-step problems in contexts, deciding which operations and methods to use and why.	Solve two-step problems involving addition and subtraction, choosing appropriate and effective calculation methods.

Preparation

Lesson 2: copy 'Target darts', one per child

Lesson 3: copy 'How did I subtract?' (for less confident learners)

Lesson 4: copy 'Subtraction pairs', one per child

Lesson 5: copy 'Money problems', one per child

You will need

Photocopiable sheets

'Target darts'; 'How did I subtract?'; 'Subtraction pairs'; 'Money problems'

General resources

'Target darts template'

Equipment

Individual whiteboards; dice; squared paper

Further practice

'Target darts template' can be used to prepare new sets of 3- and 4-digit numbers to support understanding of columnar addition

Oral and mental starters for week 1

See bank of starters on pages 44, 45 and 126. Oral and mental starters are also on the CD-ROM.

1	Place value chains (1)
6	Fact practice (addition)
7	Fact practice (subtraction)
18	Operation follow-on

Overview of progression

During this week the children will consolidate and extend their abilities to mentally add and subtract three- and four-digit numbers using ideas of place value and appropriate mental methods and will use column methods of addition and subtraction. They will use inverses to check their calculations and will make and use estimates to check whether answers are sensible. It is important that children are given opportunities to decide when a particular calculation approach is best and during lessons 2, 4 and 5 they will be encouraged to select the best strategies for calculations. In lesson 5 they will use and apply these calculation strategies in solving two-step problems.

Watch out for

Ensure that children are confident in place value ideas and look out for children who fail to appreciate the ease of adding or subtracting numbers like 30, 200, 5000 to a number. Provide such children with a place value chart and ask them to partition numbers before adding (for example, $2314 + 300 = 2000 + 300 + 10 + 4 + 300$). Help them to appreciate the value of each digit in four-digit numbers. This will help them with mental methods and when practising written methods of addition and subtraction, as it can help them appreciate the place value implications of why we carry and exchange.

Creative context

Look out for opportunities to perform addition and subtraction in real-life contexts, such as number of absent children, dinner numbers, cooking situations.

Vocabulary

add, altogether, carry, column, difference, digit, equals, exchange, fewer, leave, less, make, minus, more, partition, plus, sign, subtract, sum, take away, total

Curriculum objectives
● To add numbers with up to four-digits.

Success criteria
● I can add numbers mentally and use place value ideas.

You will need
Equipment
Individual whiteboards; dice

Differentiation
Less confident learners
Provide children with only three dice per pair and ask them to create pairs of three-digit numbers to add.

More confident learners
Let these children use the digits 1–6 on the dice rather than 0–5 for the paired activity. They could also explore five-digit numbers in the same way.

Lesson 1
Oral and mental starter 6

Main teaching activities

Whole-class work: Explain that in this lesson children will use ideas of place value and other mental strategies to add numbers. Begin by drawing two large 'bags' of numbers on the board; the first with four-digit numbers made from digits less than 5 (including zeroes) and the second with multiples of 1, 10, 100, 1000 made from digits less than 6. For example:

1020, 3024, 4444, 2114,   400, 5000, 3, 30,

4303, 2202, 3013, 1114   200, 1000, 50, 4000

Underline a number from each 'bag' and ask children to say the number names for each and then add them, such as: *one thousand and twenty add four hundred*, 1020 + 400 = ? Ask: *How can you say the answer without doing much 'work'?* Encourage children to explain what makes these questions easy. Point to the first number and say *How many hundreds does 1020 have? How many hundreds are we adding to it?* Help children to see that we simply replace the 0 with 4 to add 400. Repeat for other pairs of numbers from the bags. Children can write answers on their individual whiteboards and hold up for checking.

Write extra numbers into the second bag that involve two or three non-zero digits (say, 3020, 1110, 4005) and continue in the same way: 4303 + 3020 = 7323. Invite children to the front to explain how they are certain about each answer.

Ask extension questions such as: *Which pair of numbers, one from each bag, has a total of 9444... 7013... 8449?* Invite children to discuss answers with a partner and to make up new similar questions of their own to ask the rest of the class.

Paired work: For this game, provide each pair with four dice, but explain to them that they must think of the 6 as a zero for this lesson. (Small stickers displaying a zero could be put on the 6s, if time). Invite each player to take turns to roll the four dice twice to create two four-digit numbers (with 6s replaced by zeros), such as 3410 and 3023. The player adds the number and records this as an addition sentence: 3410 + 3023 = 6433. Then the second player does the same. The player with the higher total scores a point and the game continues.

Progress check: Invite children to explain the additions they are creating. *What is the name of this number? How many thousands/hundreds/tens/units has it? How can you partition this number into thousands, hundred, tens and units?*

Review

Select the number 4444 and say you are going to keep adding 10. Invite the children to count along with you: 4454, 4464, 4474, 4484, 4494... Ask them what will happen next, when another 10 is added (4504). Repeat for repeatedly adding 100 in the same way: 4444, 4544, 4644, 4744, 4844, 4944, 5044... Ask children to describe how the digits change when 1 is added to 9 in each of the columns.

Curriculum objectives
● To add numbers with up to four-digits using columnar addition where appropriate.
● To estimate to check answers to a calculation.

Success criteria
● I can add four-digit numbers using column addition, estimating to check.

You will need
Photocopiable sheets
'Target darts'; 'Target darts template'
Equipment
Squared paper

Differentiation
Less confident learners
Modify the 'Target darts template' to include only three-digit numbers and 1 or 2 lower four-digit numbers (for example, 1129, 1031).
More confident learners
Invite these children to find new targets by adding pairs from the darts. Can they find the largest target?

Lesson 2   Oral and mental starter 1

Main teaching activities

Whole-class work: Explain that this lesson is about adding four-digit numbers, but that, unlike the previous lesson when questions were place value additions, today they will require a written or mental method.

Write the numbers 3826 and 5158 on the board. Ask: *What is the approximate total of these two numbers?* Discuss children's answers, expressing 3826 as nearly 4000 or close to 3800, and 5158 as more than 5000 or close to 5100. Approximate answers might be 9000 or 8900. Focus attention on the importance of finding an approximate answer before calculating exactly.

Ask: *How could we find the exact total mentally?* Invite two or three children to come to the board and to explain ways that this could be done. Encourage a variety of methods, such as using an empty number line or partitioning each number and then adding. Then ask children to identify the thousands, hundreds, tens and units/ones digit of each number. Write the column headings Th H T and U. *It can be helpful to write the numbers under these column headings.* Set out the numbers vertically and demonstrate the link between partitioned mental strategies and the more formal written method involving carrying across one 10. For example:

		Th	H	T	U
		3	8	2	6
	+	5	1	5	8
		8	9	8	4
				1	

$$3000 + 800 + 20 + 6$$
$$+ 5000 + 100 + 50 + 8$$
$$8000 + 900 + 70 + 14$$

Compare the answers with the approximation/estimate and check that it is sensible.

Repeat for other questions that involve carrying once, in different positions, such as:

$$2000 + 500 + 60 + 2$$
$$+ 7000 + 300 + 60 + 4$$
$$9000 + 800 + 120 + 6$$

		Th	H	T	U
		2	5	6	2
	+	7	3	6	4
		9	9	2	6
				1	

Invite children to instruct you as to how to do the written method and to explain in their own words why we carry digits across from a column to the column to its left. In the same way, include some questions that involve more than one exchange.

Independent work: Ask children to complete photocopiable page 'Target darts' from the CD-ROM. They should choose pairs of numbers to add and try to hit as many targets as possible. The activity encourages children to estimate the total first before committing themselves to calculating. Provide children with squared paper and ask them to use a column method of addition.

Progress check: Invite children to discuss the decisions they made when attempting to choose a pair that might hit a particular target. *What estimates did you make? What made you think that these two numbers might make this target number? What did you round these two numbers to? What do you notice about the sum of the two units digits?*

Review

Take feedback on the photocopiable sheet. Ask: *Why do we need to estimate an answer before we calculate it?* Invite children to share their answers and their written methods and to explain how they were able to guess which arrows made which targets.

Curriculum objectives

● To subtract numbers with up to four-digits using columnar subtraction where appropriate.
● To estimate to check answers to a calculation.

Success criteria

● I can subtract numbers, using mental methods and place value, estimating to check.

You will need

Photocopiable sheets

'How did I subtract?'

Differentiation

Less confident learners

Provide children with photocopiable page 'How did I subtract?' if they did not use it in Autumn 1 or, if they did, numbers could be altered slightly.

More confident learners

Ask children for further appropriate subtraction questions for each method.

Lesson 3   Oral and mental starter 1

Main teaching activities

Whole-class work: Explain that this lesson is about revising strategies of mental subtraction that the children already know. Give some place value subtractions as a warm-up, such as 4862 − 800, 3526 − 20, 4637 − 1020. Then list these subtractions: 5004 − 4897, 5783 − 152, 4618 − 598. Ask children to discuss in pairs how they would answer each question mentally. Take feedback and list strategies used, such as:

- finding the difference by counting up (for example, from 4897 to 5004)
- counting back in hundreds, tens and then ones (5783 − 100 − 50 − 2)
- subtracting near multiples of 100 and adjusting (4618 − 600 + 2).

Ask: *Which method is best for each question? Why?* Explain that counting up from the smaller number is useful when two numbers are close together (such as 5004 and 4897) and counting back is useful when the number being subtracted is quite small (such as 152). *Now let's estimate, calculate and check.* Demonstrate the strategies on the board, including using empty number lines.

Paired work: Write a range of questions such as: 4003 − 2989, 2723 − 42, 3915 − 798, 7003 − 5889. Ask children in pairs to sort them into groups to show which method of mental subtraction is most appropriate for each. They should then estimate, calculate and check.

Progress check: Remind children to use their estimates to check. Invite them to suggest other questions that could be answered using each of the strategies.

Review

Write the question 5643 − 4765 and discuss why some questions are more difficult to solve mentally than others. Explain that written methods are useful for some questions that are hard to solve mentally.

Curriculum objectives

● To subtract numbers with up to four-digits using columnar subtraction where appropriate.
● To use inverse operations to check answers to a calculation.

Success criteria

● I can use a written column method of subtraction and can check by adding.

You will need

Photocopiable sheets

'Subtraction pairs'

Differentiation

Less confident learners

Provide place value cards to support children with this work.

More confident learners

When the children have completed the photocopiable sheet, provide them with additional four-digit numbers to complete on the back of the sheet.

Lesson 4   Oral and mental starter 7

Main teaching activities

Whole-class work: Introduce the column method of subtraction to the class, making the link between its expanded form and the condensed/compact form, using the following example:

					Th	H	T	U
9000	800	80	16		9	8	$\overset{8}{\cancel{9}}$	$^{1}6$
− 5000	100	50	8		− 5	1	5	8
4000	700	30	8		4	7	3	8

Ask: *How could we check whether our answer is correct?* Remind children to make estimates before beginning but show also how the answer can be added to the number subtracted to see if this gives the first number (4738 + 5158 = 9896). Repeat for other written subtraction examples involving exchange once, but in other columns, such as 7442 − 5271 or 8463 − 6752.

Independent work: Give each child photocopiable page 'Subtraction pairs' from the CD-ROM to complete.

Progress check: Invite children to explain how they subtracted each time and ask them to say the inverse calculation they used.

Review

Provide a range of four-digit subtractions, including those that could be solved mentally and ask children to say which approach they would use and why.

Curriculum objectives

● To solve addition and subtraction two-step problems in contexts.

Success criteria

● I can solve two-step problems involving addition and subtraction, choosing an appropriate and effective calculation method.

You will need

Photocopiable sheets

'Money problems'

Differentiation

Less confident learners

Invite children to sketch a quick picture or diagram to help them decide which operation or operations to use when solving each problem. The prices could also be adjusted before photocopying if necessary.

More confident learners

Encourage children to create their own one- and two-step problems for other children to solve.

Main teaching activities

Whole-class work: Remind children that this week they have been adding and subtracting four-digit numbers in different ways, including using column methods. Explain that today they will be able to use these strategies to solve money problems. Ask: *How many pence in £1? How many pence is £1.50? How many pence is £12.32?* Encourage children to convert amounts in pounds into pence and to see that prices such as £41.19 can be thought of in pence (4119p).

Give four items with prices less than £50 each (not whole pounds), such as £37.49, £16.32, £36.98, £26.76. Point to two items (say, £16.32 and £36.98) and ask what they would cost in total. *Would you use a written method or a mental method for this addition?* Ask children to discuss in pairs how they would answer this and take feedback. For example: *We would add £37 to £16.32 and then take off the 2p*, or *We would write this as a written addition 1632 + 3698*. Ask them to justify their decisions and discuss which might be the most effective method. Repeat for other pairs of additions and also for addition of three of the items.

Next, ask children to say how they would find the difference between pairs of prices, such as: *How much more expensive is this item than that one?* Revise the subtraction strategies explored this week and choose the most appropriate method for each question. Demonstrate how a written method of subtraction could be used. For example, for £37.49 − £26.76 = £10.73:

$$
\begin{array}{r}
3 \;\; {}^6\!\!\!\not{7} \;\; {}^1\!4 \;\; 9 \\
- \; 2 \;\; 6 \;\; 7 \;\; 6 \\
\hline
1 \;\; 0 \;\; 7 \;\; 3
\end{array}
$$

Now introduce several two-step problems involving the prices on the board:

- *Chloe bought these two items and paid with a £50 note. How much change did she get?*
- *Jack is saving to buy this item. He has £15.84 and his mum gives him an extra £12.50. Does he have enough money? How much more does he need?*

Invite children in pairs to discuss each problem and to work on their whiteboards to solve it, using appropriate addition and subtraction strategies.

Paired work: Provide each child with photocopiable page 'Money problems' from the CD-ROM. Invite them to work together to solve the problem on each card, using appropriate addition and subtraction strategies, and estimating and checking solutions.

Progress check: Ask children to show the methods and checking approaches they used to solve each problem. *How did you decide what to do? Did you estimate first? What checking strategy did you use? How can you check using an inverse strategy?*

Review

Take feedback on how the children solved the problems on the photocopiable sheet. Ask: *Which methods of addition and subtraction did you use?* Encourage children to summarise the addition and subtraction strategies used this week and to explain how these were applied in this problem-solving work.

Multiplication: times tables to 12 × 12 and written methods

Expected prior learning

Children should be able to:

● recall and use multiplication facts for the 1, 2, 3, 4, 5, 6, 8 and 10 multiplication tables

● write and calculate mathematical statements for multiplication using the multiplication tables that they know, using mental methods.

Topic	Curriculum objectives	Expected outcomes
Multiplication and division	**Lesson 1**	
	To recall multiplication and division facts for multiplication tables up to 12 × 12. To recognise and use factor pairs and commutativity in mental calculations.	Recall tables facts and identify factor pairs.
	Lesson 2	
	To recall multiplication and division facts for multiplication tables up to 12 × 12. To recognise and use factor pairs and commutativity in mental calculations. To use place value, known and derived facts to multiply and divide mentally, including: multiplying by 0 and 1; dividing by 1; multiplying together three numbers.	Recall tables facts. Multiply mentally, including multiplying three numbers.
	Lesson 3	
	To multiply two-digit and three-digit numbers by a one-digit number using formal written layout.	Multiply two-digit numbers by a one-digit number using, a written method.
	Lesson 4	
	To multiply two-digit and three-digit numbers by a one-digit number using formal written layout.	Multiply two- and three-digit numbers by a one-digit number, using a written method.
	Lesson 5	
	To solve problems involving multiplying and adding, including using the distributive law to multiply two digit numbers by one digit, integer scaling problems and harder correspondence problems such as which n objects are connected to m objects.	Solve one- and two-step problems involving multiplication.

Preparation

Lesson 1: copy 'Factor seeds', one per child

Lesson 3: copy 'Grids for multiplication', one per child; prepare 'Grids for multiplications' for display on the interactive whiteboard (or enlarge to A3)

You will need

Photocopiable sheets
'Factor seeds'; 'Grids for multiplication'

General resources
Interactive teaching resource 'Multiplication square'

Equipment
Individual whiteboards; dice; squared or dotty paper

Further practice

Photocopiable sheets
'Multiples grid game'

Oral and mental starters for week 2

See bank of starters on pages 85, 86, 126 and 127. Oral and mental starters are also on the CD-ROM.

17	True or false
12	9-times table
16	Multiply by 10 and 100
11	Magic square (1)
20	Bingo

Overview of progression

During this week the children will consolidate and extend their abilities to recall multiplication facts and mentally multiply numbers. In the early part of the week they consolidate and revise facts from the 7-, 9-, 11- and 12-times tables in particular and explore factors of numbers. They will multiply numbers mentally and begin to be introduced to more formal written methods of multiplication, initially for multiplying two-digit by one-digit numbers in lesson 3, and moving on to three-digit by one-digit in lesson 4. Lesson 5 gives opportunity for children to use and apply their facts and skills to solve multiplication problems.

Watch out for

For those children who struggle to recall particular times tables facts, provide cards with the questions on one side and answers on the other and encourage them to take them away to learn at home. Ensure that a range of visual, aural and kinaesthetic approaches are used when teaching tables facts to appeal to all learning styles.

Creative context

Look out for opportunities to perform multiplication in real-life contexts, such as getting into teams in PE, sitting on benches in the hall, giving out items such as coloured pencils to children, cooking situations, and so on.

Vocabulary

factor, facts, groups of, lots of, multiple, multiply, **product**, tables, times

Curriculum objectives
● To recall multiplication facts for multiplication tables up to 12 × 12.
● To recognise and use factor pairs and commutativity in mental calculations.

Success criteria
● I can recall tables facts and identify factor pairs.

You will need
Photocopiable sheets
'Factor seeds'
General resources
Interactive teaching resource 'Multiplication square'

Differentiation
Less confident learners
Provide these children with a multiplication square to support them with this work.
More confident learners
Challenge these children with questions such as: *Is it true or false to say that all numbers have an even number of factors? Is it true or false to say that square numbers always have an odd number of factors?*

Lesson 1 — Oral and mental starter 17

Main teaching activities

Whole-class work: Display the interactive teaching resource 'Multiplication square' on the CD-ROM. Take the opportunity to revise some of the more difficult multiplication facts, such as $7 \times 8 = 56$ or $7 \times 6 = 42$. Then ask: *Look at the multiples in the multiplication square. Which numbers appear several times? Why is this?* Encourage children to discuss that there are different ways of making some multiples – for example, 24 can be made from 3×8 and 4×6. *Tell me multiples that only appear once?* Look at the number 49 and discuss that there aren't many numbers that can be multiplied together to make 49: just 7×7 and 1×49. *What numbers don't appear at all in the multiplication square?* Choose a number like 31 and help children to realise that it cannot be made by multiplying numbers other than 1×31. Ensure children understand that every number can be made by multiplying itself by 1.

Tell the children that we call the numbers that are multiplied to make a number 'factors' of the number – for example, the factors pair of 49 are 1×49 and 7×7. Explain that we consider 49×1 the same as 1×49 in this instance.

Choose a number that appears several times in the multiplication square (say, 24) and list all of its factors pairs: 1×24, 2×12, 3×8, 4×6. Encourage the children to work through from 1, making decisions as to whether the number is divisible by the next number and so on. Explain that sometimes the multiplication facts might not be in the times table itself (for example, we don't usually continue the 1-times table up to 24) but that these are still appropriate factor pairs if they lie beyond the times table. Show how, once factor pairs have been written, they can be rearranged in order: $49 \longrightarrow 1, 7, 49$. Explain that the 7 is not repeated in this list.

Independent work: Provide children with photocopiable page 'Factor seeds' from the CD-ROM to complete.

Progress check: As children are writing pairs of factors ask: *Are there any other factors of this number? How can you be sure? Which numbers have you tried dividing this by?*

Review

Ask: *How many numbers can you think of that have an odd number of factors?* Discuss that square numbers (4, 9, 16, 25...) have an odd number of factors. *What do you notice about numbers that have an odd number of factors? Which number between 1 and 100 do you think has the most factors?* (The answer is 96.) List the factors and discuss the factors of other numbers (48, 64, 36 and so on).

Lesson 2 — Oral and mental starter 12

Main teaching activities

Whole-class work: Explain that this lesson focuses on mental multiplication. Write the numbers 24 and 36 on the board. Ask children to come to the front and to write multiplication questions with either answer (4 × 6, 9 × 4 and so on). Keep asking children for further facts and remind them that these are pairs of factors: 3 and 8 are factors of 24 as 3 × 8 is 24. When children have found all the pairs of factors, keep asking them for more multiplications. Without prompting, see if any child thinks of multiplying three or more numbers together, such as 2 × 2 × 6. Once this has been thought of, invite children to keep coming to the front and writing more facts. Encourage them to say which pair of factors they might have split to create a new fact (8 × 3 could become 2 × 4 × 3). Continue for as many other multiplications that involve three, four or more numbers.

Paired work: Ask children in pairs to write as many different multiplication questions with a particular answer, such as 42, 56, 28.... Encourage them to include multiplications with more than two numbers.

Progress check: Ask: *How did you work out this question? Did you use another fact? Have you checked to make sure that this gives the correct answer?*

Review

Take feedback on the number of questions the children have written. Discuss that × 1 can be put on the end of any fact to give another multiplication as it will not change the answer.

Lesson 3 — Oral and mental starter 16

Main teaching activities

Whole-class work: Project onto the interactive whiteboard or use an enlarged copy of photocopiable page 'Grids for multiplication' from the CD-ROM. Remind children that when multiplying a multiple of 10 (such as 20), we can multiply by the single digit and then multiply by 10. Using the first example on the sheet, demonstrate the grid method to multiply 24 by 6 – partitioning, multiplying and then adding the answers together. Invite children to the front to answer other questions on the sheet. Then show that it is not necessary to set it out in the grid arrangement, which takes time and space. Set out the question in columns, go through the formal written method and encourage children to see the links between the grid method and these expanded and condensed arrangements. For example:

```
  H T U    or     H T U    or     H T U
    2 4               2 4             2 4
×     6         ×       6       ×       6
  1 2 0             2 4           1 4 4
    2 4           1 2 0              2
  1 4 4           1 4 4
```

Independent work: Give each child photocopiable page 'Grids for multiplication' from the CD-ROM to complete, using whichever method is appropriate (grid method, expanded or condensed/compact method).

Progress check: Ask: *Which method do you find easiest and why?*

Review

Invite children to demonstrate their answers using each of the methods of multiplication. Discuss the advantages of each method, encouraging children to see that the condensed form is neater and quicker.

Curriculum objectives
● To multiply two-digit and three-digit numbers by a one-digit number using formal written layout.

Success criteria
● I can multiply three-digit numbers by a one-digit number using a written method.

You will need
Equipment
Dice

Differentiation
Less confident learners
Give these children two dice only and ask them to multiply by 3, 4, 5 or 6.

More confident learners
Rather than dice, provide children with a set of 0–10 number cards. Some could also begin to use the condensed method to multiply four-digit numbers, if appropriate.

Lesson 4   Oral and mental starter ▮▮

Main teaching activities

Whole-class work: Begin by revising the grid method explored in the previous lesson. Invite a child who used the more formal expanded or condensed method when working through the questions on their photocopiable sheet to come to the front and show a different way of setting out the multiplication and answering it. For example:

```
  H T U      or      H T U      or      H T U
    2 6                2 6                2 6
x     3            x     3            x     3
  ───────          ───────          ───────
    6 0                1 8                7 8
    1 8                6 0                ¹
  ───────          ───────
    7 8                7 8
```

Help children to see that, whilst in the grid method we start by multiplying the tens digits first, it doesn't make any difference to the answer if we start with the units digit. Show how, for the condensed method, we start by multiplying the units digits and carry any tens if necessary. Then we multiply the tens digit and add any tens carried to complete the answer. Work through several examples of this type.

Now introduce a question involving multiplying a three-digit by a one-digit number, such as 245×3. Ask: *How do you think we could work this out using a grid method?* Invite a child to show this. For example:

×	200	40	5
3	600	120	15

Then set it out using column arrangements, in expanded and condensed form. For example:

```
  H T U      or      H T U      or      H T U
  2 4 5              2 4 5              2 4 5
x     3            x     3            x     3
  ───────          ───────          ───────
  6 0 0                1 5              7 3 5
  1 2 0              1 2 0              ¹ ¹
    1 5              6 0 0
  ───────          ───────
  7 3 5              7 3 5
```

Paired work: Give each pair three dice to create a three-digit number. They should then choose a number between 3 and 9 to multiply by. The children should choose an appropriate method to use and should work together to find the answer. Encourage them to try the different methods and to say which they prefer and which they find quicker and neater.

Progress check: During the paired work ask: *Which method do you find quicker? Why do you think that is?*

Review

Ask children to imagine that a new child had just arrived in the classroom. Invite them to explain the condensed method of multiplication to the new child as clearly as they can. Provide them with an example to use in their explanation (say, 74×3 or 124×4). *What would you tell the child to do? How do you explain why you are writing this digit here? Do you think this explanation is clear enough? Could you do better?* Invite some children to try to give an explanation, encouraging them to make them as clear as possible.

Curriculum objectives
● To solve problems involving multiplying and adding.
Success criteria
● I can solve one- and two-step problems involving multiplication.

You will need
Equipment
Squared or dotty paper; individual whiteboards

Differentiation
Less confident learners
Ask these children to explore a smaller number of rows of vegetables, such as three rows of six cauliflowers, to investigate in the same way.
More confident learners
Select a greater number of rows of vegetables to investigate. Children can also explore the plank in both a vertical or horizontal position (when viewed from above).

Lesson 5   Oral and mental starter 20

Main teaching activities

Whole-class work: Introduce the following theme: *Ralph is a gardener. He plants rows of vegetables on his allotment, which he then sells to the local market. Here are the vegetables and how many he plants in each row.*

Cabbage 13   Onions 17   Leeks 18

Potatoes 24   Beetroot 26   Carrots 29   Baby lettuce 32

Ask questions such as:
● *How many does Ralph plant if he plants: Four rows of leeks? Six rows of carrots? Five rows of beetroot?*
● *How many rows does he plant if he plants: 320 baby lettuce? 34 onions? 130 beetroot?*

Invite children to show answers on their individual whiteboards.

Now introduce several two-step problems about the same theme, such as: *Last year he planted six rows of leeks, which sold well, so this year he decides to plant double the number?* ($6 \times 18 \times 2$). Introduce a problem that might involve some pictorial strategies: *Part-way along his six rows of cabbage he places a plank to walk along. How many cabbages could there be on each side of the plank?* With six rows of 13 there are 78 cabbages altogether. Discuss all the different positions that the plank could be, such as:

6×4	6×9	6×8	6×5
x x x x	x x x x x x x x x	x x x x x x x x	x x x x x
x x x x	x x x x x x x x x	x x x x x x x x	x x x x x
x x x x	x x x x x x x x x	x x x x x x x x	x x x x x
x x x x	x x x x x x x x x	x x x x x x x x	x x x x x
x x x x	x x x x x x x x x	x x x x x x x x	x x x x x
x x x x	x x x x x x x x x	x x x x x x x x	x x x x x
24	54	48	30

Show that the total number of cabbages on each side is always 78.

Paired work: Working in pairs, ask children to investigate all the different positions that Ralph could put a straight plank, splitting four rows of onions or eight rows of leeks (or another appropriate choice) and identifying the number of vegetables each side of the plank for the different positions. Encourage children to record their solutions in whatever way they choose – for example, using squared or dotty paper, drawing diagrams or recording number sentences.

Progress check: Ask: *Why have you decided to record your solutions this way? How do you know this is correct? What do you notice about each pair of totals? Why is that?* Encourage children to explain how they know they have found all the solutions.

Review

Invite children to show the rest of the class their recorded solutions and to talk about what they discovered. Play a short quiz, inviting children to write answers on their whiteboards to show their answers. Explain that there are 10 rows of 17 onions. Then say how many are on one side of the plank and ask children to work out how many are on the other – for example, 70 (100), 120 (50), 65 (105), and so on.

Multiplication and division

Expected prior learning

Children should be able to:

- recall and use multiplication and division facts for the 3, 4 and 8 multiplication tables
- write and calculate mathematical statements for multiplication and division using the multiplication tables that they know, using mental methods.

Topic	Curriculum objectives	Expected outcomes
Multiplication and division	**Lesson 1**	
	To recall multiplication and division facts for multiplication tables up to 12 × 12.	Divide two-digit by one-digit numbers (without and with remainders) within tables.
	Lesson 2	
	To use place value, known and derived facts to multiply and divide mentally, including: multiplying by 0 and 1; dividing by 1; multiplying together three numbers.	Divide two-digit by one-digit numbers (without and with remainders) beyond tables. Divide multiples of 10 and 100.
	Lesson 3	
	To use place value, known and derived facts to multiply and divide mentally, including: multiplying by 0 and 1; dividing by 1; multiplying together three numbers.	Recognise divisibility of two-digit numbers by single-digit numbers. Divide two-digit by one-digit numbers beyond tables.
	Lesson 4	
	To use place value, known and derived facts to multiply and divide mentally, including: multiplying by 0 and 1; dividing by 1; multiplying together three numbers.	Begin to use a short division for dividing two-digit by one-digit numbers (without remainders) but beyond tables (such as 81 ÷ 3).
	Lesson 5	
	To solve problems involving multiplying and adding, including using the distributive law to multiply two-digit numbers by one digit, integer scaling problems and harder correspondence problems such as which n objects are connected to m objects.	Solve division word problems, including interpreting remainders appropriately.

Preparation

Lesson 2: copy 'Target grids (1)', one per pair

Lesson 3: copy 'Definitely division', one per child

Lesson 4: copy 'Written division (1)', one per child

You will need

Photocopiable sheets

'Definitely division'; 'Written division (1)'

General resources

'Target grids (1)'

Equipment

Individual whiteboards; squared paper; counting stick

Further practice

Photocopiable sheets

'Sorting out the multiples'

Oral and mental starters for week 3

See bank of starters on pages 85, 86 and 126. Oral and mental starters are also on the CD-ROM.

17 True or false

16 Multiply by 10 and 100

13 Targets

9 Story time

Overview of progression

During this week the children will practise recalling and deriving division facts, including using a range of mental and written methods. In the early part of the week they consolidate and revise facts from the times tables up to 12 × 12. They will write division facts related to tables facts and will divide multiples of 10 and 100. In lesson 4 short division is introduced. lesson 5 gives opportunity for children to use and apply their facts and skills to solve division problems, where rounding is required in the answer.

Watch out for

Some children struggle to recall particular times tables facts or fail to appreciate the link between division facts and tables facts. Provide cards with the questions on one side and answers on the other and encourage children to take them away to learn at home. Ensure that a range of visual, aural and kinaesthetic approaches are used when teaching tables facts to appeal to all learning styles.

Creative context

Look out for opportunities to perform sharing and grouping division in real-life contexts, such as getting into teams in PE, sitting on benches in the hall, sharing items such as coloured pencils, cooking situations, and so on.

Vocabulary

divide, divisor, divisible, **factor**, facts, groups of, lots of, multiple, share, tables,

■ SCHOLASTIC

Curriculum objectives
● To recall multiplication and division facts for multiplication tables up to 12 × 12.

Success criteria
● I can divide two-digit by one-digit numbers (without and with remainders) within tables.

You will need
Equipment
Counting stick; squared paper

Differentiation
Less confident learners
Ask children to write division facts related to an easier times table, such as 3 or 4.

More confident learners
Children can choose divisors from harder times tables, including 11 and 12.

Main teaching activities

Whole-class work: Explain that today's lesson is about using tables to help you divide numbers. Hold up a counting stick and ask children to count in 7s from zero to 70, as you point to each mark on the counting stick. Count forwards and then backwards and then ask tables questions, pointing to different marks out of order, such as 5 times 7, 2 times 7, 9 times 7 and so on. Remind children that the marks are the multiples of 7 and list them on the board in a line.

7	14	21	28	35	42	49	56	63	70

Now ask related division questions (42 divided by 7, 56 divided by 7...), encouraging children to describe how they worked out each answer. Introduce a question involving dividing a number by 7 that is not a multiple of 7, such as: *What is 44 divided by 7?* or *How many 7s are in 44?* Help children to see that when you divide a number that is a not a multiple of the divisor you will get a remainder – there are six 7s with 2 left over. Demonstrate how we can record the remainder: $44 \div 7 = 6 \text{ r } 2$. Repeat dividing by 7 for a range of numbers that are not multiples of 7. Invite children to the front to write the answers and to explain how they might have used the counting stick to help them 'see' the answer. Ask: *Tell me a 'dividing by 7' question that has the answer 4 r 5?* ($33 \div 7$) *How can you be sure? How did you work it out?* Ask children to give you other 'dividing by 7' questions with other answers (8 r 2, 9 r 1, 10 r 5...).

Give children opportunity in pairs to discuss possible answers for this question: *Give me at least five questions that have r1 in the answer?* (8, 15, 22, 29... ÷ 7)

Look together at the patterns and encourage children to describe how the counting stick helps them to be confident in their answers.

Independent work: Tell each of the children which times table they should focus on for this work – more confident learners should choose 6, 8, 11, 12 and less confident can choose 3 or 4. Ask children to draw a simple counting stick on squared paper and to list the first 10 (or 12) multiples of their number. They should then write and answer as many division questions as they can in the time, some with and some without remainder answers, using their counting stick to help them.

Paired work: Children should then get into pairs and alternately test each other on the facts they have written. For example, the child who wrote 'dividing by 8' questions should be asked to give answers to the questions he/she wrote, without referring to his/her counting stick line. Scores can be kept to see who answers most of the questions correctly.

Progress check: During the paired work, encourage each child to choose the more difficult questions from the list. Ask: *How do you remember this fact? Which multiple of X is the number close to?*

Review

Ask children to read out the questions they wrote and for others to give the answers. *Which tables fact can you use to help you work out this division question? Which is your favourite question?* As a final activity invite children to provide as many division questions as they can with the answer 5 r 2.

Curriculum objectives
● To use place value, known and derived facts to multiply and divide mentally.
Success criteria
● I can divide two-digit by one-digit numbers (without and with remainders) beyond tables.
● I can divide multiples of 10 and 100.

You will need
General resources
'Target grids (1)'
Equipment
Individual whiteboards

Differentiation
Less confident learners
Ask children to focus only on the first activity. Give them a number to divide by (say, 6), to allow them to focus on the multiples and to work out remainders.

More confident learners
Encourage children to divide by more difficult numbers, such as 7, 11 or 12.

Curriculum objectives
● To use place value, known and derived facts to divide mentally, including by 1.
Success criteria
● I can recognise divisibility of two-digit numbers by single-digit numbers.
● I can divide two-digit by one-digit numbers beyond tables.

You will need
Photocopiable sheets
'Definitely division'

Differentiation
Less confident learners
Invite a more confident child to explain their methods to a less confident learner (peer tutoring).

More confident learners
Ask children to use a more formal written method.

Lesson 2 — Oral and mental starter 16

Main teaching activities

Whole-class work: Choose a two-digit number less than 50 (say, 28). Ask children, in pairs, to devise as many different division questions as they can starting with this number, recording their questions and answers on their individual whiteboards (28 ÷ 4 = 7; 28 ÷ 5 = 5 r 3; 28 ÷ 6 = 4 r 4…). Then collect a list of questions and answers on the board. Discuss strategies used to find the answers. Highlight those facts that do not have a remainder and remind children that this is because the divisor is a factor of the first number. Choose one of these facts and ask: *What if we make the first number 10 or 100 times larger? What will the answer be?*

Paired work: Give each pair photocopiable page 'Target grids (1)' from the CD-ROM. They should choose numbers from the first grid (two-digit numbers), write ten division questions starting with those numbers and answer them, including remainders. Next, ask them to choose any multiples of 100 from the second grid, where the first two digits form a multiple of a one-digit number, to write a division and answer it. They should only choose multiples that they recognise from their tables and should not give answers with remainders for this activity.

Progress check: For questions involving multiples of 100 ask children to say how many times larger each number is than the one in the related division fact from the table.

Review

Use the questions generated by the pairs of children to form a class quiz. Choose children to stand and read out several of their questions and invite the others to answer them. Include questions with and without remainders and those with multiples of 100. Discuss strategies used to find answers.

Lesson 3 — Oral and mental starter 13

Main teaching activities

Whole-class work: Write some two-digit numbers and begin by discussing how you can recognise when a number is divisible by 2, 3, 5 (and so on), including numbers beyond the times tables. Point out that every whole number is divisible by 1 or has the factor 1 as we can always write a multiplication for that number involving multiplying by 1 (for example, 38 = 38 × 1 or 1 × 38). Explain that today's lesson will involve using mental division to divide two-digit numbers by small numbers. List several questions on the board, such as 78 ÷ 3, 93 ÷ 4, 89 ÷ 6, 87 ÷ 3. Discuss different approaches to solving these – for example, partitioning the number into parts (78 = 60 + 18) and dividing each part separately, or taking out chunks from the number (78 − 30 − 30 − 9 − 9). Invite children to demonstrate any method that they have previously used and discuss the advantages and disadvantages.

Independent work: Provide children with photocopiable page 'Definitely division' from the CD-ROM to complete, using different mental strategies and jottings.

Progress check: While children are working on the photocopiable sheet ask: *Which strategy do you think is best for this question? Why?*

Review

Call out divisions from the photocopiable sheet. Ask children to say which strategy they used and why. Revise the more difficult division facts.

Curriculum objectives
● To use place value, known and derived facts to divide mentally.

Success criteria
● I can use a short division for dividing two-digit by one-digit numbers (without remainders).

You will need
Photocopiable sheets
'Written division (1)'

Differentiation
Less confident learners
Provide practical equipment such as cubes to support children with this work.

More confident learners
Give these children three-digit numbers to divide.

Lesson 4   Oral and mental starter 13

Main teaching activities

Whole-class work: Explain that in this lesson the children will be exploring short division, a written method of division. Write some of the questions from the previous lesson on the board – for example, 78 ÷ 3, 93 ÷ 4, 89 ÷ 6, 87 ÷ 3. Show how each can be written in the more formal division form:

$$\begin{array}{r} 2\ \ 6 \\ 3\overline{)\ 7\ {}^18} \end{array}$$

Demonstrate the method of short division: *How many 3s in 7 (tens)?* Write the answer 2 (tens) above the number in the tens column and carry the remainder 1 (ten) across to the units column to make 18. *How many 3s in 18?* Write the answer 6 above to complete the answer (26). Multiply 26 by 3 to check by showing that the answer is 78. Repeat for the other examples on the board, encouraging children to tell you what to do at each stage.

Independent work: Provide each child with photocopiable page 'Written division (1)' from the CD-ROM to complete, using a written method and another alternative method of their choosing.

Progress check: Ask: *Which method do you prefer? Why might the written method be more suitable on occasions?*

Review

Provide a written division calculation with an error in it and ask children to say where the mistake has been made.

Curriculum objectives
● To solve problems involving division.

Success criteria
● I can solve division word problems including interpreting remainders appropriately.

You will need
Equipment
Individual whiteboards

Differentiation
Less confident learners
If necessary, give children a multiplication square to support them in their divisions.

More confident learners
Invite children to make up more of their own rounding up or down division problems.

Lesson 5   Oral and mental starter 9

Main teaching activities

Whole-class work: Ask some word questions that involve either rounding up or rounding down, such as: *Jo has 25p to spend on as many 6p stamps as she can. How many can she buy and how much money would she have left?* or *Each minibus can hold eight people. How many minibuses are needed to transport 94 people?* Discuss each problem as a division statement first (for example, 25 ÷ 6 = 4 r 1 and 94 ÷ 8 = 11 r 6). Discuss them in context to show how giving a remainder isn't always appropriate.

Paired work: Write several general problems on the board, such as:
- I want to buy an item costing £[   ]. I save £[   ] each week. I must save for [   ] weeks to buy it and I will have £[   ] left over.
- A shop sells CDs for £[   ] each. How many can I buy with [   ] and how much will I have left over?

Ask children to fill in missing numbers and to make up their own rounding up or down division problems of this type.

Progress check: Ask: *Did you round up or down? Why?*

Review

Give children a few moments to discuss with a partner what all the questions that needed rounding down (or up) had in common. Draw attention to the fact that if you are buying as many things as you can or filling as many things as you can, you usually round down. If you are fitting things into boxes, minibuses, on pages, around tables (and so on) you usually need to have an extra box for the remainder so you round up.

Fractions

Expected prior learning

Children should be able to:

- count up and down in tenths; recognise that tenths arise from dividing an object into 10 equal parts and in dividing one-digit numbers or quantities by 10
- recognise and use fractions as numbers: unit fractions and non-unit fractions with small denominators
- recognise, find and write fractions of a discrete set of objects: unit fractions and non-unit fractions with small denominators
- know the role of the numerator and denominator.

Topic	Curriculum objectives	Expected outcomes
Fractions (including decimals)	**Lesson 1**	
	To solve problems involving increasingly harder fractions to calculate quantities, and fractions to divide quantities, including non-unit fractions where the answer is a whole number.	Understand and recognise fractions as areas of shapes, as sets of objects and on a number line. Find unit fractions of a set or quantity. Find non-unit fractions of a set or quantity (whole number answers).
	Lesson 2	
	To solve problems involving increasingly harder fractions to calculate quantities, and fractions to divide quantities, including non-unit fractions where the answer is a whole number.	Find unit fractions of a set or quantity. Find non-unit fractions of a set or quantity (whole number answers).
	Lesson 3	
	To count up and down in hundredths; recognise that hundredths arise when dividing an object by one hundred and dividing tenths by ten.	Understand the relationship between tenths and hundredths and can find tenths and hundredths of numbers.
	Lesson 4	
	To recognise and show, using diagrams, families of common equivalent fractions.	Understand the link between the numerators and denominators of equivalent fractions. Identify fractions equivalent to a given fraction using multiplication or division. Give missing numbers in equivalent fraction pairs.
	Lesson 5	
	To solve problems involving increasingly harder fractions to calculate quantities, and fractions to divide quantities, including non-unit fractions where the answer is a whole number.	Solve problems involving fractions.

Preparation

Lesson 1: copy 'Kaleidoscopes', one per child

Lesson 3: copy 'Fraction game', one per pair

Lesson 4: copy 'Equivalent fraction teams' and 'Equivalent fractions', one per child

Lesson 5: copy: 'Fraction questions (1)', one per child

You will need

Photocopiable sheets

'Kaleidoscopes'; 'Fraction game'; 'Equivalent fraction teams'; 'Equivalent fractions'; 'Fraction questions (1) and (2)'

Equipment

Individual whiteboards; number fans; coloured pencils; counting stick; metre stick; counters; dice

Further practice

'Fraction questions (2)' offers further practice in solving fractions problems in the context of money and measures. 'Fractions of shapes' provides practice with finding fractions as areas of shapes.

Oral and mental starters for Week 4

See bank of starters on pages 86, 126, 127 and 167. Oral and mental starters are also on the CD-ROM.

20 Bingo

22 Fraction action

16 Multiply by 10 and 100

13 Targets

Overview of progression

Lesson 1 provides revision of fractions as areas of shapes, sets of objects and on a number line. It also makes the link between finding unit fractions of quantities with division. Lesson 2 takes this further to include non-unit fractions. These ideas are then continued into lesson 3 which focuses particularly on tenths and hundredths. Lesson 4 provide opportunities for finding and identifying equivalent fractions and all the ideas of the week are drawn together in the problem-solving activities of lesson 5.

Watch out for

Children develop many misconceptions about fractions that result from assuming that things that work for whole numbers will also work for fractions (for example, a fraction with a bigger number on the bottom is smaller than one with a smaller number on the bottom). It is important that children are given opportunity to talk about the differences between whole numbers, fractions and decimals to challenge these misconceptions.

Creative context

Take opportunities to link this fraction work to real-life situations – for example, by asking children to describe sets of the class: *19 out of the 28 children in our class are girls; three quarters of our class have school dinners* (and so on).

Vocabulary

denominator, equal parts, **equivalent fraction**, fraction, hundredth, numerator, set, tenth

Curriculum objectives
● To solve problems involving fractions to calculate quantities, and fractions to divide quantities.

Success criteria
● I can find unit fractions of a set or quantity.

You will need
Photocopiable sheets
'Kaleidoscopes'

Equipment
Coloured pencils (red, yellow, blue and orange); number fans

Differentiation
Less confident learners
Remind children to count the numbers of each section and to calculate how many squares they should colour, by dividing.

More confident learners
Ask children to record the colours of each circle using fraction notation and check each using division.

Lesson 1 — Oral and mental starter 20

Main teaching activities

Whole-class work: Explain that today's lesson is about solving problems related to fractions. Draw a 3 × 4 rectangle of squares. Revise that one out of 12 equal parts of a whole is described as *one twelfth* and is written $\frac{1}{12}$. Remind children that the parts must be equal in size. Revise the words *denominator* (the bottom number) and *numerator* (the top number). Say that you wish to shade one quarter of the rectangle. *How many squares would I colour? How could I split the shape into four equal parts?* Invite children to explain how this could be done and establish that one quarter of the rectangle would be three squares. Write ¼ of 12 squares is 3 squares. Discuss that any three squares of the shape can be coloured for one quarter of it to be coloured.

Explore other fractions of the rectangle and determine how many squares would be shaded. For example: *How many squares would you shade if you wanted to shade one half /one third?* Record them using fraction notation: $\frac{1}{6}$ of 12 = 2, $\frac{1}{3}$ of 12 = 4 and so on. Help children to see the link between fractions and divisions – for example, to find one third we divide by 3. *What would you divide by to find one sixth?* Make the link between this work and fractions represented on a number line: *One quarter of 12 is 4, which is the same as 12 divided by 4.* Show also the link between tables – if you know that 3 × 4 is 12, then 12 ÷ 4 (or one quarter of 12) is 3.

0	1	2	3	4	5	6	7	8	9	10

Independent work: Provide each child with photocopiable page 'Kaleidoscopes' from the CD-ROM and some coloured pencils. Ask them to find and colour the correct number of parts of each circle. Explain that not every part of a circle will necessarily be coloured. Some circles will have several parts left uncovered. Remind children to check that they have coloured the correct number of parts each time using division – for example, not just to colour one half of the circle, but to divide the total number of parts by 2 and ensure that this is the number of parts they have coloured. If time, children can also record the colours of each circle using fraction notation, such as $\frac{1}{6}$ of 6 = 1, $\frac{1}{3}$ of 6 = 2 and so on.

Progress check: Ask: *How did you work out how many parts of this circle to colour? What tables or division fact would you use to check $\frac{1}{9}$ of 36? How could you record this using fraction notation?*

Review

Provide children with number fans and ask them to hold up the answers to some quick-fire fraction questions (testing their recall of division facts). For example: *What is $\frac{1}{9}$ of 18? $\frac{1}{6}$ of 42?* Use only unit fractions at this stage and explain that in the next lesson the children will be exploring non-unit fractions of sets of objects and quantities – where fractions have numerators other than 1.

Curriculum objectives

● To solve problems involving fractions to calculate quantities, and fractions to divide quantities.

Success criteria

● I can find unit fractions of a set or quantity.
● I can find non-unit fractions of a set or quantity (whole number answers).

You will need

Equipment
Number fans

Differentiation

Less confident learners

Provide children with 24 cubes or counters and ask them to check their answers by putting the cubes into the correct number of equal groups.

More confident learners

Ask children to list the numbers from 3 to 23 and to give a fraction question for each.

Lesson 2   Oral and mental starter 22

Main teaching activities

Whole-class work: Draw a 4 × 5 rectangle of squares. Revise that one out of 20 equal parts of a whole is described as *one twentieth* and is written ¹⁄₂₀. Say that you wish to shade one quarter of the rectangle. *How many squares would I colour? What division fact could I use to help me decide how many to colour?* Establish that finding one quarter is the same as dividing by 4 and that 20 ÷ 4 = 5. Write ¼ of 20 = 5. Discuss that any five squares of the shape can be coloured for one quarter of it to be coloured. *How could I work out how many to colour if I coloured three-quarters of the rectangle?* Demonstrate that we can calculate this by first dividing to find one part and then multiplying to find several parts. *We know that one quarter is 5, by dividing 20 by 4. Then we multiply by 3 to find three quarters, 15.* Write ¾ of 20 = 15. Explore other fractions of the rectangle and determine how many squares would be shaded.

Paired work: Draw a 4 × 6 rectangle on the board. Ask children in pairs to generate as many different fraction statements as they can, using non-unit fractions (fractions with a numerator that is not 1) for this rectangle. Remind them that they can only use denominators that are factors of 24. Encourage them to work systematically.

Progress check: Encourage children to notice that some fractions are equivalent and give the same answers: *Are there different fractions of 24 that give the same answer? Why is that?*

Review

Ask children to hold up number fans to show their answers to some quick-fire fraction questions: *What is ⅔ of 18? ⅚ of 42?*

Curriculum objectives

● To count up and down in hundredths; to recognise that hundredths arise when dividing an object by 100 and dividing tenths by 10.

Success criteria

● I can find tenths and hundredths of numbers.

You will need

Photocopiable sheets
'Fraction game'
Equipment
Counting stick; metre stick; counters; dice; number fans

Differentiation

Less confident learners

Support children in dividing numbers by 10 and 100 and provide them with a place value chart if necessary.

More confident learners

Children can record the questions and answers of the game using decimal notation.

Lesson 3   Oral and mental starter 16

Main teaching activities

Whole-class work: Hold up a counting stick. Describe the left end (as viewed by the children) as zero and the right-hand end as 1. *If this stick is one whole, how much of the whole is the first section? In what different ways can we describe that?* Invite children to suggest ways in which the first section can be described or written – for example, one out of ten equal parts, one tenth, ¹⁄₁₀. Some children may draw on previous decimal work and suggest 0.1. Point to each division of the counting stick in turn and ask children to count in fractions (one tenth, two tenths ...). Discuss that ten tenths is the same as one whole.

Now hold up a metre stick. Point to the 1cm mark. *If the whole stick is one metre, what fraction of the whole stick is this first section?* Discuss hundredths, how they can be represented and count in hundredths of a metre as you point to each centimetre. Draw attention to the fact that one hundredth is found by dividing one whole by 100 or by dividing one tenth by 10. Revise finding fractions of numbers explored in the previous lessons and show how to find tenths and hundredth of multiples of 10 and 100.

Paired work: Provide each pair with photocopiable page 88 'Fraction game' a counter and dice and ask them to play the game on the sheet.

Progress check: Ask: *How did you find one tenth... one hundredth?*

Review

Ask children to hold up number fans to answer some quick-fire fraction questions involving tenths and hundredths.

Curriculum objectives

- To recognise and show, using diagrams, families of common equivalent fractions.

Success criteria

- I can identify fractions equivalent to a given fraction, using multiplication or division.
- I can give missing numbers in equivalent fraction pairs.

You will need

Photocopiable sheets

'Equivalent fraction teams'; 'Equivalent fractions'

Equipment

Fraction wall (optional); coloured pencils (yellow, blue and green)

Differentiation

Less confident learners

Provide children with a fraction wall to use as support.

More confident learners

Ask children to write different fractions equivalent to $\frac{1}{2}$ and $\frac{1}{4}$.

Lesson 4 — Oral and mental starter 22

Main teaching activities

Whole-class work: Demonstrate how to use a fraction wall (if you have one) to find fractions that are worth the same, and remind children that we use the word *equivalent*. Write several fractions on the board and invite children to come to the front and write equivalent fractions to form different fraction families (for example, those equivalent to $\frac{1}{2}$, those equivalent to $\frac{3}{4}$, those equivalent to $\frac{6}{8}$ and so on).

For each list ask: *What patterns do you notice in the numerators and denominators? How could you use this to make up more equivalent fractions?* Show that you can multiply or divide the numerator and denominator by the same number to give an equivalent fraction:

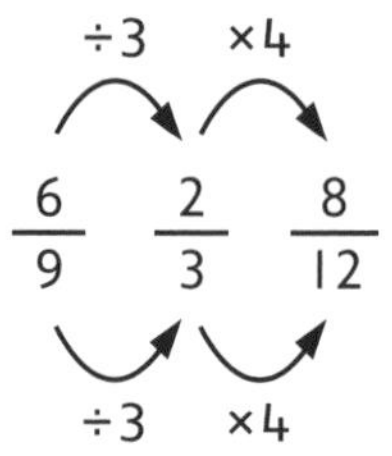

Independent work: Provide each child with coloured pencils and photocopiable page 'Equivalent fraction teams' from the CD-ROM and ask them to colour the sports shirts in the correct colours. After this, give them photocopiable page 'Equivalent fractions' from the CD-ROM to complete.

Progress check: Ask: *How can you check whether these two fractions are equivalent? How can you use this diagram? Do you use multiplication or division? Do you still think they are equivalent?*

Review

Explain that someone has been writing pairs of equivalent fractions but they have made errors. Write different pairs on the board including some that are incorrect (such as $\frac{1}{4} = \frac{2}{6}$, $\frac{3}{6} = \frac{1}{2}$, $\frac{2}{4} = \frac{1}{8}$). Go through the pairs in turn and say which are true and which are false. *How could we change this to make it true?*

Curriculum objectives

- To solve problems involving increasingly harder fractions to calculate quantities.

Success criteria

- I can solve problems involving fractions.

You will need

Photocopiable sheets

'Fraction questions (1)'; 'Fraction questions (2)'

Differentiation

Less confident learners

Provide children with a metre stick and coins as support.

More confident learners

Ask children to make up questions of this type for a partner to solve.

Lesson 5 — Oral and mental starter 13

Main teaching activities

Whole-class work: Discuss some problems involving fractions, such as:

- *There are 30 apples in a box. Five of them are green. The rest are red. What fraction of the apples are green/red?*
- *In a class of 27, two thirds are girls. How many are girls/boys?*

Draw out aspects learned this week, including how multiplication and division can be used to find fractions of amounts and how some fractions can be written as equivalent ones. Invite children in pairs to make up some of their own fraction problems for the class to solve.

Independent work: Provide each child with photocopiable page 'Fraction questions (1)' from the CD-ROM to complete.

Progress check: Invite children to give feedback on their solutions and to explain the strategies they used.

Review

Draw a tube of sweets and explain the tube holds eight sweets. *If I eat one sweet, what fraction of the whole tube have I eaten? If I have eaten three of the sweets, what fraction of the whole tube have I eaten/got left?* ($\frac{3}{8}$; $\frac{5}{8}$). Mark each eighth on the drawing and revise equivalent fractions such as $\frac{4}{8} = \frac{1}{2}$, $\frac{2}{8} = \frac{1}{4}$ and $\frac{6}{8} = \frac{3}{4}$. If time is available 'Fractions questions (2)' offers further practice.

Geometry: shapes, position and direction

Expected prior learning

Children should be able to:

- identify and name shapes according to the numbers of sides
- identify and recognise right angles in shapes
- understand the nature of parallel sides.

Topic	Curriculum objectives	Expected outcomes
Geometry: properties of shapes	**Lesson 1** To compare and classify geometric shapes, including quadrilaterals and triangles, based on their properties and sizes.	Identify different types of triangles and describe their properties.
	Lesson 2 To compare and classify geometric shapes, including quadrilaterals and triangles, based on their properties and sizes.	Identify different types of quadrilaterals and describe their properties.
Geometry: position and direction	**Lesson 3** To describe positions on a 2D grid as coordinates in the first quadrant. To plot specified points and draw sides to complete a given polygon.	Describe positions and plot points on a coordinate grid.
Geometry: properties of shapes	**Lesson 4** To identify acute and obtuse angles and compare and order angles up to two right angles by size.	Identify acute and obtuse angles. Compare and order angles.
	Lesson 5 To compare and classify geometric shapes, including quadrilaterals and triangles, based on their properties and sizes.	Solve problems involving 2D shapes.

Preparation

Lesson 1: copy 'Tons of triangles', one per child

Lesson 3: copy 'Coordinates', one per pair; prepare 'Coordinate grid' for display on the interactive whiteboard

Lesson 4: copy 'Angles', one per child

Lesson 5: copy 'Shape investigation', one per child

You will need

Photocopiable sheets

'Tons of triangles'; 'Coordinates'; 'Angles' 'Shape investigation'

General resources

'Dotty paper'; 'Coordinate grid'; interactive activity 'Shapes and coordinates'

Equipment

Individual whiteboards; rulers dotty paper; large sheets of paper; scissors; glue; geostrips; paper fasteners

Further practice

Ask children to plot different points on the 'Coordinates grid' or to describe the position of items (for example, a treasure chest).

Oral and mental starters for week 5

See bank of starters on pages 85 and 126. Oral and mental starters are also on the CD-ROM.

15 Twenty questions

18 Operation follow-on

9 Story time

Overview of progression

During this week the children will consolidate and extend their knowledge of the properties of 2D shapes and will learn to describe and classify triangles (lesson 1) and quadrilaterals (lesson 2). In lesson 3 children are given opportunities to plot and identify points on a coordinate grid and in lesson 4 they are introduced to the terms *acute* and *obtuse* as a means of describing angles less than two right angles. The final lesson of the week draws together the topics explored in an investigative situation.

Watch out for

Common errors made by children include the following:

- identifying rectangles as regular (they do not have equal sides)
- identifying a rhombus as regular (the angles are not equal)
- looking at a square twisted round and thinking it is a rhombus (the angles are still right angles)
- thinking that a parallelogram that is not a rectangle or a rhombus is symmetrical (show that it isn't by folding a piece of paper).

Creative context

Link this shape work to art activities, including creating patterns and angles using colour and shapes.

Vocabulary

acute, angles, equal, **equilateral triangle**, horizontal, irregular, **isosceles triangle**, **line of symmetry**, names of quadrilaterals, **obtuse**, **pair of coordinates**, parallel, perpendicular, **regular polygon**, right, **scalene triangle**, shape, sides, vertex, vertical, vertices

Curriculum objectives
- To compare and classify geometric shapes based on their properties and sizes.

Success criteria
- I can identify different types of triangles and describe their properties.

You will need

Photocopiable sheets
'Tons of triangles'

General resources
'Dotty paper'

Equipment
Individual whiteboards; rulers

Differentiation

Less confident learners

Provide children with a list of the names and spellings of the different types of triangles (scalene, isosceles, equilateral).

More confident learners

Ask children to write information about the perimeter of each triangle.

Lesson 1 — Oral and mental starter 15

Main teaching activities

Whole-class work: Explain that today's lesson is about different types of triangles. Using photocopiable page 'Dotty paper' from the CD-ROM, ask the children to draw a triangle using a ruler. Encourage them to think of an unusual triangle or orientation that they think might be different from what the others are drawing. Invite each child to show their triangle and discuss each of them. *What is special about this triangle? What can you say about its sides?* Ask children to look at their own triangle and invite several to describe theirs without showing it to the rest of the class. Invite other children to draw what they think the triangle might look like. Show a range of different triangles drawn and ask children to point out any right angles. Establish that any triangles with right angles are called right-angled triangles.

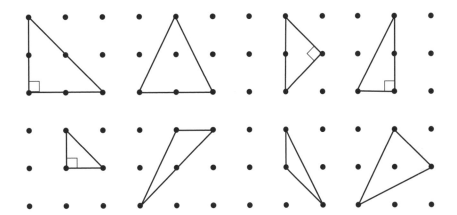

Discuss the terms *equilateral* (three equal sides and three equal angles), *isosceles* (two equal sides and two equal angles) and *scalene* (no equal sides or angles) and ask children to identify which is which. Note that none of these are equilateral triangles, the second shape is actually isosceles. Ask the children to use a ruler to check the lengths of the sides of triangles that they have drawn. Remind them that an equilateral triangle is the only regular triangle – *all* its sides and angles are equal. Discuss too that a right-angled triangle can be scalene or isosceles and that equilateral triangles have three lines of symmetry, isosceles have one line and scalene triangles have no lines of symmetry.

Independent work: Give each child photocopiable page 'Tons of triangles' from the CD-ROM. They should write the name of each shape and on a separate piece of paper describe its properties in as much detail as they can, including references to symmetry, whether or not it is regular, its angles and sides. Encourage them to use rulers to check whether sides are equal in length.

Progress check: While children are describing their shapes ask: *What can you say about the angles in this triangle? What about its symmetry? What is special about its sides? Is this equilateral, scalene or isosceles? Is it right-angled?*

Review

Play a 'Guess my name' game. Read out statements and ask children to identify the triangle. For example: *I have one right angle and no equal sides* (right-angled scalene). *I have one line of symmetry* (isosceles), *I have three lines of symmetry* (equilateral). The children's descriptions from the independent work can be used to provide further clues.

Curriculum objectives
● To compare and classify geometric shapes based on their properties and sizes.

Success criteria
● I can identify different types of quadrilaterals and describe their properties.

You will need
Equipment
Dotty paper; large sheets of paper; scissors; glue

Differentiation
Less confident learners
Give children geostrips or straws in three different lengths. Ask them to make different four-sided shapes and name them.

More confident learners
Encourage children to identify if any of the shapes on their poster are congruent (same size and shape).

Main teaching activities

Whole-class work: Explain to the children that today's lesson is about different types of four-sided shapes. *What do we call all shapes with four straight sides?* (Quadrilaterals) *Can anyone tell me the special names of any of these quadrilaterals?* Draw a range of quadrilaterals on the board:

Invite children to name any quadrilaterals they know, asking them to explain what properties each shape has: *It is a square because it has four right angles and four equal sides.* Ensure children realise that they should be able to describe all the properties of the shapes that distinguish them from other types of quadrilaterals – for example, that it is not good enough to say *a square has four sides* or *a square has four right angles* as other non-square quadrilaterals have these properties also. Describe the different type of quadrilateral and their properties, identifying which drawing is which.

- A **parallelogram** has two sets of parallel lines.
- A **rectangle** has four right angles. It is a type of parallelogram.
- A **square** has four right angles and four sides of equal length. It is a type of rectangle and a spiral type of parallelogram.
- A **rhombus** has two sets of parallel lines and four sides of equal length. It is a type of parallelogram.
- A **trapezium** has one set of parallel lines (one of the parallel lines is longer than the other).
- A **kite** has two short sides adjacent and of equal length and two longer ones adjacent and of equal length.
- Any shape that is not any of the shapes above, is just called a quadrilateral.

Ensure children understand that a quadrilateral can be called by more than one name – for example, a square can be called a quadrilateral, and can also be called a parallelogram since it has two sets of parallel sides, and it is also a rectangle since it has four right angles, but its special name is a square.

Ask the children to secretly pick a quadrilateral and to work out what makes it different from the others on the board. Pick some children to describe the quadrilateral they have chosen. Can the other children work out which it is?

Group work: Give the children sheets of 4 × 4 dotty paper. Ask them to draw as many quadrilaterals as they can. They should organise their shapes into groups, naming them and writing group descriptions of them. The shapes and descriptions can be stuck onto a group poster to help other children learn about quadrilaterals. Encourage them to give precise descriptions, giving reference to symmetry, regularity and so on.

Progress check: While children are describing the shapes ask: *What can you say about the angles in this quadrilateral? What about its symmetry? What is special about its sides? Does this quadrilateral have a special name?*

Review

Extend questions to include other shape work. For example: *Are any of the quadrilaterals regular shapes?* (Squares, which are the only quadrilaterals with equal sides and equal angles.) *Which of the quadrilaterals have lines of symmetry?*

Curriculum objectives

- To describe positions on a 2D grid as coordinates in the first quadrant.
- To plot specified points.

Success criteria

- I can describe positions and plot points on a coordinate grid.

You will need

Photocopiable sheets

'Coordinates'

General resources

'Coordinate grid'; interactive activity 'Shapes and coordinates'

Differentiation

Less confident learners

Support children in identifying which coordinate comes first in a pair of coordinates.

More confident learners

Ask children to measure and find the perimeters of shape.

Lesson 3 — Oral and mental starter 15

Main teaching activities

Whole-class work: Use the interactive activity 'Shapes and coordinates' on the CD-ROM with the whole-class. To remind children which coordinate comes first, use phrases such as *In the house and up the stairs* or *Along the corridor and up the stairs* and *x is across, x is a cross*. Invite children to give coordinates for the vertices of each shape. Ask questions such as: *What shape is this? How many sides does it have? What angles does this shape have? Is the shape symmetrical?*

Paired work: Provide each pair with photocopiable page 'Coordinates' from the CD-ROM. Ask them to work together to play the game.

Progress check: While children are giving and identifying pairs of coordinates ask: *Which coordinate comes first? What other coordinates are along the same vertical/horizontal line as this point?*

Review

Display photocopiable page 'Coordinate grid' from the CD-ROM on the interactive whiteboard. Draw three of the vertices of a square – for example, at the points (7, 1) (7, 4) (10, 4). Ask children to give the coordinates for these points. *These three points are three of the vertices of a square. What are the coordinates for the fourth vertex of this square?* (10, 1) Discuss strategies that children could use to help them find the fourth vertex. Repeat for another square or other quadrilaterals.

Curriculum objectives

- To identify acute and obtuse angles and to compare and order angles up to two right angles by size.

Success criteria

- I can identify acute and obtuse angles and can compare and order angles.

You will need

Photocopiable sheets

'Angles'

Equipment

Geostrips; paper fasteners

Differentiation

Less confident learners

Let children use the angle-makers to make the angles on the sheet and to relate them to the idea of angle as an amount of turn.

More confident learners

Ask children to use a protractor to measure the angles.

Lesson 4 — Oral and mental starter 15

Main teaching activities

Whole-class work: Use two strips of cards (or geostrips) fastened with a paper fastener to make a flexible angle maker. Turn one arm of the angle to show a right angle and discuss its name. Turn the angle to different orientations so that children realise a right angle does not have to have a horizontal or vertical arm. Change it to an angle smaller than a right angle. *Does anyone know what we call an angle that is smaller than a right angle?* (An acute angle.) Show a range of acute angles with the strips in different orientations. Now show an angle that is larger than a right angle but less than a half turn and introduce the term *obtuse* in the same way. Draw five or six angles on the board to show them in static positions and ask children to identify if they are acute, obtuse or right angles and to put them in order of size. Ensure children realise that angle is the amount of turn and not related to the lengths of the lines or to the distance between the end points of the lines.

Independent work: Ask children to complete photocopiable page 'Angles' from the CD-ROM.

Progress check: Ask: *What type of angle is this? How do you know? Is it smaller or larger than a right angle? What do we call this angle then?*

Review

Draw an irregular shape on the board with a range of angles. Ask children to identify each type of angle. *How do you know whether these angles are acute, right or obtuse angles? Find and tell me an example of each of these angles in the classroom?*

Curriculum objectives
● To compare and classify geometric shapes based on their properties and sizes.
Success criteria
● I can solve problems involving 2D shapes.

You will need
Photocopiable sheets
'Shape investigation'

Differentiation
Less confident learners
Provide children with paper and scissors and ask them to fold and cut the shapes, if necessary.
More confident learners
Ask children to group the results of the investigation in different ways and to write more detailed descriptions of the shapes formed.

Lesson 5   Oral and mental starter 9

Main teaching activities

Whole-class work: Discuss the ideas learned this week and introduce the investigation activity 'Split it' which children will undertake during the independent work part of the lesson. Ask children to visualise the following: *Imagine I am holding a square piece of paper. I fold it and crease it along a straight line before opening it back out again. What two shapes do you think I have split my square into?* Discuss the many possible options, although children initially may be likely to assume that the crease formed a line of symmetry, thus either two rectangles were made or two triangles. *What type of triangle would it be?* Encourage children to visualise that the triangles would be right-angled isosceles triangles, if the fold was along a line of symmetry of the square. Discuss that other folds could be made – for example, creating a triangle and a trapezium, like this:

Spend time discussing other folds that children may have visualised and describe the shapes with relation to their angles, lengths of sides, symmetries and names. For example: *We could make a right-angled isosceles triangle and a pentagon that has three right angles. The two long sides of the pentagon are equal and two short sides are equal:*

Independent work: Hand out copies of photocopiable page 'Shape investigation' from the CD-ROM. Ask children to investigate all the different possible ways in which Farmer Jones could split his rectangular field using straight fences. Encourage them to describe each of the shapes created in as much detail as possible, including references to angles, symmetries, lengths of sides, and so on.

Progress check: Invite children to describe the different shapes they have investigated. *What are the differences between these two fields? What three shapes have you made here? What about here? Are these the same?*

Review

Take feedback about the investigation and explore the range of solutions. For example, for the second part:

Three rectangles

Three triangles

One rectangle, two triangles

Two triangles, one quadrilateral

Two triangles, one parallelogram

One trapezium, one rectangle, one triangle

One rectangle, one pentagon, one triangle

Ask further questions about the investigation, such as: *Is it possible to split a rectangle in this way and form an equilateral triangle? Why is that? What do you know about its angles?*

Statistics and time

Expected prior learning

Children should be able to:

● give the number of seconds in a minute and the number of days in each month, year and leap year

● understand simple scales (for example, 2, 5, 10 units) in pictograms and bar charts.

Topic	Curriculum objectives	Expected outcomes
Measurement	**Lesson 1**	
	To read, write and convert time between analogue and digital 12- and 24-hour clocks.	Read, write and convert time between analogue and digital 12-hour clocks.
	Lesson 2	
	To solve problems involving converting from hours to minutes; minutes to seconds; years to months; weeks to days.	Know different units of time and convert between them.
Statistics	**Lesson 3**	
	To interpret and present discrete and continuous data using appropriate graphical methods, including bar charts and time graphs.	Interpret and present discrete data using bar charts.
	Lesson 4	
	To solve comparison, sum and difference problems using information presented in bar charts, pictograms, tables and other graphs.	Solve comparison, sum and difference problems using information presented in bar charts and tables.
	Lesson 5	
	To solve comparison, sum and difference problems using information presented in bar charts, pictograms, tables and other graphs.	Solve comparison, sum and difference problems using information presented in pictograms and tables.

Preparation

Lesson 1:. prepare sets of cards cut out from 'Time Pelmanism', one set per pair

Lesson 3: copy 'Tally charts', one per child, 'Frequency chart', one per group, and 'Bar chart (2)', one per child

Lesson 4: copy 'Bar chart (1)', one per child

Lesson 5: copy 'Interpreting pictograms', one per child

You will need

Photocopiable sheets

'Time Pelmanism'; 'Tally charts'; 'Frequency chart'; 'Bar chart (1)'; 'Bar chart (2)'; 'Interpreting pictograms'

General resources

Interactive teaching resource 'Clocks'; interactive teaching resource 'Data handling'

Equipment

Individual whiteboards; clock faces with moving hands; rulers; magazines

Further practice

Photocopiable sheets

'Reading tally charts'

Oral and mental starters for week 6

See bank of starters on pages 45, 86 and 126. Oral and mental starters are also on the CD-ROM.

16 Multiply by 10 and 100

6 Fact practice

14 Measurement facts

Overview of progression

During the first part of the week the children will revise, consolidate and extend their knowledge of units of time and the relationships between them. They will revise telling times in analogue and digital 12-hour form and using roman numerals. In lesson 3 children will collect data and create tally chart and bar charts in groups. In lessons 4 and 5 children will solve problems involving interpreting bar charts and pictograms with different scales and keys.

Watch out for

The most common error in interpreting charts such as pictograms and bar charts is that children fail to notice and use the key or scale appropriately. Watch out for children, particularly with pictograms, who interpret one picture as one person or item.

Creative context

Link this time work to science activities, cooking, athletics and other sporting activities and draw attention to bar charts and pictograms used in real-life situations.

Vocabulary

am ante meridiem, pm post meridiem, bar chart, century, chart, data, day, frequency, hour, key, minute, month, pictogram, scale, second, tally, time, week, year, unit

Curriculum objectives
● To read, write and convert time between analogue and digital 12-hour clocks.
Success criteria
● I can read, write and convert time between analogue and digital 12-hour clocks.

You will need
Photocopiable sheets
'Time Pelmanism'
General resources
Interactive teaching resource 'Clocks'
Equipment
Small clock faces with moving hands

Differentiation
Less confident learners
Provide these children with small clock-faces with moving hands for support.
More confident learners
Encourage children to make several of their own new clock cards to include as part of the Pelmanism game.

Lesson 1
Oral and mental starter 16

Main teaching activities
Whole-class work: Use the interactive teaching resource 'Clocks' on the CD-ROM to show some analogue times. Use the random button to generate these, asking: *What time is this?* Invite children to read the times correctly in words, using *to* or *past* vocabulary, such as *quarter past six, twenty-five minutes to seven.* Then use 'Options' display a digital clock (12-hour mode) and again ask children to say the times using *correct vocabulary.* Children often find it difficult to give digital times using *to* vocabulary and instead just read out the digits – for example, they say *Four forty* rather than *twenty minutes to five.* Provide lots of practice of this. Return to the analogue clock and select the 'Roman numerals' option and repeat activity again, using the random button.

As you are working together with the class ask children to suggest things that they might be doing at these times (at school, watching TV, having lunch...) and invite them to say whether the time would then be an am or a pm time. Revise that am comes from the Latin *ante meridiem* (meaning before noon) and pm is *post meridiem* (meaning after noon). Give children opportunities to describe activities at different times of day and to give them as am and pm times.

Return to the analogue times and as you click the random button, encourage children to say how this time could be written as a digital time (12-hour clock). *If it was in the afternoon, would this be an am or pm digital time?*

As an assessment activity to see how well they understand the link between digital times and analogue times, give each child (or pair) a small clock face with moving hands. Use the interactive teaching resource to set some digital times and ask children to show the same time on their clock face.

Paired work: Provide each child with the cards cut out from photocopiable pages 'Time Pelmanism' from the CD-ROM. Invite them to play the game in pairs, matching a digital to an analogue time.

Progress check: As children are playing the game ask: *If this time was an am/pm time what might you be doing then? Will it be morning, afternoon, evening or night? What time is one minute later than 11:59 pm?*

Review
Set the clocks from the interactive teaching resource to different times and ask problems about them, such as: *What time would it be in 10/20 minutes time? What time was one hour before this? How did you work that out?* Children can give answers in words or as digital times or can again use their small clock faces to show the answers as analogue times.

Curriculum objectives

● To solve problems involving converting from hours to minutes; minutes to seconds; years to months; weeks to days.

Success criteria

● I know different units of time and can convert between them.

Differentiation

Less confident learners

Give children specific situations and the time in one unit and ask them to give this time in a different unit, such as *the length of a film is two hours or 120 minutes.*

More confident learners

Encourage children to use a wider range of units of time, such as decades or centuries.

Lesson 2 Oral and mental starter 16

Main teaching activities

Whole-class work: Explain that in today's lesson the focus will be on converting between units of time. Ask: *What units of time do we use? How long can things take?* Invite children to answer which unit would be used to measure:

- the age of a tree
- the length of a TV advert
- how long it takes for a daffodil to grow
- how old your grandma is
- the length of time to take the register
- the length of an episode of Coronation Street
- how long between episodes of Eastenders
- the length of time since Queen Victoria died
- the age of a baby
- how long until your birthday
- the length of time since the year 1AD
- how long it takes to run a marathon. Up the stairs. From Land's End to John O'Groats
- how long until Saturday
- the length of a film
- how long until you are 19 or 20.

Draw the following headings along the top of the board and ask children to say what we would multiply by each time to convert from one unit of time to the next:

years $\longrightarrow \times ? \longrightarrow$ months   weeks $\longrightarrow \times ? \longrightarrow$ days   days $\longrightarrow \times ? \longrightarrow$ hours

hours $\longrightarrow \times ? \longrightarrow$ minutes   minutes $\longrightarrow \times ? \longrightarrow$ seconds

Revise the correct multipliers for each conversion (such as 12, 7, 24, 60 and 60) and give some simple numbers for the larger unit to convert to the smaller unit – for example, 4 years, 5 weeks, 2 days. Discuss appropriate multiplication strategies, including multiplying by units of 10: *If you know that 4 × 6 = 24, then what is 4 × 60?* List examples under the headings and provide practice of this.

Paired work: Ask children in pairs to make up situations and describe the approximate lengths of time that each would take in at least two different ways. Encourage them to use examples like the questions listed above and to give each time in at least two units. For example: *How long until my birthday* might be 8 weeks or 56 days or *My age* might be 9 years or 108 months.

Progress check: Ask children to describe how they solved a problem from their sheet: *How did you convert from this unit to this one? What number did you multiply or divide by?*

Review

Take feedback and ask pairs to share their examples with the rest of the class. Discuss any where one unit could be given more accurately than the other – for example, *How long until Saturday* might be two days or more specifically 39 hours until Saturday starts, rather than 48. Encourage children to realise that some units are better for giving more accurate times.

Curriculum objectives
● To interpret and present discrete data using bar charts.

Success criteria
● I can interpret and present discrete data using tallying and bar charts.

You will need

Photocopiable sheets
'Tally charts'; 'Frequency chart'; 'Bar chart (2)'

General resources
Interactive teaching resource 'Data handling'

Equipment
Individual whiteboards; magazines; rulers

Differentiation

Less confident learners
Ask this group to select fewer magazines and to focus on a bar chart with a scale of no more than 5 units.

More confident learners
Challenge this group to select their own scales/vertical axis for the bar charts.

Lesson 3
Oral and mental starter 16

Main teaching activities

Whole-class work: Open interactive teaching resource 'Data handling' on the CD-ROM. Display screen 1 and use the tools to hide the numbers in the y-axis, leaving the countries visible on the x-axis. Ask children in pairs to work out how many medals each country won using the bar chart and record the frequencies chart on their individual whiteboards, such as: USA 39, China 32, Russia 27, Australia 16 (and so on).

Group work: Arrange the children into groups of four or five. Give each group a pile of magazines and ask them to test the statement *Half of the pages in these magazines are made up of adverts*. Give each group photocopiable page 'Frequency chart', and provide each child with a copy of 'Tally charts' and 'Bar chart (2)' from the CD-ROM. Ask them to firstly look through and then tally the proportion of adverts on the pages of different magazines. They can then total all their tallies to complete a joint frequency chart. Finally each child can draw a bar chart of their group's information and draw conclusions from it.

Progress check: Ask: *Do you think you have enough of a sample? How can you draw conclusions from this much information? Do you need to check more magazines?*

Review

Invite each group to present their findings. *Who thinks that the statement 'Half of the pages in these magazines are made up of adverts' is correct?* Ask children to explain their answers.

Curriculum objectives
● To solve comparison, sum and difference problems using information presented in bar charts, pictograms and tables.

Success criteria
● I can solve comparison, sum and difference problems using information presented in bar charts and tables.

You will need

Photocopiable sheets
'Bar chart (1)'

General resources
Interactive teaching resource 'Data handling'

Differentiation

Less confident learners
Ask children to complete the photocopiable page in pairs.

More confident learners
Ask children to complete the photocopiable sheet individually.

Lesson 4
Oral and mental starter 6

Main teaching activities

Whole-class work: Open interactive teaching resource 'Data handling' on the CD-ROM. Display screen 2, use the tools to hide the numbers in the y-axis. Explain that a class of children counted up the total number of each pet that they owned and that this chart shows that information. Ask a range of questions involving adding or subtracting the heights of the bars, such as:

● *Which pet are there most/least of?*
● *How many more _____ are there than _____?*
● *How many _____ and _____ are there altogether?*
● *How many pets does our class have in total?*

Work through the answers with the class, discussing the scale and how to find each total or difference.

Paired/Independent work: Provide each child with photocopiable page 'Bar chart (1)' from the CD-ROM to complete.

Progress check: Ask: *How did you work out the answer to this question? What method of addition/subtraction did you use to find the total/difference of these numbers?*

Review

Take feedback on the photocopiable sheet. Collect information about the children's own favourite wild animals and draw a simple frequency diagram of this information. Ask questions involving adding or subtracting, such as: *Which is the most popular animal in our class? How many more children chose lions as their favourite animal than chose giraffes?*

Curriculum objectives
● To solve comparison, sum and difference problems using information presented in bar charts, pictograms and tables.

Success criteria
● I can solve comparison, sum and difference problems using information presented in pictograms and tables.

You will need
Photocopiable sheets
'Interpreting pictograms'

Differentiation
Less confident learners

Before copying, mask and alter photocopiable page 'Interpreting pictograms' so that the first chart has a key of 2, and change 100 to read 20 in the instructions.

More confident learners

Before copying, mask and alter the photocopiable sheet so that the first chart has a key of 20, and change 100 to read 200 in the instructions.

Lesson 5 — Oral and mental starter 14

Main teaching activities

Whole-class work: Copy the following pictogram on to the whiteboard and ask children to explain what they think it might show.

Favourite days of the week

Monday	◯ ◖
Tuesday	◯ ◯ ◯
Wednesday	◯ ◯ ◯ ◯ ◯ ◯ ◯
Thursday	◯ ◯
Friday	◯ ◯ ◯ ◯ ◯
◯ = ☐ children	

Ask questions and help children to see that without a number in the key they cannot answer them: *How many children chose Monday?* Ask them to say what they think the key might be and establish that it cannot be that the face = 1 child since there is half a picture. Fill 2 into the key and ask questions for them to answer, including those that involve adding and subtracting, such as: *How many more chose Wednesday than Monday?*

Now change the key to 10 and repeat for a range of similar questions. *How could we show two people when we have the key 10?* Explore drawing one fifth of a face (like a slice of pie) to represent two people. Emphasise the importance of using the key when interpreting pictograms.

Independent work: Give each child photocopiable page 'Interpreting pictograms' from the CD-ROM. Ask them to read the key carefully and to answer the questions about the pictograms.

Progress check: During independent work ask: *How did you work out the answer to this question? What method of addition/subtraction did you use to find the total/difference of these numbers?*

Review

Take feedback on the photocopiable sheet. *What did you discover about the pictograms?* Use data from the previous lesson about the children's favourite wild animals and choose an appropriate key to display that information in a pictogram. Invite children to the front to draw faces (or part faces) to represent the data.

Curriculum objectives
● To add and subtract numbers with up to four-digits using the formal written methods of columnar addition and subtraction where appropriate.

You will need
1. Check

Oral and mental starter
29 Place value additions and subtractions

2. Assess
'Target grids (2)'; squared paper

3. Further practice

Oral and mental starters
13 Targets

Photocopiable sheets
'Sum practice'

Adding four-digit numbers

Most children should be able to add four-digit numbers using a column method of addition.

Some children will require further practice in adding three-digit numbers and digits that require fewer incidents of carrying.

1. Check
29 Place value additions and subtractions

Ask children to add pairs of numbers, choosing one from each list. Observe which children understand place value ideas and are confident in adding digits from the same columns correctly. For those lacking confidence, draw the column headings and write the numbers vertically before asking them to add.
● *What is the sum of the two numbers? How could you find out?*
● *Which are the hundreds digits of the two numbers? What is their total?*

2. Assess
Children choose pairs of numbers from the second grid on photocopiable page 'Target grids (2)' from the CD-ROM to add together using a vertical method. Challenge the more confident to choose pairs from the third grid, whose totals will be five-digit numbers. Check that all children can identify which digit is which and can align the numbers correctly in columns. If children are unsure, help them to set out each question on squared paper in the correct columns first. Observe also whether any children do not know their number bonds and are resorting to counting on or using fingers to add. Record the outcomes.

3. Further practice
Use the suggested oral and mental starter to provide further reinforcement. The photocopiable page 87 'Sum practice' gives further experience of adding four-digit numbers using the column method.

Curriculum objectives
● To use place value, known and derived facts to multiply and divide mentally, including: multiplying together three numbers.

You will need
1. Check

Oral and mental starter
11 Magic square (1)

2. Assess
2–9 number cards

3. Further practice

Oral and mental starters
8 Function machine
10 Multiplication and division facts for 8
16 Multiply by 10 and 100

Photocopiable sheets
'Quick times'

Multiplying three numbers together

Most children should be able to multiply three small numbers together, choosing the most appropriate order to do so.

Some children will require further practice in recognising which pairs of numbers to multiply first to make each question simpler.

1. Check
11 Magic square (1)

Start by revising tables facts from the 6-times table. Complete a new magic square (×6) and observe which children are confident in recalling the facts. Then create a third magic square by multiplying all the numbers in the square by 2. Observe whether children see that the answers are 12 times the numbers in the first grid.
● *Which number in the third magic square is the answer to 4 × 6 × 2?*
● *What is the answer to 2 × 9 × 6? How could you work it out?*

2. Assess
Children make a multiplication question by picking three 2–9 number cards to multiply together. Challenge the more confident to use the digits 5, 8, 6, 7 (for example, 5 × 8 × 6). Give those who experience difficulty the 2 and 5 cards and ask them to select a third card to make their multiplications. Observe children who are able to confidently multiply numbers by multiples of 10. Record the outcomes.

3. Further practice
The oral and mental starter activities provide practice in the recall of tables facts and also in multiplying numbers by 10 and by multiples of 10.

Curriculum objectives
● To recognise and show, using diagrams, families of common equivalent fractions.

You will need
1. Check
Oral and mental starter
27 Run around fractions

2. Assess
'Fraction wall'

3. Further practice
Oral and mental starters
22 Fraction action
41 Fifths of a metre
38 Decimal divisions

Equivalent fractions

Most children should be able to write fractions that are equivalent to any proper fraction made with small numbers and 10 and 100.

Some children will not have made such progress and will require further practice in colouring shapes or using a fraction wall to help them recognise equivalence.

1. Check

27 Run around fractions

Observe which children are confident in identifying fractions equivalent to another. Ask questions such as:

- *What does equivalent mean?*
- *How can you tell whether two fractions are equivalent or not?*
- *Tell me three fractions equivalent to ¾.*
- *Are ⁸⁰⁄₁₀₀ and ⅕ equivalent?*

2. Assess

Ask children to write three fractions that are equivalent to each of these fractions: ⅓, ⅕, ⅞ and ⁶⁰⁄₁₀₀. Observe the children at work, and note those who work quickly and accurately. Let children lacking confidence refer to photocopiable page 210 'Fraction wall' if necessary. Give further fractions to the more confident children, asking them to give them in their simplest form. Record the outcomes.

3. Further practice

The recommended oral and mental starter activities provide further practice in understanding the nature of fractions and equivalence.

Curriculum objectives
● To read, write and convert time between analogue and digital 12- and 24-hour clocks.

You will need
1. Check
Oral and mental starter
32 Time trials

2. Assess
Small clock-faces with moving hands

3. Further practice
Oral and mental starters
33 What's the time, Mr Wolf?

Photocopiable sheets
'Time after time cards'

Analogue and digital 12-hour times

Most children should be able to read times on both analogue and digital 12-hour clocks and be able to convert between them.

Some children will not have made such progress and may still need to develop an understanding of how digital time relates to a clock-face.

1. Check

32 Time trials

Ask questions involving both analogue and digital times, including holding up a clock-face to show times. Observe whether children can recognise the relationship between digital and analogue time and whether they are able to read digital times using words *past* and *to* the hour.

- *What time does this digital clock show? How could the same time be shown on a clock-face?*
- *How many minutes to 12 o'clock is 11:45? How do you know?*

2. Assess

Write a list of 12-hour digital times and ask the children to copy them onto paper, to make each time on their small clock-face and write the time in words, using *past* and *to* the hour. Observe the children at work, and note those who work confidently. Children lacking confidence could be shown a clock-face with the multiples of 5 written at each five-minute interval to make linking digital times with analogue ones easier. Record the outcomes.

3. Further practice

The recommended oral and mental starter activities and photocopiable page 'Time after time cards' from the CD-ROM can provide further practice in exploring the link between analogue and digital 12-hour times.

Oral and mental starters

Addition, subtraction, multiplication and division

8 Function machine

Draw a simple function machine on the board and write a single- or multi-step operation such as 4 or ×3 + 1 into the machine. Call out input numbers and ask the children to give output numbers – for example, Input 10 (×4, output 40) and so on. Extend in subsequent sessions to ×6, ×8 and ×12.

Extension

For a single-step function give the output number and ask the children to say the input number. Alternatively, give the input and output numbers and ask the children to guess the function.

9 Story time

Write a number statement on the board (say, 30 ÷ 5 = 6) and ask the children, in pairs, to devise a story to match the statement. For example: *Thirty children played football in the Games lesson. Each team had five players and there were six teams.* The class can decide which was the most interesting story. Include questions that contain a missing number other than the answer, such as 28 − [ ] = 19, [ ] + 29 = 58.

10 Multiplication and division facts for 8

Use the interactive activity 'Multiplication and division facts for 8' on the CD-ROM. Screen 1: Invite the children to make links between the questions and their correct answers from the 8-times table. Screen 2: Use the same approach for related division facts.

11 Magic square (1)

Copy a magic square onto the board:

4 3 8
9 5 1
2 7 6

Explain that the sum of each row, column and diagonal is the same. (15)

Choose a times table (for example, 7), and multiply each number in the magic square by that number to create a new grid of numbers. Encourage the children to check to see if the numbers still form a magic square and to say what the total is.

12 9-times table

Practise the 9-times table on your fingers with the children: Hold up both hands, palms towards you. For 1 × 9 hold down the first finger of the left hand. There are nine fingers to the right of the finger held down so the answer is 9. For 2 × 9 hold down the second finger. There is one finger to the left (worth 10) and 8 to the right so the answer is 18. For 3 × 9 hold down the third finger. There are two fingers to the left (worth 20) and 7 to the right so the answer is 27 and so on. Call out questions up to 10 × 9 and ask the children to give the answers, using their fingers to check.

13 Targets

Write several numbers on the board (for example, 80, 50, 9, 6, 4) and a target number (say, 244). Set the children the challenge of hitting, or getting as close as possible to, the target number using some or all of the numbers and whatever operations they wish. In this case 9 − 6 = 3, 3 × 80 = 240, and 240 + 4 = 244.

Measurement

14 Measurement facts

Draw a 4 × 5 rectangle on the board, with a measurement in each section. For example:

55cm	0.72m	8cm	0.3m	1m
½m	30cm	0.35m	72cm	0.2m
7.2m	0.5m	0.2m	50cm	0.75m
35cm	92cm	720cm	¾m	45cm

Invite the children to create number statements from the measurements in the rectangle, such as 0.5m = 50cm, 0.72m = 72cm, 92cm + 8cm = 1m. It can be useful to draw the template on card and laminate it. New numbers can then be written whenever required.

Name: _____   Date: _____

Sum practice

1.

```
  4 1 5 2
+ 3 7 4 5
─────────
```

2.

```
  8 5 7 3
+ 1 4 2 6
─────────
```

3.

```
  4 4 5 8
+ 1 4 8 0
─────────
```

4.

```
  5 6 2 9
+ 1 2 1 6
─────────
```

5.

```
  4 6 2 9
+ 1 2 8 3
─────────
```

6.

```
  3 8 2 7
+ 1 6 1 4
─────────
```

7.

```
  7 9 6 7
+ 7 4 7 1
─────────
```

8.

```
  4 8 2 6
+ 6 8 7 1
─────────
```

9.

```
  6 5 3 8
+ 4 7 9 8
─────────
```

10.

```
  9 8 8 7
+ 7 5 7 6
─────────
```

I can add four-digit numbers.

How did you do?

Fraction game

- Play this game with a partner. Use a counter and a dice.
- Take turns to roll the dice and move your counter around the track, crossing off the answer in your grid below. The winner is the first player to cross off all their numbers.

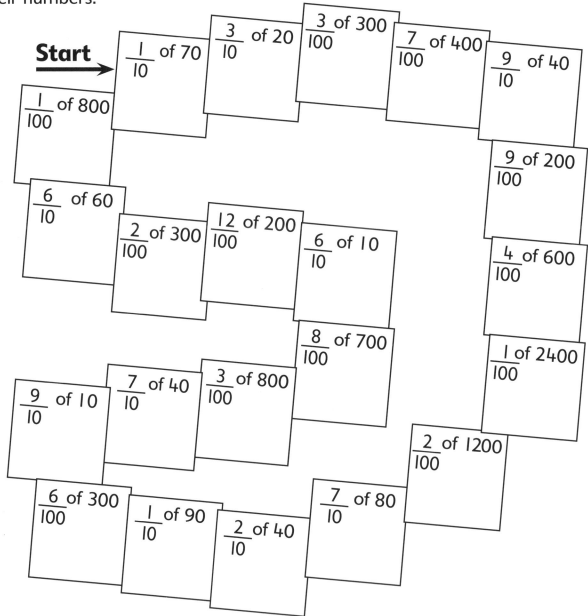

Start →

$\frac{1}{10}$ of 70

$\frac{3}{10}$ of 20

$\frac{3}{100}$ of 300

$\frac{7}{100}$ of 400

$\frac{9}{10}$ of 40

$\frac{1}{100}$ of 800

$\frac{9}{100}$ of 200

$\frac{6}{10}$ of 60

$\frac{2}{100}$ of 300

$\frac{12}{100}$ of 200

$\frac{6}{10}$ of 10

$\frac{4}{100}$ of 600

$\frac{8}{100}$ of 700

$\frac{1}{100}$ of 2400

$\frac{9}{10}$ of 10

$\frac{7}{10}$ of 40

$\frac{3}{100}$ of 800

$\frac{2}{100}$ of 1200

$\frac{6}{100}$ of 300

$\frac{1}{10}$ of 90

$\frac{2}{10}$ of 40

$\frac{7}{10}$ of 80

Player 1

28	24	36
18	6	7
8	9	56

Player 2

28	24	36
18	6	7
8	9	56

PHOTOCOPIABLE

Name: _____   Date: _____

Reading tally charts

- Answer the questions below about this tally chart.

Dog   ⅢⅢ ⅢⅢ ⅢⅢ
Cat   ⅢⅢ ⅢⅢ ⅠⅠ
Hamster   ⅢⅢ
Goldfish   ⅢⅢ ⅢⅢ
Rabbit   ⅢⅢ ⅠⅠ

1. What do you think the chart shows? _____

_____

2. What was the least popular animal? _____

3. How many animals are in the chart altogether? _____

4. What do you think the title of the chart should be? _____

_____

- Answer the questions below about this tally chart.

Car   ⅢⅢ ⅢⅢ ⅢⅢ ⅢⅢ Ⅰ
Bus   ⅢⅢ ⅠⅠⅠⅠ
Train   ⅢⅢ ⅢⅢ Ⅰ
Bike   ⅢⅢ
Aeroplane   ⅢⅢ ⅢⅢ ⅢⅢ ⅢⅢ ⅢⅢ

1. What do you think the chart shows? _____

_____

2. What was the most popular transport? _____

3. How many things are in the chart altogether? _____

4. What do you think the title of the chart should be? _____

_____

I can read tally charts.

How did you do?

Number, place value and rounding

Expected prior learning

Children should be able to:

- recognise the place value of each digit in a three-digit number (hundreds, tens, ones)
- compare and order numbers up to 1000
- identify, represent and estimate numbers by using different representations
- read and write numbers to at least 1000 in numerals and in words.

Topic	Curriculum objectives	Expected outcomes
Number and place value	**Lesson 1**	
	To find 1000 more or less than a given number.	Give the value of each digit in a four-digit number and order and compare them.
	To recognise the place value of each digit in a four-digit number (thousands, hundreds, tens, and ones).	Find 1000 more or less than a four-digit number.
	To order and compare numbers beyond 1000.	
	Lesson 2	
	To identify, represent and estimate numbers using different representations.	Identify, position and estimate four-digit numbers on number lines.
	Lesson 3	
	To round any number to the nearest 10, 100 or 1000.	Round four-digit numbers to the nearest 10, 100 or 1000.
	Lesson 4	
	To read Roman numerals to 100 (I to C) and know that over time, the numeral system changed to include the concept of zero and place value.	Read Roman numerals to 100.
	Lesson 5	
	To solve number and practical problems that involve all of the above and with increasingly large positive numbers.	Solve number and practical problems.

■SCHOLASTIC

Preparation

Lesson 1: copy 'The comparing game', one per pair

Lesson 2: modify and copy 'Blank number lines', one per pair (see lesson plan)

Lesson 4: prepare 'Roman numerals' for display on the interactive whiteboard; modify and copy the sheet, one per pair (see lesson plan)

Lesson 5: copy 'Potato crisis', one per pair

You will need

Photocopiable sheets
'The comparing game'; 'Potato crisis'

General resources
'Blank number lines'; 'Roman numerals'

Equipment
Individual whiteboards; place value cards (four-digit numbers); large sheets of paper; scissors; counters; number fans; place value charts; 0–9 number cards

Further practice

Photocopiable sheets
'A bigger place?'

Oral and mental starters for week 1

See bank of starters on pages 44 and 167. Oral and mental starters are also on the CD-ROM.

23 Place value chains (2)

3 Writing numbers

24 Secret numbers

Overview of progression

During this week the children will consolidate and extend their place value ideas of four-digit numbers, including comparing, ordering, positioning them on number lines and rounding them. In lesson 1 they will explore the value of digits in four-digit numbers and will compare them using the > and < symbols. In lesson 2 they will explore different representations of numbers on number lines and in lesson 3 they will round numbers to the nearest 10, 100 and 1000. Lesson 4 introduces Roman numerals and you can discuss these rules with the class: A letter can be repeated to show itself two or three times, such as XXX = 30, CC = 200. *But we don't use VV or LL – why not?* (Because there is another letter we can use for 10 and 100.)

If one or more letters are placed after another letter of greater value, add that amount: VI = 6 (5 + 1 = 6), LXX = 70 (50 + 10 + 10 = 70).

If a letter is placed before another letter of greater value, subtract that amount: IV = 4 (5 − 1 = 4), XC = 90 (100 − 10 = 90).

By the end of the week children will be exploring all aspects of four-digit numbers through a problem-solving activity set in a real-life context.

Watch out for

Ensure that children are confident with the place value of four-digit numbers and that they appreciate the different values of the digits. Children often experience difficulty writing in words numbers that include the digit zero, particularly in the middle of the number (for example, 6047). Where this mistake occurs, provide place value arrow cards and encourage children to place the 40 and 7 cards correctly onto the 6000 card to create the number 6047.

Creative context

Make links between measurement topics in science and technology that involve four-digit numbers.

Vocabulary

compare, digit, estimate, figure, hundreds, multiples, ones, order, **place value**, rounding, sequences, tens, thousands, units

Curriculum objectives
- To find 1000 more or less than a given number.
- To recognise the place value of each digit in a four-digit number (thousands, hundreds, tens, and ones).
- To order and compare numbers beyond 1000.

Success criteria
- I can give the value of each digit in a four-digit number and can order and compare them.
- I can find 1000 more or less than a four-digit number.

You will need
Photocopiable sheets
'The comparing game'

Equipment
Place value cards (four-digit numbers); scissors; counters

Differentiation
Less confident learners
Adapt the cards to encompass three-digit numbers and ask children to compare numbers between 100 and 999.

More confident learners
Adapt the cards to encompass five-digit numbers and ask children to compare numbers between 10,000 and 99,999.

Lesson 1
Oral and mental starter 23

Main teaching activities

Whole-class work: Explain that today's lesson will involve saying the value of each digit in a four-digit number and comparing and ordering them. Write a four-digit number on the board (say, 6574) and write Th H T U above the digits. Ask a range of questions: *What do these letters stand for? Which digit is the tens digit? What is the digit 6 worth?* Invite a child to come to the front and write the number in partitioned form: 6574 = 6000 + 500 + 70 + 4. Use place value cards to reinforce this idea. Revise adding and subtracting 1000 to and from this number. Draw attention to the fact that the hundreds, tens and units digits remain unchanged.

Revise the symbols < and > and ask: *What do these signs mean?* Remind children that, like the jaws of a greedy shark or crocodile, the sign opens towards the larger number. Write 6574 > [ ] and 6574 < [ ] and invite a child to write a number to the right of each sign to make the statement true. Ask the rest of the class to say whether these are correct and to explain how they know (for example, 6574 > 6354 and 6574 < 8835). Provide other similar questions, but give several digits and explain that the numbers to the right of the sign must be made from these digits. For example:

3437 < [ ]

3437 > [ ] using the digits 3, 3, 4 and 2.

Look at all the possible solutions, for example:

3437 < 4233 (or 4323 or 4332)

3437 > 2334 (2343, 2433, 3243, 3234, 3324, 3342, 3423, 3432)

Ask: *How can we be sure we are correct?* Encourage children to partition numbers and to compare them, starting with the most significant digit (the thousands digit) first.

Paired work: Each child should begin by drawing a large 6 × 6 grid on a sheet of paper to write a different four-digit number into each section of the grid. Give each pair photocopiable page 'The comparing game' from the CD-ROM. Ask them to cut out the cards on the sheet and use them to play a game. The cards are placed face down in a pile. Taking turns, the children pick a card and find a number in their own grid that matches the description. The other player must agree that it is correct. The number is covered with a counter and the game continues. The winner is the first player to get four counters in a line.

Progress check: Ask: *Which digit has the largest value in the number 1234?* Watch out for children who incorrectly say 4 as this can indicate that they have failed to grasp the relative values of the digits. Invite them to partition the number and ask the question again.

Review

Create a chain of four-digit numbers on the board that involve adding or subtracting 1000 or 2000. For example:

4378 — +1000 → 5378 — – 2000 → 3378 — – 1000 →

2378 — +2000 → ...

As children continue each step, partition the numbers on the board to reinforce the place value ideas and encourage children to put the numbers created in order at the end.

Curriculum objectives
● To identify, represent and estimate numbers using different representations.

Success criteria
● I can identify, position and estimate four-digit numbers on number lines.

You will need

General resources
'Blank number lines'

Differentiation

Less confident learners
Focus on only one type of number line interval (say, 1000) and provide lines with adjacent multiples of 1000 at either end.

More confident learners
Include several number lines with adjacent multiples of 10,000 at either end of the line where children give five-digit answers.

Lesson 2   Oral and mental starter 23

Main teaching activities

Whole-class work: Draw a number line with 0 at the left-hand end and 1000 at the right.

0   1000

Mark a point part way along the line and ask children to estimate what approximate number they think the mark might be pointing to (230, 780 and so on). *How can you be sure?* Split the line into ten equal parts to help them estimate and check. Select and mark several points and repeat. Then call out some numbers and invite children to estimate the position of each on the number line.

Change the number line by altering 0 to 1000 and 1000 to 2000. Mark similar points.

1000   2000

What number do you think this might be? How do you know? Continue in this way for the other numbers on the line, inviting children to say and write the names of each and to mark it on a number line.

Now alter the start and end numbers so that the line shows a range of 10,000 rather than 1000:

0   10,000

Ensure that children realise that you have changed the scale and that each interval will be worth ten times more than before. Mark the halfway point, establish that this is 5000 and continue to split the line into ten equal parts to show each 1000. *Where should I mark 2500? 7500? 500?*

Finally, alter the end numbers so that the line shows a range of only 100:

3400   3500

Mark ten intervals and discuss that each interval is now only worth 10 (3410, 3420, 3430...).

Paired work: Before copying photocopiable page 'Blank number lines' from the CD-ROM, mark on the following numbers at each end of the lines and draw a range of arrows to points on the line. Ask children in pairs to discuss and estimate the numbers of the points marked by the arrows. They should write the numbers in figures and in words. For the core children, write the following numbers at the ends of the lines: 0 and 1000; 5000 and 6000; 9000 and 10,000; 3500 and 3600; 4200 and 4300; 7000 and 7100; 0 and 10,000.

Progress check: Ask: *How can you split the line into ten equal parts to help you check? What number do you think this might be? How can you be sure?*

Review

Take feedback on the number lines work. Children can copy one of their lines onto the board and mark a point for the others to estimate.

Curriculum objectives
● To round any number to the nearest 10, 100 or 1000.

Success criteria
● I can count on in ones to add.

You will need
Equipment
Individual whiteboards

Differentiation
Less confident learners
Ask these children to round three-digit numbers.

More confident learners
These children can include five-digit numbers in their first column.

Lesson 3
Oral and mental starter 3

Main teaching activities

Whole-class work: Draw these number lines on the board:

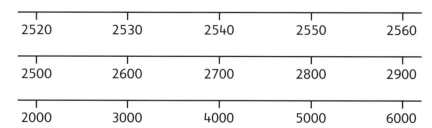

| 2520 | 2530 | 2540 | 2550 | 2560 |

| 2500 | 2600 | 2700 | 2800 | 2900 |

| 2000 | 3000 | 4000 | 5000 | 6000 |

Point out that the numbers are multiples of 10, 100 or 1000. Give a four-digit number that appears in the range of each line (say, 2548). Point to the first line and ask children to identify where on the line 2548 would be. *Which multiple of 10 is it closest to? So if we round 2548 to the nearest 10, what is the answer?* (2550) Then ask children to say what the same number would be rounded to the nearest 100. *Where on the second line would 2548 come? Which multiple of 100 is it closest to?* (2500) Finally, look at rounding to the nearest 1000. *Where would we mark 2548 on the third line? Which multiple of 1000 is it closest to?* (3000) Repeat for rounding other numbers to the nearest 10, 100 and 1000. Remind children that numbers half way between multiples (those ending in 5, 50 or 500), round up.

Independent work: Ask children to draw a table with four columns and label each column: Number, Rounded to the nearest 10, Rounded to the nearest 100 and Rounded to the nearest 1000. They should write a range of four-digit numbers into the first column and then round them to the nearest 10, 100 and 1000.

Progress check: Ask: *What is this to the nearest 10/100? How do you know?*

Review
Call out a four-digit multiple of 10, 100 or 1000 and ask children to say numbers that would round to it. For example: *What numbers when rounded to the nearest 1000 round to 5000? Which would be the highest/lowest number?*

Curriculum objectives
● To read Roman numerals to 100 (I to C).

Success criteria
● I can read Roman numerals to 100.

You will need
General resources
'Roman numerals'

Differentiation
Less confident learners
Mask fewer of the numbers and choose the easier ones involving adding or subtracting I or X mainly.

More confident learners
Mask a greater number of the numerals in the chart.

Lesson 4
Oral and mental starter 24

Main teaching activities

Whole-class work: Write I V X L C on the board, explaining that in Roman times these were numerals. Write I 5 10 50 and 100 under the letters respectively. Introduce the rules given in 'Overview of progression' on page 91.

Display photocopiable page 'Roman numerals' from the CD-ROM and discuss how the numbers to 100 are made. Explain that there are several limits on what you can do when subtracting – for example, you cannot subtract V or L from another letter. Go through the numbers in turn and explore the patterns.

Paired work: Before copying photocopiable page 'Roman numerals' from the CD-ROM, mask some of the Roman numerals for children to work out in pairs.

Progress check: Ask: *Are Roman numerals easier or harder to work with? Why is this?*

Review
Explain that the Romans didn't have a symbol for zero and that, over time, a simpler number system was invented using the digits 1 to 9 and zero. Zero as a place holder allowed for much larger numbers to be written using fewer digits/symbols.

Curriculum objectives
● To solve number and practical problems that involve increasingly large positive numbers.

Success criteria
● I can solve number and practical problems.

You will need
Photocopiable sheets
'Potato crisis'

Equipment
A bag of supermarket potatoes and weighing scales (optional)

Differentiation
Less confident learners

Encourage children to round each bag's weight to the nearest 10, 100 and 1000g first and then to look for the solutions.

More confident learners

As a follow-on activity children could write six more of their own weights and provide labels for them.

Lesson 5
Oral and mental starter 24

Main teaching activities

Whole-class work: Introduce the following real-life context to explore the ideas encountered this week: *A factory puts potatoes into bags and then weighs them and sorts the bags according to how heavy they are.* Explain that the bags are weighed in grams. List five weights (for example, 2014g, 1894g, 1869g, 2100g, 2301g) and ask children to say each aloud and then put them in order of heaviness (lightest first). Draw a long number line on the board from 1000 to 3000 and ask children to estimate where on the line the numbers would go. Discuss how close to 2000 each of the numbers is and draw intervals on the line to help children place them more accurately:

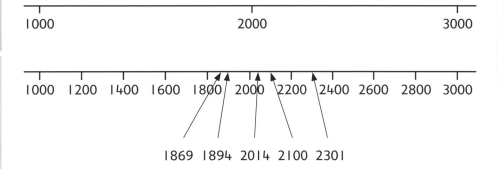

Ask: *Would it be fair for the bags of potatoes to be labelled as 2kg? Why or why not?* Revise that 2000g is 2kg. *What is each of these measurements rounded to the nearest 10g, 100g or 1000g (or kilogram)?* Draw a table to show the numbers rounded to each and discuss children's own opinions about what might be fair to put on a bag of potatoes. If available, hold up a bag of potatoes from a supermarket and weigh it to see how closely it matches the weight given on the bag. *Do you think it is fair to give that weight? Should the label show how the weight has been rounded? Has it been rounded to the nearest 10g? 100g? 1kg?* Ensure that children realise that just because an answer is a multiple of 1000, it can still have been rounded to the nearest 10 (for example, 4996 rounded to the nearest 10 is 5000).

Paired work: Provide each pair with photocopiable page 'Potato crisis' from the CD-ROM. Explain that the bags of potatoes have lost their labels and that the children must match each label with the correct bag. Make it clear that for some bags several labels are appropriate but that they must work out which label must have come from which bag as only one way allows each bag to have a label.

Progress check: Discuss strategies that children used to solve the problem on the photocopiable sheet. *Did anyone draw a table and round the all the measurements to the nearest 10g, 100g, 1kg?* Encourage the children to explain what they did. *Which other bag of potatoes could this label have matched? How do you know?*

Review

Go through the solutions together and see if any pairs disagree. Discuss any difficulties encountered in the activity and ask children to describe successful strategies that they used for solving the problems. *Did you put the bags in order? How did that help you?*

Addition and subtraction: mental and written methods

Expected prior learning

Children should be able to:

- rapidly recall and use addition and subtraction facts to 20
- recognise the place value of each digit in four-digit numbers
- accurately add and subtract numbers mentally, including one- and two-digit numbers.

Topic	Curriculum objectives	Expected outcomes
Addition and subtraction	**Lesson 1**	
	To add and subtract numbers with up to four-digits using the formal written methods of columnar addition and subtraction where appropriate.	Add and subtract numbers with up to four-digits (using place value ideas).
	Lesson 2	
	To add and subtract numbers with up to four-digits using the formal written methods of columnar addition and subtraction where appropriate.	Subtract near multiples of 1000 and amounts of money near to whole pounds, counting up to find the difference.
	Lesson 3	
	To add and subtract numbers with up to four-digits using the formal written methods of columnar addition and subtraction where appropriate. To estimate and use inverse operations to check answers to a calculation.	Use a written column method of addition. Estimate to check answers to a calculation.
	Lesson 4	
	To add and subtract numbers with up to four-digits using the formal written methods of columnar addition and subtraction where appropriate. To estimate and use inverse operations to check answers to a calculation.	Use a written column method of subtraction and check by adding.
	Lesson 5	
	To solve addition and subtraction two-step problems in contexts, deciding which operations and methods to use and why. To estimate, compare and calculate different measures, including money in pounds and pence.	Solve two-step money problems involving addition and subtraction, choosing appropriate and effective calculation methods.

■SCHOLASTIC

Preparation

Lesson 5: prepare 'At the fair' for display on the interactive whiteboard; copy 'At the fair', one per group

You will need

Photocopiable sheets
'At the fair'

Equipment
Individual whiteboards; number cards (or a random number generator); place value cards

Further practice

Photocopiable sheets
'Number differences questions'

Oral and mental starters for week 2

See bank of starters on pages 45 and 167. Oral and mental starters are also on the CD-ROM.

6 Fact practice (addition)

25 Rounding round

24 Secret numbers

Overview of progression

This week, children will consolidate and extend their abilities to mentally add and subtract four-digit numbers using ideas of place value and mental methods and will use column methods of addition and subtraction with increasing complexity. They will use inverses to check their calculations and will make and use estimates to check whether answers are sensible. Children are given opportunities to decide when a particular calculation approach is best and work with money problems in lessons 2 and 5. At the end of the week they will use and apply these calculation strategies in solving problems.

Watch out for

Ensure that children are confident in place value ideas and look out for children who fail to appreciate the ease of adding or subtracting numbers like 3001, 2300, 5000 to a number where exchange is not required. Provide such children with a place value chart and ask them to partition numbers before adding – for example, $2314 + 300 = 2000 + 300 + 10 + 4 + 300$. Help them to appreciate the value of each digit in four-digit numbers. This will help them with mental methods and when practising written methods of addition and subtraction, as it can help them appreciate the place value implications of why we carry and exchange.

Creative context

Look out for opportunities to perform addition and subtraction in real-life contexts, such as number of absent children, dinner numbers, cooking situations.

Vocabulary

add, altogether, carry, column, difference, digit, equals, exchange, fewer, leave, less, make, minus, more, partition, plus, sign, subtract, sum, take away, total

Curriculum objectives

● To add and subtract numbers with up to four-digits.

Success criteria

● I can add and subtract numbers with up to four-digits (using place value ideas).

You will need

Equipment

Individual whiteboards; place value cards; 0–9 number

Differentiation

Less confident learners

Provide children with place value charts showing Th, H, T and U and digit cards. They should make each pair of numbers by placing the digits into the correct columns before adding and subtracting.

More confident learners

After they have done some calculations, provide children with some harder ready-made puzzles to solve.

Lesson 1
Oral and mental starter 6

Main teaching activities

Whole-class work: Explain that in this lesson children will use ideas of place value and other mental strategies to add and subtract numbers. Begin by drawing two large 'bags' of numbers on the board: the first with four-digit numbers made from the digits 3, 4, 5 and 6, the second with numbers made from digits less than 4, including zeroes. For example:

3433, 3544, 6345, 5555, 5635   120, 3023, 32, 3303, 2110,

4443, 3435, 4455, 3466   303, 2002, 3313, 112

Keep the sets of numbers on the board for the rest of the lesson. Underline a number from each 'bag' and ask children to say the number names for each and then add them. For example: *Three thousand, four hundred and thirty-three add two thousand and two, 3433 + 2002 = ?* Ask: *How can you say the answer without doing much 'work'?* Encourage children to explain what makes these questions easy. Point out that these are easy place value additions where we simply add to the appropriate digits: add 2 to the thousands digit and 2 to the units digit to give the answer 5435. Repeat for other pairs of numbers from the bags. Ask children to write answers on their individual whiteboards and hold them up for checking.

Then repeat for subtraction. *How can we find the difference between these two numbers?* (say, 4455 − 3023). Discuss again that these are easily solved through place value work, simply subtracting from the appropriate digits (for example, subtracting 3 from the thousands, 2 from the ten and 3 from the units columns).

Ask extension questions such as: *Which pair of numbers, one from each bag, has a total/difference of 8568... 3313... 130?* Invite children to discuss answers with a partner and to make up new similar questions of their own to ask the rest of the class.

Independent work: Leaving the same set of numbers on the board, or including extra numbers that meet the given criterion, ask children to use mental addition and subtraction and place value ideas to find the sum and the difference of pairs of numbers and use them to write puzzles for the review part of the lesson. They should initially build up a table showing sums and differences, such as:

Secret number 1	Secret number 2	Sum	Difference
[3466]	[112]	[3578]	[3354]

Puzzles in the following form can then be written: *I chose one number from each bag. Their sum is 3578 and their difference is 3354. Which two numbers did I choose?*

Progress check: Invite children to explain the calculations they are doing. *What is the name of this number? How many thousands/hundreds/tens/units has it? Tell me if you can partition this number into thousands, hundred, tens and units?*

Review

Invite children to read out the puzzles and for the rest of the class to try to solve them.

Curriculum objectives
● To subtract numbers with up to four-digits.

Success criteria
● I can subtract near multiples of 1000 and amounts of money near to whole pounds, counting up to find the difference.

You will need
Equipment
Individual whiteboards

Differentiation
Less confident learners
Provide children with two sets of three-digit numbers either side of a multiple of 100. This will create easier pairs of numbers to work with.

More confident learners
Ask children to create their own numbers to work with that are more than 10 away from the multiple of 1000 (say, 4985 and 5016) or pairs that are over 1000 away (say, 2991 and 4018).

Lesson 2
Oral and mental starter 6

Main teaching activities
Whole-class work: Begin by writing these two sets of numbers on the board:

| 4996 | 3994 | 7999 | 6991 | | 3003 | 8007 | 5002 |
| 8993 | 2995 | 1998 | | | 4001 | 2005 | 9009 | 7008 |

Ask: *What have the numbers in each set got in common?* Children may notice that two digits of each number in the first set are 9 and in the second set are 0. Describe the numbers in the first set as numbers that are a few less than multiples of 1000 and numbers in the second set as a few more than multiples of 1000. Ask children to pair numbers that are close together and give the multiple of 1000 that lies between them –for example, 3994 and 4007 with 4000 that lies between them. Remind them of the meaning of the word *difference* and explain that today's lesson is about finding the difference between pairs of numbers like these.

Demonstrate how to find the difference by counting up from the lower number to the multiple of 1000 and then up from that to the second number of the pair, adding the two numbers together. *What is the difference between 6991 and 7008?* (9 + 8 = 17) Sketch a simple number line section to illustrate the difference. Then discuss the difference between numbers that are over 1000 apart (for example, 3998 and 5002). Sketch a simple number line section to illustrate the difference:

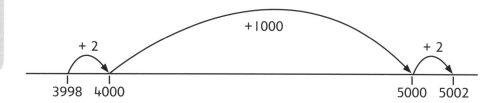

Find the difference between similar pairs in this way. Also demonstrate how this approach can be used for finding differences in amounts of money, such as £39.98 and £50.02, counting up 2p, then £10, then 2p.

Independent work: Ask children to find the difference between pairs of numbers, one from each bag on the board. After answering at least six of these questions they should write the following on their whiteboards, then find differences between them:

Set 1

£29.99, £31.98, £30.95, £28.91

Set 2

£33.09, £32.01, £40.10, £36.11

Progress check: Invite children to describe their strategies for finding the difference. *How did you work out this difference? Which is the multiple of 1000 that lies between them? Which is the next whole number of pounds as you count up?*

Review
Challenge children to guess two numbers or amounts of money that have a particular difference (say, 37), found on either side of 5000 on a number line, or £1.07 found either side of £10. Create similar questions with smaller or larger differences.

Curriculum objectives

- To use a written column method of addition.
- To estimate to check answers to a calculation.

Success criteria

- I can add numbers, using a column method of addition.
- I can estimate to check answers.

You will need

Equipment

0–9 number cards (or a random number generator)

Differentiation

Less confident learners

Select numbers for the children that generally only involve carrying once, such as 2644, 1326, 3811, 4253, 2272.

More confident learners

Ask children to generate four-digit numbers between 5555 and 9999 to ensure a greater number of carrying opportunities and to give many answers as five-digit numbers.

Main teaching activities

Whole-class work: Explain that this lesson is about adding four-digit numbers that require a written or mental method. Write the numbers 2562 and 7364 on the board. Ask: *What is the approximate total of these two numbers?* Discuss children's answers, expressing 2562 as less than 3000 (or close to 2600) and 7364 as more than 7000 (or close to 7400). An approximate answer might be 10,000. Focus attention on the importance of finding an approximate answer before calculating exactly.

Ask: *How could we find the exact total mentally?* Invite two or three children to come to the board and to explain ways that this could be done. Encourage a variety of methods – for example, using an empty number line or partitioning each number and then adding. Then ask children to identify the thousands, hundreds, tens and units/ones digit of each number. Write the column headings Th H T and U. *It can be helpful to write the numbers under these column headings.* Set out the numbers vertically and demonstrate the link between partitioned mental strategies and the more formal written method involving carrying once:

$$
\begin{array}{r}
2000 + 500 + 60 + 2 \\
+\ 7000 + 300 + 60 + 4 \\
\hline
9000 + 800 + 120 + 6
\end{array}
\qquad
\begin{array}{r}
\text{Th}\ \ \text{H}\ \ \text{T}\ \ \text{U} \\
2\ \ \ 5\ \ \ 6\ \ \ 2 \\
+\ 7\ \ \ 3\ \ \ 6\ \ \ 4 \\
\hline
9\ \ \ 9\ \ \ 2\ \ \ 6 \\
\scriptstyle 1
\end{array}
$$

Invite children to instruct you as to how to do the written method and to explain in their own words why we carry digits across from a column to the column to its left. Repeat for other pairs of numbers in the same way, including some questions that involve more than one exchange:

$$
\begin{array}{r}
3000 + 700 + 30 + 8 \\
+\ 4000 + 500 + 50 + 4 \\
\hline
7000 + 1200 + 80 + 12
\end{array}
\qquad
\begin{array}{r}
\text{Th}\ \ \text{H}\ \ \text{T}\ \ \text{U} \\
3\ \ \ 7\ \ \ 3\ \ \ 8 \\
+\ 4\ \ \ 5\ \ \ 5\ \ \ 4 \\
\hline
8\ \ \ 2\ \ \ 9\ \ \ 2 \\
\scriptstyle 1\ \ \ \ \ \scriptstyle 1
\end{array}
$$

Remind children to check their answers using the estimates they made.

Paired work: Let children use a random number generator (such as the one at www.random.org), to produce five numbers between 1000 and 9999. (Alternatively they can select sets of four-digit cards to create the four-digit numbers.) They should record these numbers and choose pairs of them to add. Encourage them to estimate first and then calculate, using the column method, to find as many different totals as they can.

Progress check: Invite children to discuss their additions. *What estimates did you make? How many times did you need to carry in this addition? Why was that? What is special about the digits in that column?*

Review

Take feedback. *Why do we need to estimate an answer before we calculate it?* Invite children to share their answers and their written methods and to explain how they checked their answers using their estimates.

Curriculum objectives
- To subtract numbers with up to four-digits using columnar subtraction.
- To use inverse operations to check answers to a calculation.

Success criteria
- I can use a written column method of subtraction and can check by adding.

Differentiation

Less confident learners

Ask children to use the expanded method for this work and provide place value cards for support.

More confident learners

Give a different set of numbers of nuts where questions involve exchanging two or three times.

Lesson 4   Oral and mental starter 25

Main teaching activities

Whole-class work: Revise the column method of subtraction with the class, making the link between its expanded form and the condensed/compact form, using this example:

Th H T U

7000	400	90	3	→	7000	400	80	13	7	4 $^{8}9$ $^{1}3$
− 4000	100	50	7		− 4000	100	50	7	− 4	1 5 7
					3000	300	30	6	3	3 3 6

How could we check whether our answer is correct? Remind children to make estimates before beginning but show also how the answer can be added to the number subtracted to see if this gives the first number (for example, 4157 + 3336 = 7493). Repeat for other written subtraction examples involving exchange once or twice, including in other columns.

Paired work: Introduce a 'Super Squirrel' who had collected and stored 8356 hazelnuts for the winter. Record this number. Tell children that each night the other animals in the wood come and steal Super Squirrel's nuts. Explain that you would like them to work out how many nuts Super Squirrel has left at the end of the week.

Number of nuts stolen each night: Mon 1532; Tue 1172; Wed 941; Thur 1371; Fri 1127; Sat 821; Sun 1217. Ask: *How many nuts did he have at the end?* (175)

Progress check: Invite children to explain how they subtracted each time and ask them to say the inverse calculation they used to check.

Review

Take feedback and discuss solutions.

Curriculum objectives
- To solve two-step addition and subtraction problems in contexts.
- To estimate, compare and calculate different measures.

Success criteria
- I can solve two-step money problems involving addition and subtraction.

You will need

Photocopiable sheets

'At the fair'

Differentiation

Less confident learners

Use mixed-ability groups and encourage peer tutoring, where more confident learners help those who are less confident.

More confident learners

Challenge children to make up their own questions for others to solve.

Lesson 5   Oral and mental starter 24

Main teaching activities

Whole-class work: Explain that today children will use the addition and subtraction strategies explored this week to solve money problems.

Show photocopiable page 'At the fair' from the CD-ROM on the interactive whiteboard. Choose two ride prices and ask what they would cost in total (say, £2.75, £1.65). *Would you use a written method or a mental method for this addition?* Ask children in pairs to discuss how they would answer this and take feedback. Ask them to justify their decisions and discuss which might be the most effective method. Then ask them to say how they would find the difference between pairs of prices. Revise the subtraction strategies explored this week and choose the most appropriate method for each question.

Group work: Invite each group to solve the three challenges on photocopiable page 'At the fair' from the CD-ROM.

Progress check: Ask children to show the methods and checking approaches they used to solve each problem. *How did you decide what to do? Did you estimate first? What checking strategy did you use?*

Review

Take feedback on the problems. *Which methods of addition and subtraction did you use?* Encourage children to summarise the addition and subtraction strategies used this week and to explain how these were applied in this problem-solving work.

Multiplication: mental and written methods

Expected prior learning

Children should be able to:

- recall and use multiplication facts for the 1, 2, 3, 4, 5, 6, 8 and 10 multiplication tables
- write and calculate mathematical statements for multiplication using the multiplication tables that they know, using mental methods.

Topic	Curriculum objectives	Expected outcomes
Multiplication and division	**Lesson 1**	
	To recall multiplication facts for multiplication tables up to 12 × 12 multiplying together three numbers.	Recall tables facts and mentally multiply several numbers.
	Lesson 2	
	To use place value, known and derived facts to multiply and divide mentally, including: multiplying by 0 and 1; dividing by 1; multiplying together three numbers. To recognise and use factor pairs and commutativity in mental calculations.	Multiply mentally, recognise and use factor pairs in mental calculations. Multiply multiples of 10.
	Lesson 3	
	To multiply two-digit and three-digit numbers by a one-digit number using formal written layout.	Multiply two-digit numbers by a one-digit number using a written method.
	Lesson 4	
	To multiply two-digit and three-digit numbers by a one-digit number using formal written layout.	Multiply two- and three-digit numbers by a one-digit number by using a written method.
	Lesson 5	
	To solve problems involving multiplying and adding, including using the distributive law to multiply two-digit numbers by one digit, integer scaling problems and harder correspondence problems such as which n objects are connected to m objects.	Solve one- and two-step problems involving multiplication.

Preparation

Lesson 3: prepare 'Merry-go-round' for display on the interactive whiteboard; copy the top or bottom half of the sheet (enlarged to A4) for each pair

Lesson 4: copy 'Three-digit cube', one per child

You will need

Photocopiable sheets

'Merry-go-round'; 'Three-digit cube'; 'Merry-go-round template'

Equipment

Individual whiteboards; interlinking cubes; counters; dice

Further practice

Adapt the 'Merry-go-round template' with appropriate two-digit and single-digit numbers for further practice of multiplication facts

Oral and mental starters for week 3

See bank of starters on pages 85, 126, 167 and 168. Oral and mental starters are also on the CD-ROM.

8 Function machine

26 Magic square (2)

16 Multiply by 10 and 100

28 Money matters

17 True or false

Overview of progression

During this week the children will consolidate and extend their abilities to mentally multiply numbers and to grow in confidence in using written methods of multiplication. In the early part of the week they multiply small numbers and use factors pairs to multiply larger numbers. In lesson 3 they use more formal written methods of multiplication, initially for multiplying two-digit by one-digit numbers, and in Lesson 4 they explore three-digit by one-digit products. Lesson 5 gives opportunity for children to use and apply their facts and skills to solve multiplication problems.

Watch out for

For those children who struggle to recall particular times tables facts, provide cards with the questions on one side and answers on the other. Encourage children to take them away to learn at home. Ensure that a range of visual, aural and kinaesthetic approaches are used when teaching tables facts to appeal to all learning styles.

Creative context

Look out for opportunities to perform multiplication in real-life contexts, such as getting into teams in PE, sitting on benches in the hall, giving out items such as coloured pencils to children, cooking situations, and so on.

Vocabulary

column method, condensed method, expanded method, **factor**, facts, groups of, lots of, multiple multiply, **product**, tables, times

Curriculum objectives
- To recall multiplication facts for multiplication tables up to 12 × 12.
- To multiply together three numbers.

Success criteria
- I can recall tables facts and multiply mentally, including multiplying several numbers.

You will need
Equipment
Individual whiteboards; interlinking cubes

Differentiation
Less confident learners
Give these children 10, 11 or 12 cubes.

More confident learners
Give children 16 cubes. You could also ask them to explore splitting the stick into four parts.

Lesson 1
Oral and mental starter 8

Main teaching activities
Whole-class work: Hold up a stick of 12 cubes joined in a line, telling the children how many there are. Snap the stick into two parts: ten cubes in one part and two in the other. *What is 10 multiplied by 2?* Explain that you are multiplying the number of cubes in one part by the number of cubes in the other part. Next, rejoin the cubes and split the stick into 9 and 3. *What is 9 multiplied by 3?* Repeat with other combinations. Ask children to record as many different multiplications as they can on their whiteboards by splitting the 12 cubes into two parts. Revise the commutative law that means that 7 × 5 will have the same answer as 5 × 7. Then ask: *What if I had 15 cubes in my stick? What different solutions could I make in the same way?* Collect and order the results and discuss any patterns noticed in the numbers. *What if I had 18 cubes? What would be the highest answer I could make?* (9 × 9 = 81)

Now return to the 12 cube stick. Ask: *What if I split the stick into three parts and multiplied the number of cubes in each part together?* Remind children that numbers can be multiplied together in any order (the associative law).

Paired work: Provide each pair with 13 or 14 cubes. Ask them to make a stick of them and then find as many different ways of splitting the stick into two or three parts, multiplying the number of cubes in each part together.

Progress check: Encourage children to work systematically. Invite them to explain how they are sure that each solution has been found.

Review
List the solutions and discuss patterns in them. Ask: *Do you get larger solutions from splitting the stick into two parts or into three parts? Why is that?*

Curriculum objectives
- To use place value, known and derived facts to multiply and divide mentally.
- To recognise and use factor pairs and commutativity in mental calculations.

Success criteria
- I can multiply mentally using factor pairs.
- I can multiply multiples of 10.

Differentiation
Less confident learners
Give children this set of numbers to work from: 5, 15, 25 and 12, 14, 18, 16.

More confident learners
For the numbers in the second set, include some as multiples of 10 (for example, change 18 to 180, 56 to 560).

Lesson 2
Oral and mental starter 26

Main teaching activities
Whole-class work: Write 4 × 35 on the board. *How could you answer this question?* Discuss different strategies before introducing the factor pair approach: *Tell me a factor pair that has the answer 35?* Revise that factor pairs are two numbers that multiply to give a number. Rewrite 4 × 35 as 4 × 5 × 7. *How can we multiply 4 × 5 × 7?* Remind children that we can multiply in any order: 4 × 5 first, or 5 × 7 first. Demonstrate multiplying multiples of 10 – say, 4 × 5 × 7 = 20 × 7 = 140. Try 5 × 72 in the same way. Allow time to discuss the approach and demonstrate that 5 × 72 is 5 × 8 × 9 = 40 × 9 = 360. Show also 35 × 14 = 35 × 2 × 7 = 70 × 7 = 490.

Paired work: Write these two sets of numbers on the board: 45, 15, 35, 55, 25 and 18, 48, 24, 14, 36, 56, 32, 44. Ask children in pairs to choose a number from each set and multiply using the factor pairs approach.

Progress check: Ask: *How did you work out this question? What factor pairs did you use? Why is that an easier multiplication to do?*

Review
Take feedback and invite children to demonstrate their working to the class.

Curriculum objectives

● To multiply two-digit numbers by a one-digit number using formal written layout.

Success criteria

● I can multiply two-digit numbers by a one-digit number using a written method.

You will need

Photocopiable sheets

'Merry-go-round'

Equipment

Counters; dice

Differentiation

Less confident learners

Ask children to answer the questions using the grid method of multiplication.

More confident learners

Let children use the two carousels from the bottom half of the 'Merry-go-round' game.

Lesson 3 — Oral and mental starter 16

Main teaching activities

Whole-class work: Display the top half of photocopiable page 'Merry-go-round' from the CD-ROM. Choose a number from each carousel to multiply together (say, 59 × 7). Set out the question in columns, go through the formal written method and encourage children to see the links between the expanded and condensed methods of written multiplication:

```
  H T U      or      H T U      or      H T U
    5 9                5 9                5 9
×     7            ×     7            ×     7
  3 5 0                6 3            _ 4 1 3_
_   6 3_          _ 3 5 0_               6
_ 4 1 3_          _ 4 1 3_
```

Paired work: Give each pair a copy of the top half of the 'Merry-go-round' game sheet, two counters and a dice. The pair should place a counter initially on each carousel to start. They should take turns to roll the dice and move both dice on that many places, clockwise. The two numbers landed on by the counters should be multiplied together using either the expanded or condensed method (as appropriate for each child). The player with the higher answer each time scores a point.

Progress check: Ask: *How did you multiply these two numbers together? What is this carried digit? Where did it come from?*

Review

Invite children to demonstrate the questions they answered using each of the methods of multiplication.

Curriculum objectives

● To multiply two-digit and three-digit numbers by a one-digit number using formal written layout.

Success criteria

● I can multiply three-digit numbers by a one-digit number using a written method.

You will need

Photocopiable sheets

'Three-digit cube'

Differentiation

Less confident learners

Choose numbers from the top face of the cube and smaller numbers to multiply by (3 to 6).

More confident learners

Choose numbers from the left-hand face of the cube and larger numbers to multiply by (4 to 9).

Lesson 4 — Oral and mental starter 16

Main teaching activities

Whole-class work: Revise the methods explored in the previous lesson before demonstrating the expanded and condensed form for three-digit × one-digit numbers:

```
 Th H T U    or     Th H T U    or     Th H T U
    8 4 6               8 4 6               8 4 6
×       3           ×       3           ×       3
  2 4 0 0               1 8          _ 2 5 3 8_
    1 2 0             1 2 0               1 1
_     1 8_          _ 2 4 0 0_
_ 2 5 3 8_          _ 2 5 3 8_
```

Independent work: Give each child photocopiable page 'Three-digit cube' from the CD-ROM. Explain that three-digit numbers can be read horizontally or vertically from each face of the cube. Ask children to choose a three-digit number from a particular face of the cube and multiply it by a single-digit number of their choice using a written method of multiplication.

Progress check: Ask: *Do you find the condensed method easier than the expanded form? Why do you think that is?*

Review

Invite volunteers to explain the condensed method of multiplication as clearly as they can.

Curriculum objectives
● To solve problems involving multiplying and adding.
Success criteria
● I can solve one- and two-step problems involving multiplication.

You will need
Equipment
Individual whiteboards

Differentiation
Less confident learners
Let these children explore what could be bought with a smaller amount of money (say, with 80p).
More confident learners
Ask children to explore what could be bought with a larger amount of money (say, £2.50 or £3).

Lesson 5

Main teaching activities

Whole-class work: Introduce the following theme: *Sara makes jewellery out of thin lengths of wire. The wire comes in three colours: silver, gold and copper. The wire costs different amounts per length: each centimetre of gold wire costs 9p, each centimetre of silver wire costs 7p and each centimetre of copper wire costs 6p.* Record the following details on the board:

Gold 9p per cm

Silver 7p per cm

Copper 6p per cm

Then ask a range of questions such as:

● *How much does it cost for 9cm of gold wire? 8cm of silver wire? 13cm of copper wire?*
● *How many centimetres can she buy if she has 48p to buy silver wire? 72p to buy gold wire?*

Ask children to show answers on their individual whiteboards.

Paired work: Ask children in pairs to investigate as many different lengths of the three types of wire that Sara could buy with £2, resulting in as little money left over as possible. For example, she could buy 12cm of gold wire, 7cm of silver wire and 7cm of copper wire with 1p left over, or she could buy 2cm of gold, 6cm of silver and 23cm of copper with 2p left over. Encourage them to look for ways that involve no money left over.

Progress check: Ask: *What did you notice about the possible solutions? Did you find a strategy for making sure Sara has no money left over?*

Review

Invite children to show the rest of the class their recorded solutions and to talk about what they discovered. Build a collective list together ordering them in a systematic way, such as in a table:

Gold	Silver	Copper	Total price
20cm	2cm	1cm	180p + 14p + 6p = 200p
19cm	3cm	1cm	171p + 21p + 6p = 198p
19cm	2cm	2cm	171p + 14p + 12p = 197p

Division: mental and written methods

Expected prior learning

Children should be able to:

- recall and use multiplication and division facts
- write and calculate mathematical statements for multiplication and division using the multiplication tables that they know, using mental methods.

Topic	Curriculum objectives	Expected outcomes
Multiplication and division	**Lesson 1**	
	To recall multiplication and division facts for multiplication tables up to 12 × 12.	Know the relationship between multiplication and division. Recall division facts for multiplication tables up to 12 × 12.
	Lesson 2	
	To recall multiplication and division facts for multiplication tables up to 12 × 12. To use place value, known and derived facts to multiply and divide mentally, including: multiplying by 0 and 1; dividing by 1; multiplying together three numbers.	Divide numbers mentally.
	Lesson 3	
	To use place value, known and derived facts to multiply and divide mentally, including: multiplying by 0 and 1; dividing by 1; multiplying together three numbers.	Use short division with exact answers when dividing by a one-digit number.
	Lesson 4	
	To use place value, known and derived facts to multiply and divide mentally, including: multiplying by 0 and 1; dividing by 1; multiplying together three numbers.	Use short division with exact answers when dividing by a one-digit number.
	Lesson 5	
	To use place value, known and derived facts to multiply and divide mentally, including: multiplying by 0 and 1; dividing by 1; multiplying together three numbers.	Solve division problems, including questions such as three cakes shared equally between 10 children.

Preparation

Lesson 2: copy 'Triangle relations', one per child

You will need

Photocopiable sheets
'Triangle relations';
'Triangle relations template'

Equipment
Individual whiteboards; interlinking cubes; small blank cards; large sheets of paper

Further practice

Adapt 'Triangle relations template' to give further practice of deriving and recalling division facts.

Oral and mental starters for week 4

See bank of starters on page 85, 86, 126 and 127. Oral and mental starters are also on the CD-ROM.

8 Function machine

16 Multiply by 10 and 100

13 Targets

20 Bingo

Overview of progression

The focus of this week is division, including mental and written strategies. During the first part of the week the children will use the relationship between multiplication and division to practise recalling and deriving division facts. In lesson 2 this will also include multiples of 10 and 100. In lesson 3 the notation of short division will be introduced, initially through multiplication and mental strategies. These ideas are then extended in lesson 4 when children will begin to use the short division method for themselves. They will find missing numbers in related multiplications and divisions. Lesson 5 explores division problems including those with answers less than one.

> ### Watch out for
> Children often experience difficulty with the layout of short division and sometimes put the wrong number to the left of the vertical line. In lesson 3 they are introduced to the layout through multiplication to help overcome this error and also to remind them of the inverse nature of multiplication and division.

Creative context

Look out for opportunities to perform sharing and grouping division in real-life contexts, such as getting into teams in PE, sitting on benches in the hall, sharing items such as coloured pencils, cooking situations, and so on.

Vocabulary

divide, facts, groups of, **inverse**, lots of, **multiply**, **product**, share, tables

Curriculum objectives

● To recall multiplication and division facts for multiplication tables up to 12 × 12.

Success criteria

● I know the relationship between multiplication and division.
● I can recall division facts for multiplication tables up to 12 × 12.

You will need

Equipment

Interlinking cubes; small blank cards

Differentiation

Less confident learners

Ask children to write division facts related to an easier times table (3 or 4). They can also use cubes to make a stick and break it to show the relationships between multiplication and division.

More confident learners

Ask children to choose facts from other times tables, including 11 and 12.

Lesson 1   Oral and mental starter 8

Main teaching activities

Whole-class work: Explain that today's lesson is about the relationship between multiplication and division. Hold up a stick of 14 cubes and split it into two groups of 7. Write 2 × 7 = 14 (*two groups of seven is fourteen)* and 14 ÷ 7 = 2 (*fourteen grouped into sevens is two groups*). Show that dividing by 7 is the inverse (opposite) of multiplying by 7 and vice versa as it 'undoes' the other.

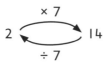

Now rearrange the cubes in seven groups of 2. *How can we describe the cubes now?* Demonstrate that this can be written as 7 × 2 = 14 (*seven groups of two is fourteen*) and 14 ÷ 2 = 7 (*fourteen grouped into twos is seven groups*). Emphasise that four facts (two multiplication and two division) can be written linking three different numbers – for example, 2, 7 and 14. Write 2, 7 and 14 into a triangle to look like this and draw several other triangles with a number missing:

Invite children to identify the missing numbers (8, 36, 132), using their knowledge of tables facts. Point out that the largest number is always at the top of the triangle, the product of the lower two numbers. Then ask them to list the four facts (two multiplication and two division) for each triangle.

Paired work: In preparation for a group game, give each pair a set of 15 small blank cards. Identify the times table you would like each pair to focus on (to ensure a wide range of tables across the class) and ask them to choose harder facts from it, such as 6 × 7 = 42. They should draw the matching triangle on one card and the four related facts on four other cards to form a set of five related cards. Ask them to do this three times.

Group work: Ask pairs to join with another pair and put their cards all together. Collect up each set of 30 cards and, without mixing them up, swap the sets of 30 cards around so that children do not work with their own sets of cards. Each group then lays the cards face down and spreads them around the table. They then take turns to lift two cards. If they are related the player keeps them. If not they turn them back face down. Continue until all the cards are collected by the players. The scoring at the end of the game is as follows:

Score 1 point for each set of 2 related cards

Score 3 points for each set of 3 related cards

Score 5 points for each set of 4 related cards

Score 10 points for each set of 5 related cards

Progress check: As children are writing the facts, ask: *How do you remember this tables fact? Have you found a fact that only has one multiplication and one related division? Why is this?* (8 × 8 = 64 only has one related division, since it is a squared number.)

Review

Take feedback on the game and revise any difficult facts that children worked with. As a final activity invite children to fill in the missing numbers to make this statement true in as many different ways as they can: [   ] days = [   ] weeks (for example, 56 days = 8 weeks), or [   ] months = [   ] years (for example, 96 months = 8 years).

Curriculum objectives

● To recall multiplication and division facts for multiplication tables up to 12 × 12.
● To use place value, known and derived facts to multiply and divide mentally.

Success criteria

● I can divide numbers mentally.

You will need

Photocopiable sheets

'Triangle relations'; 'Triangle relations template'

Differentiation

Less confident learners

Alter the numbers on the 'Triangle relations template' to include facts from an easier times table.

More confident learners

Children can make up their own questions related to multiples of 10 and 100 linked to other times tables.

Lesson 2

Oral and mental starter 16

Main teaching activities

Whole-class work: Leading on from the previous lesson, begin by writing a difficult multiplication statement beyond the times tables, such as 27 × 12 = 324. Explain that you know that this multiplication is correct. Ask children to answer the following questions:

324 ÷ 27 = [   ]   12 × 27 = [   ]   324 ÷ 12 = [   ]

Remind children that, as multiplication and division are related, they can answer the questions using the given multiplication fact. Draw a triangle to remind them of the previous work:

Now draw the following set of triangles and ask children to fill in the missing numbers at the tops of them.

Draw attention to the fact that if one number is ten times larger, the answer will be ten times larger, but if both numbers multiplied are ten times larger, the answer will be one hundred times larger.

Invite children to write four related facts for each of the last three triangles above. For example: 2 × 60 = 120; 60 × 2 = 120; 120 ÷ 60 = 2; 120 ÷ 2 = 60. If time, repeat for another set of triangles in the same way (42, 6, 7 and 420, 60, 7, and so on).

Independent work: Provide each child with photocopiable page 'Triangle relations' from the CD-ROM to complete. A blank 'Triangle relations template' has been included if you wish to adapt for early finishers or for differentiation.

Progress check: Ask children to say how many times larger each number is than the one in the related division fact from the table: *Will the answer be 10 or 100 times larger? How do you make a number 10 or 100 times larger?*

Review

Choose questions from the photocopiable sheet and ask them in words. For example: *How many sixties in four thousand eight hundred? How do you know?*

⚓SCHOLASTIC

Lesson 3   Oral and mental starter 13

Main teaching activities

Whole-class work: Introduce the notation of short division as follows. Draw a horizontal line and write 26 above it and a vertical line and write 3 to the left of it:

$$3\overline{\smash{)}}\;\;^{2\;6}$$

Ask children to multiply 26 by 3 and work it out on their whiteboards. Record the answer under the line:

$$3\overline{\smash{)}7\;8}\;\;^{2\;6}$$

Repeat for other multiplications in the same way, always recording the answer below the line. Next write:

$$4\overline{\smash{)}9\;6}$$

Ask: *What calculation could we do to find the missing number above the line?* Draw attention to the fact that they divide. Invite children to work out the answer (24) and record it above the line. Allow children to use any appropriate strategy for dividing as the focus here is on the layout for division.

Paired work: List the following numbers in sets on the board:

Set A (divide by 3)	Set B (divide by 4)	Set C (divide by 6)
81, 96, 72, 128	96, 72, 128, 136	78, 96, 84, 132, 144

Children divide each number in the set by the number shown, setting out the questions with the large number under the line and the divisor to the left. Pairs should discuss strategies for solving each division and write answers above the line.

Progress check: Ask: *Which will be the largest number? Why?*

Review

Invite children to write some of their divisions on the board and describe strategies they used to work out each one.

Lesson 4   Oral and mental starter 20

Main teaching activities

Whole-class work: The focus of today's lesson is to introduce more formal short division, following on from the previous lesson. Write:

$$4\overline{\smash{)}9\;6}$$

Ask children to say what question we are trying to solve (96 divided by 4). Demonstrate the following: *Look at the tens digit. How many fours in 9? There are 2 fours with 1 left over. Write 2 above in the tens column and carry the one left over.*

$$4\overline{\smash{)}9\,^1 6}\;\;^{2}$$

Look at the units. We now have 16. How many fours in 16? There are 4 fours so we write 4 above to complete the answer.

$$4\overline{\smash{)}9\,^1 6}\;\;^{2\;4}$$

Remind children that they can multiply 24 by 4 to give 96 as a means of checking their answer. Demonstrate other examples in the same way.

Paired work: List the following numbers in sets on the board:

Set A (divide by 5): 80, 95, 65, 70, 95

Set B (divide by 3): 45, 81, 96, 57, 78, 87

Set C (divide by 4): 52, 96, 72, 64, 76, 92

Set D (divide by 6): 72, 78, 84, 96, 138, 150

Children use short division to divide the set numbers by the given divisor.

Progress check: Say: *Describe what you did to reach this answer?*

Review

Perform 136 ÷ 4 = 34 using written division. Remind children that the division can be checked by multiplying and invite them to check it on their whiteboards.

Curriculum objectives
● To solve two-step problems in context.

Success criteria
● I can solve division problems, including questions such as three cakes shared equally between ten children.

You will need

Equipment
Individual whiteboards; large sheets of paper

Differentiation

Less confident learners
Adjust the numbers to include sharing between 2 and 5 people, using 20, 15, 5, 2 and 1 pizzas.

More confident learners
Adjust the numbers to include sharing between 3 and 10 people, using the same number of pizzas as given.

Lesson 5

Main teaching activities

Whole-class work: Remind children that division can be thought of as 'sharing' and so $64 \div 4$ can mean 64 cakes shared between four people. Call out some questions, related to tables facts, that involve sharing cakes between people, such as: *What is 36 cakes shared between 12 people? 48 cakes shared between eight people? 56 cakes shared between seven people?*

Then introduce a number of cakes smaller than the divisor: *What is three cakes shared between six people?* Help children to see that the answer would be a fraction (in this case one half). *How could we write this as a division question?* ($3 \div 6 = \frac{1}{2}$) Repeat for other simple questions where the answer will be ½ or ¼, such as: *What is three cakes shared between 12?* ($3 \div 12 = \frac{1}{4}$) or *What is five pizzas shared between 20?* ($5 \div 20 = \frac{1}{4}$). Sketch related diagrams to help any children struggling to visualise this.

Invite children to come to the front and write further division statements where the answer will be one half or one quarter.

Then draw three identical rectangles on the board to represent bars of chocolate.

What if we wanted to share this chocolate equally between ten people? Give children time in pairs to discuss this and to try to work out an answer on their whiteboards. Take feedback and see what difficulties children experienced in trying to answer the question. *Did anyone get an answer?* Discuss their suggestions and ask them to explain any strategies they may have used, such as splitting each bars into parts. *How many parts did you split each bar into?*

Split each bar on the board into ten equal parts. *Does splitting the bars into ten equal parts help you?* Again, give time for children in pairs to discuss this. Draw out that the answer is three-tenths of a bar each. Ask several children to explain in their own words how we could follow a similar approach for sharing five bars of chocolate between 12 people. *How many equal parts can we split each bar into to help us?* (12)

Invite children to find the answer on their whiteboards (⁵⁄₁₂), and to talk about patterns they notice.

Group work: Group children into fours and ask them to draw the following table with six columns on a large sheet of paper. They should work together to investigate how much/many pizzas each person would get if there were three or six people. If you choose to group the children by ability, the numbers can be adjusted to make them harder or easier.

	24 pizzas	18 pizzas	15 pizzas	3 pizzas	2 pizzas
Shared between three people					
Shared between six people					

Progress check: Ask: *Which of the divisions produce whole-number answers? Why is that? What strategies did you use to find the answers? Did you draw pictures?*

Review

Ask: *What have you learned about dividing small numbers by larger numbers?* Explain that during the following week the focus of the lessons will be on fractions and these ideas will be explored further.

Fractions

Expected prior learning

Children should be able to:

- know the role of the numerator and denominator
- recognise and use fractions as numbers: unit fractions and non-unit fractions with small denominators
- recognise, find and write fractions of a discrete set of objects: unit fractions and non-unit fractions with small denominators.

Topic	Curriculum objectives	Expected outcomes
Fractions (including decimals)	**Lesson 1**	
	To solve problems involving increasingly harder fractions to calculate quantities, and fractions to divide quantities, including non-unit fractions where the answer is a whole number.	Find unit fractions of a set or quantity. Find non-unit fractions of a set or quantity.
	Lesson 2	
	To recognise and show, using diagrams, families of common equivalent fractions.	Identify fractions equivalent to a given fraction using multiplication or division.
	Lesson 3	
	To recognise and show, using diagrams, families of common equivalent fractions.	Identify fractions equivalent to a given fraction using multiplication or division. Simplify fractions.
	Lesson 4	
	To count up and down in hundredths; recognise that hundredths arise when dividing an object by one hundred and dividing tenths by ten.	Understand the relationship between tenths and hundredths and can find tenths and hundredths of numbers.
	Lesson 5	
	To solve problems involving increasingly harder fractions to calculate quantities.	Solve problems involving fractions.

Preparation

Lesson 1: copy 'Fractions to go', one per child

Lesson 3: copy 'Fraction cones', one per child

Lesson 5: copy 'Clock face', one per child

You will need

Photocopiable sheets

'Fractions to go'; 'Fraction cones'; 'Fraction cones template'

General resources

'Clock face'

Equipment

Individual whiteboards; number fans; large sheets of paper; coloured pencils; metre stick; 0–9 number cards; large clock face; paper fasteners; scissors

Further practice

Adapt the 'Fraction cones template' to give further practice of identifying equivalent fractions or simplifying fractions.

Oral and mental starters for week 5

See bank of starters on pages 127, 167 and 168. Oral and mental starters are also on the CD-ROM.

22 Fraction action

27 Run-around fractions

24 Secret numbers

Overview of progression

Lesson 1 provides practice for finding unit and non-unit fractions of quantities using division and multiplication. Lessons 2 and 3 focus on finding and identifying equivalent fractions and these ideas are continued into lesson 4 where children are given opportunity to explore fractions of a metre, including tenths and hundredths of a metre. They are given further practice of finding equivalent fractions and to simplify them. Lesson 5 takes these ideas further through exploring fractions of an hour.

Watch out for

Children develop many misconceptions about fractions that result from assuming that things that work for whole numbers will also work for fractions – for example, a fraction with a bigger number on the bottom is smaller than one with a smaller number on the bottom. It is important that children are given opportunity to talk about the differences between whole numbers, fractions and decimals to challenge these misconceptions.

Creative context

Take opportunities to link this fraction work to real-life situations, such as by asking children to describe sets of the class: *19 out of the 28 children in our class are girls* or *three quarters of our class have school dinners*.

Vocabulary

fraction, denominator, equal parts, **equivalent fraction**, hundredth, numerator, set, simplify, tenth

Curriculum objectives
- To solve problems involving increasingly harder fractions to calculate quantities, and fractions to divide quantities.

Success criteria
- I can find unit and non-unit fractions of a set or quantity.

You will need

Photocopiable sheets
'Fractions to go'

Equipment
Number fans

Differentiation

Less confident learners
Ask children to work in pairs and to discuss each question together before answering it.

More confident learners
Challenge the children by changing the last question to £2 instead of £1.

Lesson 1

Oral and mental starter 22

Main teaching activities

Whole-class work: Tell the children that today's lesson is about finding unit fractions of sets of objects. Explain that there are 12 people on a station platform. *If one quarter of the people are children, how many are children?* Revise that we find one quarter by dividing by the *denominator* (bottom number), and write the question and answer using fraction notation: $\frac{1}{4}$ of 12 = 3. *One half are female, one sixth are wearing jeans and one third of the people are carrying a bag. How many are female? Wearing jeans? Carrying a bag?* Discuss how to find each fraction of 12 and record them on the board using fraction notation.

Explain that on Platform B there are 36 people. List that: $\frac{1}{4}$ are girls, $\frac{1}{9}$ are wearing boots, $\frac{1}{6}$ are reading, $\frac{5}{6}$ have a suitcase, $\frac{7}{12}$ are wearing hats, $\frac{2}{3}$ are on their mobile (and so on). Revise how to find non-unit fractions of quantities, by dividing to find one part and multiplying to find several: $\frac{7}{12}$ of 36 is found by dividing 36 by 12 to find one twelfth and then multiplying by 7 to find seven twelfths. Remind children: *Divide for one, multiply for many.*

Independent work: Provide each child with photocopiable page 'Fractions to go' from the CD-ROM. They should solve each problem using appropriate multiplication and division strategies.

Progress check: Ask: *How did you work out this answer? What tables or division fact did you use? How could you record this question using fraction notation?*

Review

Ask children to hold up number fans as they answer some quick-fire fraction questions involving non-unit fractions, such as: *What is $\frac{2}{9}$ of 90? $\frac{5}{6}$ of 420?*

Curriculum objectives
- To recognise and show, using diagrams, families of common equivalent fractions.

Success criteria
- I can identify fractions equivalent to a given fraction using multiplication or division.

You will need

Equipment
Large sheets of paper; coloured pencils

Differentiation

Less confident learners
Support children in finding sets of fractions equivalent to one half, one quarter, one third, three quarters.

More confident learners
Ask children to choose more difficult non-unit fractions as the starting point for their sets of equivalent fractions.

Lesson 2

Oral and mental starter 22

Main teaching activities

Whole-class work: Sketch eight faces on the board, as below:

Ask: *What fraction of the faces are smiling/wearing hats/wearing glasses?*

Invite children to write the fractions on the board, in eighths initially, $\frac{6}{8}$, $\frac{4}{8}$, $\frac{2}{8}$. *Could I have used a different fraction here?* Encourage them to see that they could have written: $\frac{3}{4}$, $\frac{1}{2}$, $\frac{1}{4}$. Point out that we say that fractions are *equivalent* when they have the same value. Revise how to multiply or divide the numerator and denominator by the same number to give an equivalent fraction:

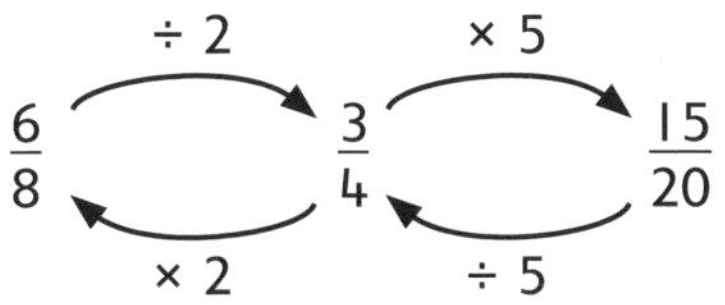

Paired work: Invite children to make up a puzzle for other pairs to solve. They should write four sets of equivalent fractions as four lists initially (for example, one list might be $\frac{2}{6} = \frac{1}{3} = \frac{5}{15} = \frac{20}{60} = \frac{4}{12}$). They should then copy the fractions from the four lists into a mixed-up arrangement on a large sheet of paper. Pairs then swap sheets and, using four different-coloured pencils, circle those that are equivalent in the same colour.

Progress check: Ask. *How can you be sure these are equivalent? What could you multiply or divide the numerator and denominator by to get this fraction?*

Review

Look at the completed puzzles and invite children to check each other's answers.

Curriculum objectives
- To recognise and show, using diagrams, families of common equivalent fractions.

Success criteria
- I can identify fractions equivalent to a given fraction using multiplication or division.
- I can simplify fractions.

You will need

Photocopiable sheets
'Fraction cones'; 'Fraction cones template'

Differentiation

Less confident learners
Adapt the photocopiable page 'Fraction cones template' to provide a simpler range of fractions to simplify.

More confident learners
Ask children to make up more fractions of their own to simplify.

Lesson 3
Oral and mental starter 27

Main teaching activities

Whole-class work: Play 'Snap'. Write a range of simple fractions and their equivalents on the board, such as:

⅙ ¾ ¼ ⅓ ⅔ ²⁄₁₂ ⁶⁄₁₂ ²⁄₆ ⁴⁄₆ ⁵⁄₁₀ ⁶⁄₈

½ ²⁄₈ ³⁄₆

Point to two of the fractions at a time. Ask children to say 'Snap' and snap their fingers if they are equivalent fractions. If they are not they should remain quiet.

Draw related shapes split equally and shaded to demonstrate how they are equivalent. *How can you be sure when two fractions are equivalent?* Remind children that if they can multiply or divide the numerator and denominator by the same number to give the other fraction then they are equivalent. Point to two fractions from the list and ask them to say which they think is *simpler* (uses smaller numbers). Explain that we simplify fractions by finding equivalent ones written with smaller numbers – for example, ⁶⁄₁₂ can be simplified to ½. Help children to realise that they can keep dividing until it is no longer possible to divide exactly into both the numerator and denominator.

Independent work: Provide each child with photocopiable page 'Fraction cones' from the CD-ROM and ask them to simply the fractions.

Progress check: Ask: *What is the largest number that divides into these two numbers? Which times table do both these numbers appear in?*

Review

Take feedback on the answers in the individual activity.

Curriculum objectives
- To count up and down in hundredths.

Success criteria
- I understand the relationship between tenths and hundredths and can find tenths and hundredths of numbers.

You will need

Equipment
Metre stick; individual whiteboards; 0–9 number cards

Differentiation

Less confident learners
Let children record lengths as fractions of a metre only rather than then simplifying the fractions.

More confident learners
Encourage children to give each fraction in its simplest form.

Lesson 4
Oral and mental starter 27

Main teaching activities

Whole-class work: Hold up a metre stick and point to the 10cm mark. *What fraction of the whole metre is ten centimetres?* Establish that this is one tenth of a metre. *How can we write this as a fraction?* Ask children to write one tenth of a metre on their whiteboards (¹⁄₁₀m) and hold up their boards. Now point to the 1cm mark of the metre stick. *From zero to this point is one centimetre. What fraction of the whole metre is one centimetre?* Establish that this is one hundredth of a metre. *How can we write this as a fraction?* Ask children to write one hundredth of a metre (¹⁄₁₀₀m). Continue to ask children to show the lengths 3cm, 7cm, 9cm, 11cm in metres as fractions in the same way. Help them to see that one tenth can be written as the fraction ¹⁄₁₀ or as ¹⁰⁄₁₀₀ and that these two fractions are *equivalent* (they have the same value). Talk about any fractions that can also be written as tenths (0.3m can be written as ³⁄₁₀ or as ³⁰⁄₁₀₀). Discuss any other fractions that could be simplified (35cm could be ³⁵⁄₁₀₀ or ⁷⁄₂₀).

Paired work: Using 0–9 number cards, pairs take turns to turn over two cards to form a two-digit number (say, 32). Explain that they should think of this as a length in centimetres. They should record this as a fraction of a metre, simplified if possible.

Progress check: *How can you check whether these two fractions are equivalent? Do you use multiplication or division? Do you still think they are equivalent?*

Review

Write different pairs of equivalent fractions on the board including some that are incorrect, such as: ⁴⁸⁄₁₀₀ = ¹²⁄₂₅, ⁶⁵⁄₁₀₀ = ¹¹⁄₂₀, ⁸⁰⁄₁₀₀ = ⁴⁄₅. Establish which are true and which are false. *How could we change this to make it true?*

 SCHOLASTIC

Curriculum objectives
● To solve problems involving increasingly harder fractions to calculate quantities.

Success criteria
● I can solve problems involving fractions.

You will need
General resources
'Clock face'

Equipment
Individual whiteboards; large clock face; paper fasteners; scissors

Differentiation
Less confident learners
Encourage children to use times from past the hour.

More confident learners
Ask children to choose times from the second half of the hour.

Lesson 5 — Oral and mental starter 24

Main teaching activities

Whole-class work: Ask children to suggest occasions where they use the word *quarter* frequently, such as a *quarter of an hour, quarter past, quarter two*. Hold up a large clock face and ask children to say how many minutes there are in a quarter of an hour. Ask: *Why is 15 one quarter? One quarter of what number is 15?* Remind children that there are 60 minutes in one hour and so we can write the fraction $\frac{15}{60}$ (*fifteen out of sixty minutes*) and then simplify it to one quarter by dividing the numerator and denominator by 15: $\frac{15}{60} = \frac{1}{4}$. Now show the clock face set to 12:20. *Through what fraction of an hour has the minute hand turned since 12 o'clock?* Encourage children to record a fraction with the denominator 60 on their whiteboards and hold them up. *Now can you simplify this fraction?* Show that $\frac{20}{60} = \frac{1}{3}$. Set the clock face to show 12:45 and ask children to work with a partner to answer the question: *Through what fraction of an hour has the minute hand turned since 12 o'clock?* Take feedback and again show that $\frac{45}{60}$ can be simplified first by dividing the numerator and denominator by 5 to give $\frac{9}{12}$ and then it can be simplified further by dividing each by 3 to give $\frac{3}{4}$.

Independent work: Provide each child with photocopiable page 'Clock face' from the CD-ROM and a paper fastener. Ask them to cut out and fix the hands onto the clock face using the paper fastener. The hour hand should point up (to the 12) and then the children should point the minute hand to any position around the clock face and work out through what fraction of an hour the minute hand has turned. This can be recorded as a digital time, followed by a fraction and then, if possible, this fraction in its simplest form. For example:

12:15 $\frac{15}{60} = \frac{1}{4}$

12:06 $\frac{6}{60} = \frac{1}{10}$

12:48 $\frac{48}{60} = \frac{4}{5}$

Paired work: As children are approaching the end of the individual activity, ask them to get together with a partner and to discuss and compare their answers.

Progress check: Invite children to give feedback on their findings. Ask: *Did you find any times where the fraction couldn't be simplified? Why is that? What different denominators did you find?*

Review

Build up a class list of results. For example:

12:01	$\frac{1}{60}$	12:07	$\frac{7}{60}$
12:02	$\frac{2}{60} = \frac{1}{30}$	12:08	$\frac{8}{60} = \frac{2}{15}$
12:03	$\frac{3}{60} = \frac{1}{20}$	12:09	$\frac{9}{60} = \frac{3}{20}$
12:04	$\frac{4}{60} = \frac{1}{15}$		
12:05	$\frac{5}{60} = \frac{1}{12}$		
12:06	$\frac{6}{60} = \frac{1}{10}$		

Discuss patterns in the fractions and draw attention to when particular denominators repeat. Ask: *Is it possible to have one sixth of an hour? How many minutes past is this?* (10)

Decimals and fractions

Expected prior learning

Children should be able to:

● count up and down in tenths; recognise that tenths arise from dividing an object into 10 equal parts and in dividing one-digit numbers or quantities by 10

● recognise, find and write fractions of a discrete set of objects: unit fractions and non-unit fractions with small denominators

● recognise and show, using diagrams, equivalent fractions with small denominators.

Topic	Curriculum objectives	Expected outcomes
Fractions (including decimals)	**Lesson 1**	
	To recognise and write decimal equivalents of any number of tenths or hundredths.	Recognise and write decimal equivalents of tenths or hundredths up to one whole.
	To recognise and write decimal equivalents to ¼; ½; ¾.	Identify decimal equivalents to ¼; ½; ¾.
	Lesson 2	
	To recognise and write decimal equivalents of any number of tenths or hundredths.	Compare numbers involving tenths or hundredths.
	To compare numbers with the same number of decimal places up to two decimal places.	
	Lesson 3	
	To find the effect of dividing a one- or two-digit number by 10 and 100, identifying the value of the digits in the answer as ones, tenths and hundredths.	Divide a one- or two-digit number by 10 and 100, identifying the value of the digits in the answer as ones, tenths and hundredths.
	Lesson 4	
	To round decimals with one decimal place to the nearest whole number.	Round decimals with one decimal place to the nearest whole number.
	Lesson 5	
	To solve simple measure and money problems involving fractions and decimals to two decimal places.	Solve simple measure problems involving decimals to two decimal places.

Preparation

Lesson 2: copy 'Decimal number line' and 'Decimal ordering', one of each per pair

Lesson 3: copy: 'Decimal bingo', one per group

Lesson 5: copy 'Accurate millimetres', one per child

You will need

Photocopiable sheets

'Decimal ordering'; 'Decimal bingo'; 'Accurate millimetres'; 'Decimal ordering template'

General resources

'Decimal number line'

Equipment

0–9 number cards; scissors; an arrow or triangle as a pointer; sharp pencils; rulers

Further practice

Give children further experience of comparing decimal numbers by adapting the 'Decimal ordering template'.

Oral and mental starters for week 6

See bank of starters on pages 167, 168, 208 and 209. Oral and mental starters are also on the CD-ROM.

23 Place value chains (2)

27 Run-around fractions

16 Multiply by 10 and 100

25 Rounding round

28 Money matters

Overview of progression

Lesson 1 provides revision of fractions as tenths and hundredths and introduces the decimal equivalents for these numbers between 0 and 1. Lesson 2 explores similar ideas for fractions and decimals beyond 1. It also provides opportunities for children to compare decimals with up to two decimal places. Lesson 3 develops place value ideas for multiplying and dividing by 10 and 100, including answers that have up to two decimal places. Lesson 4 provides opportunities for rounding decimals to the nearest whole number and the ideas of the week are drawn together in lesson 5, which makes links between measurement topics and decimals.

Watch out for

Children develop many misconceptions about decimals that result from assuming that things that work for whole numbers will also work for decimals. Misconceptions include: (a) a longer number is larger; (b) 25 is larger than 3, so 2.5 must be larger than 3; (c) putting a zero on the end of a number makes it 10 times as large – for example, 310 is 10 times as large as 31, so 3.10 must be 10 times as large as 3.1. It is important that children are given opportunities to talk about the differences between whole numbers, fractions and decimals to challenge these misconceptions.

Creative context

Take opportunities to link decimal work to real-life situations, such as looking at athletics times (9.8 seconds), food items and cooking activities (1.2kg), and money situations such as collecting dinner money.

Vocabulary

decimal, decimal place, decimal point, **equivalent fraction**, fraction, hundredth, integer, tenth,

Curriculum objectives

• To recognise and write decimal equivalents of any number of tenths or hundredths.
• To recognise and write decimal equivalents to ¼; ½; ¾.

Success criteria

• I can recognise and write decimal equivalents of tenths or hundredths up to one whole.
• I can identify decimal equivalents to ¼; ½; ¾.

You will need

Equipment

0–9 number cards

Differentiation

Less confident learners

Children turn over only one card and write fractions and decimal equivalents for tenths.

More confident learners

Ensure children give fractions in their simplest form. Then ask them to put the decimals they have made in order, starting with the smallest.

Lesson 1

Main teaching activities

Whole-class work: Draw a very long line on the board and split it into ten equal parts. Write zero at the left-hand end and 1 at the right-hand end. Point to the first division and ask children to say what fraction of the whole stick this point represents ($\frac{1}{10}$). Continue to mark, above the line, each division with a fraction with the denominator 10. Discuss any equivalent fractions ($\frac{2}{10} = \frac{1}{5}$, $\frac{4}{10} = \frac{2}{5}$, $\frac{5}{10} = \frac{1}{2}$, and so on) and demonstrate how the line could have been split equally into five or two equal parts to show these fractions.

Now point to the first division. *How could we write the value of this point using decimals?* (0.1) Remind children that each tenth can be written as the decimal 0.1. Write 0.1 below the line to correspond with $\frac{1}{10}$. Revise that the column to the right of the decimal point stands for tenths and that 0.1 is said as *zero point one*. Determine the decimals for each division (0.2, 0.3, 0.4... 0.9), and write them below the number line. Draw attention to 0.5 being equivalent to one half and 0.2, 0.4, 0.6... being fifths.

Then point to any position between zero and the first division. *What decimals can we use to describe points between zero and zero point one?* Ask children to talk to a partner for a minute, before taking feedback. Listen to their suggestions and allow them to come to the front and make any marks if necessary. It might be necessary to draw a new line under the existing one and to enlarge the section between zero and 0.1, splitting it into ten intervals.

Revise the fractions $\frac{1}{100}$, $\frac{2}{100}$... and invite children to say the decimals 0.01, 0.02 up to 0.09. Show how a zero can be put on the end of 0.1 to make the decimal 0.10. Remind children that 0.1 and 0.10 both stand for the same amount – no units, one tenth and no hundredths. Ask children to continue to describe the decimals for points between 0.1 and 0.2, 0.2 and 0.3 (and so on) to see patterns in the numbers. Draw attention to 0.25 being equivalent to one quarter of the whole.

Leave the number line on the board to refer to later in the lesson.

Paired work: Provide each pair with 0–9 number cards. On a piece of paper, each player should draw around two cards (face down) and put zero and a decimal point in front of them, to create 0 . ▢ ▢ Children then turn over the pairs of digit cards to create decimals between zero and 0.99. The decimals should be recorded and then written as fractions, simplifying them where possible.

Progress check: Ask: *What is the decimal equivalent of three hundredths? What about three tenths? What about 33 hundredths?*

Review

Write the following on the board and ask children to work in pairs to decide whether the statements written are true or false:

0.50 is larger than 0.49   0.81 is smaller than 0.90   0.63 is smaller than 0.60

0.2 > 0.02   0.72 > 0.07   0.44 < 0.04   0.70 < 0.7   0.90 = 0.09

Give children sufficient time to talk to each other about the statements.

■SCHOLASTIC

Curriculum objectives

- To recognise and write decimal equivalents of any number of tenths or hundredths.
- To compare numbers with the same number of decimal places up to two decimal places.

Success criteria

- I can compare numbers involving tenths or hundredths.

You will need

Photocopiable sheets
'Decimal ordering'

General resources
'Decimal number line'

Equipment
Scissors

Differentiation

Less confident learners

Enlarge photocopiable page 'Decimal number line' to A3. Ask children to write numbers on the number line first.

More confident learners

Ask children to turn over four or five cards at a time and order them.

Lesson 2
Oral and mental starter 27

Main teaching activities

Whole-class work: Play the game 'Think of a number'. Explain that you are thinking of a number between zero and 100 (say, 37). By asking questions that you can only answer *yes* or *no* to, children should try to guess the number. They should do this in as few questions as possible. Questions could be of the type *Is it higher than 40? Is it lower than 70?* Encourage children to ask good questions, those that narrow down the possibilities most effectively, for example, *Is it larger than 50?* is more helpful than the question *Is it 26?* Children are often conditioned from an early age to believe that *yes* answers are more valuable than *no* answers. Help them to see that just as much information can be gained from a *no* answer, as would be the case for the question *Is it larger than 50?*

Discuss strategies with the children as to how they can try to reduce the number of guesses and repeat for another whole number in the same range (say, 21). You can encourage children to keep track of the numbers using a number line. For example: *We know it is between zero and 100. Then Mel's question showed us it is higher than 20 and Sam's question that it is lower than 30. How could we show this on a number line?* Zoom in on the number as the possibilities are narrowed.

Then repeat for another number in the same range but, without telling the children, choose a number that lies between 17 and 18, such as 17.2. Gradually get closer to the number until children have found out that the number is higher than 17 but lower than 18. *What numbers are between 17 and 18?*

Invite children to make suggestions as to the nature of the number – for example, it could involve fractions such as 17½ or a decimal such as 17.5. Develop a number line and discuss that hundredths also lie between the tenths. For example, between 17.3 and 17.4 are decimals such as 17.31, 17.32, 17.33 (and so on).

Play the game one more time, this time choosing a decimal between 0 and 10 with hundredths such as 9.58.

Paired work: Give each pair photocopiable pages 'Decimal number line' and 'Decimal ordering' from the CD-ROM. Ask them to cut out the cards and put them face down. In pairs they pick three cards, identify where on the number line each should go and record them in order, smallest first – for example, 3.02, 3.17 and 3.52.

Progress check: Ask children to order 3.2, 3.02 and 3.12. *Which is the largest of the three decimals? How do you know? How many tenths has each number? How many hundredths? Where on the number line would this go?*

Review

Write the following on the board and ask children to work in pairs to decide whether the statements written are true or false.

3.5 is larger than 3.49   3.81 is smaller than 3.9   3.63 is smaller than 3.6

3.2 > 3.02   3.72 > 3.07   3.44 < 3.04   3.70 < 3.7   3.9 = 3.09

Give children sufficient time to talk to each other about the statements.

Curriculum objectives
- To find the effect of dividing a one- or two-digit number by 10 and 100.

Success criteria
- I can divide a one- or two-digit number by 10 and 100, identifying the value of the digits in the answer as ones, tenths and hundredths.

You will need
Photocopiable sheets
'Decimal bingo'

Differentiation
Less confident learners

Support children in dividing numbers by 10 and 100 and provide them with a place value chart if necessary.

More confident learners

Adapt the questions before copying to include dividing by 1000.

Lesson 3   Oral and mental starter 16

Main teaching activities

Whole-class work: Invite children to the front to give answers to these questions one at a time. *Find a pattern in the digits of the answers. What do you notice about dividing by 10 or 100?* Ensure they are able to correctly say the decimals aloud. Remind children that as we multiply by 10 or 100 the digits move to the left and as we divide by 10 or 100 the digits move to the right.

$$36 \boxed{\times 100} =$$
$$36 \boxed{\times 10} =$$
$$36 \boxed{\times 1} =$$
$$36 \boxed{\div 10} =$$
$$36 \boxed{\div 100} =$$

For decimal answers ask: *How many tenths or hundredths has this number? How many times larger is the tenths digit 6 in 3.6 than the hundredths digit in 0.36?*

Remind children of the link between fractions and decimals. For example, 6, $\frac{6}{10} = 0.6$ and $\frac{6}{100} = 0.06$.

Group work: Divide the class into groups of four or five. Provide each group with photocopiable page 'Decimal bingo' from the CD-ROM. In each group one child should be the caller and should be given the instructions and questions to read.

Progress check: Ask: *What is this number divided by 10? By 100? How many tenths/hundredths has it?* Ask children to describe the effect of multiplying and dividing by 10 and 100 in their own words.

Review

Choose some questions from the bingo sheet, inviting children to describe the movement of the digits and giving answers.

Curriculum objectives
- To round decimals with one decimal place to the nearest whole number.

Success criteria
- I can round decimals with one decimal place to the nearest whole number.

Equipment
An arrow or triangle as a pointer; 0–9 number cards

Differentiation
Less confident learners

Provide children with a 10 square or a number line showing decimals with tenths from 0 to 10.

More confident learners

Children can turn over three cards to create a decimal with two decimal places (such as 3.56, 6.35, 5.63) and round to the nearest integer.

Lesson 4   Oral and mental starter 25

Main teaching activities

Whole-class work: On the board, draw a number line marked from 0 to 4. Place an arrow or plastic triangle at a point along the line. *What number do you think is being pointed to?* Write the agreed number on the board (for example, 1.7). *Which whole number (integer) is 1.7 nearest to?* Ensure children understand that an integer is a whole number and that this includes zero. Invite individuals to come to the front and reposition the arrow and repeat for other numbers. Build a table with headings 'arrow' and 'nearest integer' and record each arrow position and nearest integer. Encourage children to see the range of numbers that will round to any given integer.

Place the arrow exactly between two integers. *Which integer is it nearest to now?* Explain that when a number is equally near to two integers we round up to the next higher number.

Paired work: Give pairs 0–9 number cards. They each write the integers 0 to 10 on a piece of paper. One player turns over two cards and arranges them to denote units and tenths (for example, 3 and 6 could be arranged as 3.6 or 6.3). The chosen decimal is rounded to the nearest integer which is then crossed from that player's 0 to 10 list. Play continues until one player has successfully rounded decimals which have allowed all the numbers from 0 to 10 to be crossed out.

Progress check: Ask: *What is the smallest decimal that rounds to the number 8? Explain what happens to numbers that are exactly halfway between two whole numbers.*

Review
Take feedback and give further puzzles to solve.

■SCHOLASTIC

Curriculum objectives
● To solve simple problems involving fractions and decimals to two decimal places.

Success criteria
● I can solve simple problems involving decimals to two decimal places.

You will need
Photocopiable sheets
'Accurate millimetres'
Equipment
Sharp pencils; rulers

Differentiation
Less confident learners
In the paired work, change ¾m to 20cm, and 98mm to 0.8cm.
More confident learners
Change the problem to include, rather than a square, a regular pentagon or hexagon with the same length sides.

Lesson 5 — Oral and mental starter 28

Main teaching activities

Whole-class work: Write cm and mm on the board and revise the abbreviations. *If I had a measurement in centimetres, such as 2cm, how do I convert it to millimetres?* Revise that each centimetre is the same length as 10 millimetres so we multiply 2 by 10. Repeat for other whole numbers, such as:

cm $\longrightarrow$ × 10 $\longrightarrow$ mm

2cm	20mm
7cm	70mm
15cm	150mm

If I had a length in millimetres, such as 15mm, how do I convert it to centimetres? Revise that the inverse of multiplying by 10 is dividing by 10. *What is 15 divided by 10?* Discuss the work covered in the previous lesson and invite a child to explain how a number can be divided by 10 to give a decimal answer (for example, 1.5). Practise converting one- or two-digit numbers (in millimetres) to centimetres:

cm $\longleftarrow$ ÷ 10 $\longleftarrow$ mm

1.5cm	15mm
0.8cm	8mm
2.4cm	24mm

Then explore the relationship between metres and centimetres and pounds and pence, first converting from whole numbers of metres and pounds:

m $\longrightarrow$ × 100 $\longrightarrow$ cm		pounds $\longrightarrow$ × 100 $\longrightarrow$ pence (p)	
3.2m	320cm	£2	200p

before then converting one- or two-digit numbers in centimetres or pence:

m $\longleftarrow$ ÷ 100 $\longleftarrow$ cm		pounds $\longleftarrow$ ÷ 100 $\longleftarrow$ pence (p)	
0.74m	74cm	£0.43	43p

Independent work: Provide children with photocopiable page 128 'Accurate millimetres', sharp pencils and a ruler, and ask them to complete the sheet.

Paired work: Ask children to work together on solving this problem: *Jo has a piece of string that is ¾m long. He draws a square with sides that are 98mm and lays the string around the perimeter. He cuts off the spare string. How much did he cut off?* (Answer: 35.8cm or 358mm)

Progress check: Invite pairs to give feedback on their solutions and to explain which unit they decided to convert the lengths to. *How did you solve this problem? What strategy did you use?*

Review

Invite children to work with a partner and to think about the ideas learned this week. Ask each pair to say something that they learned and to remind the rest of the class of different maths ideas that they remember.

Curriculum objectives
● To find 1000 more or less than a given number.

You will need
1. Check
Oral and mental starter
23 Place value chains (2)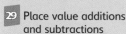

2. Assess
0–9 number cards; place value cards

3. Further practice
Oral and mental starters
29 Place value additions and subtractions

Photocopiable sheets
'Target grids (2)'

Find 1000 more or less

Most children should be able to add or subtract 1000 to and from a two-, three- or four-digit number with ease.

Some children will require further practice in partitioning and using place value cards.

1. Check
23 Place value chains (2)

Start by adding or subtracting 1, 10 or 100, asking children to say which is the hundreds, tens or units digit. Extend this to adding or subtracting 1000 to and from any number and note whether children understand how the thousands digit will change. Include numbers between 9000 and 9999 for children to add 1000 to. *Which is the thousands digit of this number? What is its value? Explain whether or not you can you add/subtract 1 to the thousands digit. How will it change the number?*

2. Assess

Children make a four-digit number with four 1–9 digit cards to which they add or subtract 1000. Challenge the more confident to begin with five-digit numbers. If children are unsure, give them place value cards to make each number and separate them to partition them (7463 = 7000 + 400 + 60 + 3, so 7463 + 1000 = 8463). Record the outcomes.

3. Further practice

Use the suggested oral and mental starter to provide further reinforcement of place value ideas. The photocopiable page can be used to provide four-digit numbers for children to add and subtract 1000 to and from.

Curriculum objectives
● To add and subtract numbers with up to four-digits using the formal written methods of columnar addition and subtraction where appropriate.

You will need
1. Check
Oral and mental starter
29 Place value additions and subtractions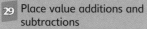

2. Assess
Photocopiable sheets
'Target grids (2)'; squared paper

3. Further practice
Oral and mental starters
13 Targets

Photocopiables sheets
'What's the difference?'

Subtracting two four-digit numbers

Most children should be able to subtract a four-digit number from another using a column method of subtraction.

Some children will still struggle with the idea of exchange and will require further practice in subtracting three-digit numbers and digits that require fewer incidents of exchange.

1. Check
29 Place value additions and subtractions

Start by asking children to find the differences between pairs of numbers, choosing one from each list on the photocopiable sheet. Observe which children understand place value ideas and who are confident in subtracting digits from the same columns together correctly. *What is the difference between these two numbers? Which are the hundreds digits of the two numbers? Which are the tens?*

2. Assess

Children choose pairs of numbers from the second grid on photocopiable page 'Target grids (2)' to find the difference between, using a vertical method. Challenge the more confident to choose pairs from the third grid, which will involve more incidents of exchange. Check that all children can identify which digit is which and can align the numbers correctly in columns. If children are unsure, help them to set out each question on squared paper in the correct columns first. Record the outcomes.

3. Further practice

Use the suggested oral and mental starter and photocopiable page 129 'What's the difference?' to provide further reinforcement of subtracting four-digit numbers.

Curriculum objectives
• To recall multiplication facts for multiplication tables up to 12 × 12.

You will need
1. Check
Oral and mental starter
11 Magic square (1)

2. Assess
Photocopiable sheets
'Multiple questions'; multiplication square

3. Further practice
Oral and mental starters
8 Function machine
20 Bingo

Photocopiable sheets
'Multiples grid game'

Curriculum objectives
• To recognise and write decimal equivalents of any number of tenths or hundredths.

You will need
1. Check
Oral and mental starter
38 Decimal divisions

2. Assess
'Tenths and hundredths'; place value chart

3. Further practice
Oral and mental starters
27 Run-around fractions
39 Divide by 10 and 100

Photocopiable sheets
'Tenths maths'; 'Hundredths maths'; 'Decimal ordering'

11- and 12- multiplication tables facts

Most children should be able to recall the multiplication facts for the 11- and 12-times tables.

Some children will not have made such progress and will require further practice in learning the multiples and then recalling the multiplication facts.

1. Check

11 Magic square (1)

Encourage the children to multiply each of the numbers in the magic square by 11 or by 12. Observe which children are confident and which need further practice. Extend by asking children to recall 11 × 11, 11 × 12 and 12 × 12. Ask questions such as: *What are eight elevens? Which multiple of 12 is 144? What is the product of 11 and 12?*

2. Assess

Provide photocopiable page 47 'Multiple questions' with 11 or 12 written into the blank space at the top. Children lacking confidence could be given a multiplication square to refer to. For the more confident, when they have finished the activity, ask them to write a word problem which uses multiplying by 11 or 12. Record the outcomes.

3. Further practice

The recommended photocopiable sheet and oral and mental starter activities can provide further practice in recall of multiplication facts for the 11- or 12-times tables and other multiplication facts.

Decimal equivalents

Most children should be able to describe fractions with the denominator of 10 or 100 as a decimal equivalent.

Some children may need more experience of working with fractions and decimals, particularly as represented on a number line.

1. Check

38 Decimal divisions

Ask the children to say tenths as fractions and decimals. Observe whether children can identify the tenths digit in a decimal and understand that fractions and decimals can show the same number. Extend this to including more than nine tenths (for example, 12 tenths is 1.2). Then repeat with hundredths. *How can you write three tenths as a decimal and as a fraction? What is 0.5 as a fraction with the denominator 10? Write an equivalent fraction. What is $\frac{17}{100}$ as a decimal?*

2. Assess

Distribute photocopiable page 130 'Tenths and hundredths'. Give children lacking confidence a place value chart showing the headings U. t h to refer to. For the more confident, when they have finished the activity ask them to write other equivalent fractions and decimals. Record the outcomes.

3. Further practice

The recommended oral and mental starter activities can provide further practice in finding equivalent fractions and decimals and dividing whole numbers by 10 and 100.

Oral and mental starters

Geometry

15 Twenty questions

Hide a shape in a bag and ask the children to find out which shape it is by asking questions. You can only answer *yes* or *no* to their questions. Challenge the children to guess the shape in 20 questions.

Addition, subtraction, multiplication and division

16 Multiply by 10 and 100

Ask four children to stand at the board and face the rest of the class. Behind them on the board write Th H T and U, so that one child is under each letter. Give the T and U children a number card each (for example, 6 and 4). Ask: *What number is this?* (64) *How do we multiply by 10?* The T child passes the card to the H child and the U child passes theirs to the T child. Give the U child a zero number card. *What is 64 × 10?* Repeat for other numbers multiplied by 10 and 100, giving zero digits to the T and U children as necessary.

Extension

This activity can be extended to dividing by 10 and 100 and, when appropriate, dividing numbers such as 364 by 10 can be explored. For example: *What does the units person do with their 4 digit? We need another volunteer to hold her card in the tenths column,* and so on.

17 True or false

Prepare some tables facts from the 6-, 8- and 9-times tables with their related division. Also, include questions such as 'the product of 6 x 8 is greater than 50'. After each question, ask the whole class to write True or False on their individual whiteboards and to raise them when you say: Show me. Check for any common misconceptions.

Extend to 11- and 12-times tables.

18 Operation follow-on

Cut out the cards from the photocopiable page 'Operation follow-on' from the CD-ROM and hand them out to the children, one card between two (or one each, if possible). Choose a child to stand and begin by reading out their card. All the children should answer the question and the child with the answer as the first number on their card should stand and then read out their question. (The answers to the questions on the cards form a loop.) Continue until the first child is reached again and all questions have been answered.

19 Multiple magic

Use the interactive activity 'Multiple magic' on the CD-ROM. Go through the riddles on screens 1 and 2 and ask the children to write answers on their individual whiteboards and hold up each time. The children can keep their own scores of correct answers, as they go.

20 Bingo

Children will need to write multiples from their times tables onto a small piece of card to play the bingo game. Use the interactive teaching resource 'Bingo: times tables' on the CD-ROM to generate tables questions. The children cover or colour answers as they come up. The first child to get a number in a row or all the numbers on their grid calls out *Bingo*. Use the 'Check grid' button to see if they were correct.

21 Follow me

Cut out the cards provided on photocopiable page 'Follow-me cards' from the CD-ROM and give one card to each child. Choose a child to start. Invite them to read out the calculation on their card. Another child will have the answer to that question as the first part of the calculation on their card. That child then reads out the next calculation, and so on.

Fractions

22 Fraction action

Split the class into two teams. Ask one team to give a fraction smaller than 1. The other team scores a point if they can give the fraction that adds to this to make 1. This team then chooses the fraction and the game continues.

Extension
Children could say the mixed number that adds to make 5 or 10.

Accurate millimetres

■ Work in pairs. Take turns to draw these lines as accurately as you can, using a sharp pencil and a ruler. Ask your partner or your teacher to check each line for accuracy before drawing the next line. In the box by the side of each measurement, write what your line measures in centimetres.

mm	cm	line
67mm		
56mm		
99mm		
112mm		
87mm		
77mm		
104mm		
65mm		
81mm		
19mm		

I can measure in millimetres.
I can convert between millimetres and centimetres.

How did you do?

What's the difference?

1.

	4	9	5	7
−	3	7	4	5

2.

	8	5	7	8
−	1	4	2	6

3.

	8	3	6	8
−	4	9	4	2

4.

	4	5	9	7
−	1	8	1	2

5.

	9	4	8	4
−	5	9	7	7

6.

	7	2	5	2
−	6	3	2	9

7.

	5	6	6	0
−		4	8	5

8.

	4	5	4	6
−	1	8	7	3

9.

	9	8	0	4
−	2	3	9	7

10.

	7	4	0	1
−	5	3	6	8

I can subtract four-digit numbers.

How did you do?

Tenths and hundredths

■ Write each of these as a decimal.

1. $\frac{1}{10}$ ☐

2. $\frac{3}{10}$ ☐

3. $\frac{5}{10}$ ☐

4. $\frac{4}{10}$ ☐

5. $\frac{6}{10}$ ☐

6. $\frac{8}{10}$ ☐

7. $\frac{1}{100}$ ☐

8. $\frac{5}{100}$ ☐

9. $\frac{11}{100}$ ☐

10. $\frac{43}{100}$ ☐

11. $\frac{73}{100}$ ☐

12. $\frac{84}{100}$ ☐

■ Write each of these as a fraction.

13. 0·7 ☐

14. 0·02 ☐

15. 0·12 ☐

16. 0·06 ☐

17. 0·88 ☐

18. 0·9 ☐

■ Draw lines to join pairs of fractions and decimals.

$\frac{99}{100}$ 9.9   0.9 $\frac{9}{10}$

0.09 $\frac{9}{100}$ 0.99 $\frac{99}{10}$

I can recognise and write decimal equivalents of tenths or hundredths.

How did you do?

Mental calculations

Expected prior learning

Children should be able to:

- rapidly recall and use addition and subtraction facts to 20
- accurately add and subtract numbers mentally, including one- and two-digit numbers
- recall and use multiplication facts for the 1, 2, 3, 4, 5, 6, 8 and 10 multiplication tables and related division facts.

Topic	Curriculum objectives	Expected outcomes
Addition and subtraction Multiplication and division	**Lesson 1**	
	To estimate and use inverse operations to check answers to a calculation. To recall multiplication tables up to 12 × 12.	Solve and check mental calculations using inverses.
	Lesson 2	
	To solve addition and subtraction two-step problems in contexts, deciding which operations and methods to use and why. To estimate and use inverse operations to check answers to a calculation.	Solve problems involving mental addition, subtraction, estimating and checking.
	Lesson 3	
	To recall multiplication and division facts for multiplication tables up to 12 × 12. To recognise and use factor pairs and commutativity in mental calculations.	Solve problems involving mental multiplication and division, estimating and checking.
	Lesson 4	
	To estimate and use inverse operations to check answers to a calculation. To recall multiplication tables up to 12 × 12.	Solve problems involving mental addition, subtraction, multiplication and division involving one and two steps.
	Lesson 5	
	To solve addition and subtraction two-step problems in contexts, deciding which operations and methods to use and why. To solve problems involving multiplying and adding, including using the distributive law to multiply two-digit numbers by one digit, integer scaling problems and harder correspondence problems such as which n objects are connected to m objects.	Solve problems involving mental addition, subtraction, multiplication and division involving one and two steps.

Preparation

Lesson 2: copy 'Beat the brain cards' one per pair

Lesson 4: copy 'Badge problems', one per child

You will need

Photocopiable sheets

'Beat the brain cards'; 'Badge problems'; 'Beat the brain template'

Equipment

Individual whiteboards; coloured pencils

Further practice

Photocopiable sheets

'Follow-me cards'

Oral and mental starters for week 1

See bank of starters on pages 127 and 167. Oral and mental starters are also on the CD-ROM.

| 13 | Targets |

| 8 | Function machine |

| 31 | Factor fun |

Overview of progression

This week, children will consolidate and extend their abilities to mentally add, subtract, multiply and divide numbers using ideas of place value and mental methods. They will use inverses to check their calculations and will make and use estimates to check whether answers are sensible. Throughout the week they are given opportunities to solve problems and decide on suitable approaches to calculation.

Watch out for

Children sometimes look for trigger words when solving word problems and fail to fully interpret the situation. For example, they may see the word *times* in the question *I went swimming four times last week and five times this week. How many times did I go?* and may incorrectly give the answer 20. Encourage children to visualise the whole situation and to even sketch pictures where necessary to help them to choose the correct operation or operations.

Creative context

Look out for opportunities to perform calculations in real-life contexts, such as number of absent children, dinner numbers, cooking situations.

Vocabulary

altogether, add, difference, divide, equals, **factor**, fewer, **inverse**, leave, less, make, minus, more, multiply, plus, sign, subtract, sum, take away, times, total, share

Curriculum objectives
● To estimate and use inverse operations to check answers to a calculation.
● To recall multiplication and division facts for multiplication tables up to 12 × 12.

Success criteria
● I can solve and check mental calculations using inverses.

You will need
Equipment
Coloured pencils

Differentiation
Less confident learners
Let children use only one or two arrows for their work.

More confident learners
Encourage children to choose more difficult calculations, involving two- and three-digit numbers.

Lesson 1   Oral and mental starter 13

Main teaching activities

Whole-class work: Explain that in this lesson children will do mental calculations and use inverses to check them. Draw the following, using a coloured pen to draw the arrow:

3 ⟹ 27

Explain that the arrow represents a function or calculation. *What could we do to turn 3 into 27?* Discuss how we could add 24 or multiply by 9. Using the same coloured arrow, write:

7 ⟹ 63

Ask: *What must the arrow stand for if it is the same in both?* (× 9) *What if the arrow was turned to face the other way?* Discuss that we can use the inverse operation to work backwards from the end number – for example, by dividing by 9 rather than multiplying by 9:

 × 9   7 ⟹ 63   ÷ 9   7 ⟸ 63

Now use a different-coloured pen for a new arrow questions, such as:

4 ⟹ 2

6 ⟹ 4

Ask: *What could the arrow stand for if it was the same calculation in both?* (− 2) Discuss the inverse operation that could be used to check them. (+ 2) Remind children that addition and subtraction are inverses and multiplication and division are inverses. Repeat for other examples and ask children to give the inverse that could be used to check.

Next, use three different colours to draw three large arrows, 5 and 8:

 5 ⟹ ⟹ ⟹ 8

Explain that each arrow represents a different calculation. Ask children in pairs to decide on three calculations that could be done one after the other to change 5 into 8, and write them on their whiteboards. For example:

 + 2   × 4   − 20   5 ⟹ ⟹ ⟹ 8

or

− 1   × 6   ÷ 3   5 ⟹ ⟹ ⟹ 8

Take feedback and go through the different suggestions to check whether they work. Discuss the inverse operations for each that could be used to work backwards from the answer, 8, to the starting number 5.

Paired work: Ask children in pairs to draw three arrows in different colours and write a start and finish number. They then choose three calculations to change the start number into the finish number. Then they follow the same arrows for a different start number. They then use inverses to work back from the end number to check that their calculations were correct.

Progress check: Invite children to explain the calculations they are doing. *What is the inverse of this calculation? How could you check this?*

Review
Invite children to read out their puzzles for the rest of the class to check them.

Curriculum objectives
● To solve addition and subtraction two-step problems.
● To estimate and use inverse operations to check answers to a calculation.

Success criteria
● I can solve problems involving mental addition, subtraction, estimating and checking.

You will need
Photocopiable sheets
'Beat the brain cards'; 'Beat the brain template'

Differentiation
Less confident learners
If more suitable, provide alternative cards with easier calculations.

More confident learners
If time, invite children to make up their own 'Beat the brain cards' to try.

Main teaching activities

Whole-class work: Revise addition and subtraction vocabulary, including sum, difference, total, subtract, take. Ask questions involving these terms, such as *What is the difference between 1846 and 2007?* Remind children of the value of making an estimate before calculating: *It will be about 150.* Discuss suitable strategies for answering the questions – for example, by counting on or jumping from 1846 to 1900 and then from 1900 to 2000 and then on 7 more. Remind children to use the estimate to check whether the answer seems sensible.

Paired work: Explain to the children that they are going to play a game to determine whether or not it is better to write down workings out or to do calculations in your head.

Give each pair a set of cards from photocopiable page 'Beat the brain cards' from the CD-ROM containing a range of word problems. Explain that both players must make an estimate of each answer. One person in each pair then must perform a written calculation, so that their workings are clear; the other works out the answer using mental calculation strategies. The first person to work out the correct answer wins the card. Once the answer has been checked against the estimate, they then pick a new card. After five completed cards, they should then swap roles.

Progress check: Invite children to say what they notice about working mentally or writing things down. *Who won most cards? Why was this? Were any problems easier to answer mentally than with jottings?*

Review

Ask children to describe the best strategies for answering the questions on the cards. Check for the mental and written strategies and address any common misconceptions. Ask the children which methods they find easiest and why. Repeat this activity at other times to give further practice of mental and written calculations by adapting the 'Beat the brain template'.

Curriculum objectives
- To recall multiplication and division facts for multiplication tables up to 12 × 12.
- To recognise and use factor pairs and commutativity in mental calculations.

Success criteria
- I can solve problems involving mental multiplication and division, estimating and checking.

Differentiation
Less confident learners
Let these children choose questions from the first part of the list.
More confident learners
Children can choose questions from the last part of the list.

Lesson 3
Oral and mental starter `31`

Main teaching activities

Whole-class work: Revise the term *factor* as meaning a number that divides into another and that we can give factor pairs of a number. Choose several two-digit numbers and list all of their factors pairs: for 24, these would be 1 × 24, 2 × 12, 3 × 8, 4 × 6. Write these questions and explain that one number in each calculation can be written as a pair of factors to make it easier to answer:

24 × 5	16 × 15	5 × 36
3 × 8 × 5	8 × 2 × 15	5 × 6 × 6

Then remind children that they can then multiply in any order to make it simpler:

3 × 40	8 × 30	30 × 6
120	240	180

Independent work: Ask children to choose eight of the following questions and to use factors to help them mentally answer them (the questions in the list become increasingly difficult).

5 × 18	12 × 5	16 × 5	5 × 14	8 × 15	15 × 6	14 × 15	12 × 15
45 × 8	35 × 4	8 × 45	35 × 8	45 × 6	35 × 6	12 × 45	45 × 14

Progress check: Ask: *Are there any other factors of this number that could have been better to use? Why is the factor 2 so useful if the other number is 5?*

Review
Take feedback and ask children to show their strategies on the board. Discuss any questions that children may have answered differently.

Curriculum objectives
- To recall multiplication and division facts for multiplication tables up to 12 × 12.
- To estimate and use inverse operations to check answers to a calculation.

Success criteria
- I can solve one- and two-step problems involving mental addition, subtraction, multiplication and division.

You will need
Photocopiable sheets
'Badge problems'
Equipment
Individual whiteboards

Differentiation
Less confident learners
Children may require support in breaking down each problem. Ask them to discuss each question with a partner.
More confident learners
Invite children to try the 'Challenge' question on the photocopiable sheet.

Lesson 4
Oral and mental starter `31`

Main teaching activities

Whole-class work: Introduce the following context: *A school is making birthday cards to sell at a school fete. The badges come in three sizes: small, medium and large. They decide on a price for each size.* Ask several one- or two-step problems:

- *Jo buys three small cards for 96p. How much is one small card?*
- *A small and a medium card together cost 48p. If the small card costs 32p, how much would two medium cards cost?*
- *Four large cards cost £2.20. How much would five large cards cost?*
- *Mary bought one of each size. How much change from £5 did she get?*

Invite children to discuss the problems in pairs and write their answers on their whiteboards. Remind them to make estimates and then use them to check.

Independent work: Provide children with photocopiable page 'Badge problems' from the CD-ROM to complete.

Progress check: Invite children to say what estimates they made for each question and to explain what calculations they used to solve them.

Review
Take feedback and discuss solutions. Explore the estimates that children made and discuss the reasons for their estimates. Review the 'Challenge' question with the whole class. Prompt for methods of solving it.

Curriculum objectives

● To solve addition and subtraction two-step problems in contexts.
● To solve problems involving multiplying and adding.

Success criteria

● I can solve one- and two-step problems involving mental addition, subtraction, multiplication and division.

You will need

Equipment

Individual whiteboards

Differentiation

Less confident learners

Give these children specific problems to solve from the list given.

More confident learners

Give children further information to write questions about, such as: *Each minibus costs £80 for the week and each coach costs £165 for the journey to and from the centre.*

Lesson 5 — Oral and mental starter 8

Main teaching activities

Whole-class work: Explain that today children will use mental strategies to solve problems. Present the following information to the class:

- *42 girls, 35 boys and 9 adults are going on to stay at a residential centre in Wales.*
- *Each child pays £72 to go on the trip.*
- *A coach to take them to the centre can carry 44 people.*
- *The minibuses at the centre can carry 12 people plus a driver.*
- *Each of the girls' dormitories can sleep 8 girls.*
- *Each of the boys' dormitories can sleep 9 boys.*

Ask: *What questions could we ask about this information?* Ask children to discuss in pairs questions that could be asked about the trip and invite them to suggest them to the class. For example:

- *How many people are on the trip altogether?*
- *How much do the children pay in total?*
- *How many coaches are needed?*
- *If some of the adults drive the minibuses, how many are needed?*
- *How many of the girls' dormitories are needed?*
- *How many of the boys' dormitories are needed?*

Paired work: Encourage each pair to write and solve as many questions as they can about the information.

Progress check: Ask children to show the methods and checking approaches they used to solve each problem. Ask questions such as: *How did you decide what to do? Did you estimate first? What checking strategy did you use?*

Review

Take feedback on the problems. *Which problem was the most difficult to solve? Why? Which methods of addition, subtraction, multiplication or division did you use?* Encourage children to summarise the strategies used this week and to explain how these were applied in this problem-solving work.

Addition and subtraction: written methods

Expected prior learning

Children should be able to:

- rapidly recall and use addition and subtraction facts to 20
- recognise the place value of each digit in four-digit numbers
- accurately add and subtract numbers mentally, including one- and two-digit numbers.

Topic	Curriculum objectives	Expected outcomes
Addition and subtraction	**Lesson 1**	
	To add and subtract numbers with up to four-digits using the formal written methods of columnar addition and subtraction where appropriate. To estimate and use inverse operations to check answers to a calculation.	Add numbers with up to four digits using columnar addition. Estimate to check answers.
	Lesson 2	
	To add and subtract numbers with up to four-digits using the formal written methods of columnar addition and subtraction where appropriate. To estimate and use inverse operations to check answers to a calculation.	Subtract numbers with up to four-digits using columnar subtraction.
	Lesson 3	
	To add and subtract numbers with up to four-digits using the formal written methods of columnar addition and subtraction where appropriate.	Add and subtract numbers with up to four-digits using columnar addition and subtraction.
	Lesson 4	
	To add and subtract numbers with up to four-digits using the formal written methods of columnar addition and subtraction where appropriate.	Add and subtract numbers with up to four-digits using columnar addition and subtraction.
	Lesson 5	
	To solve addition and subtraction two-step problems in contexts, deciding which operations and methods to use and why.	Solve two-step measurement problems involving addition and subtraction, choosing an appropriate and effective calculation method.

Preparation

Lesson 1: copy 'Target grids (2)', one per child

Lesson 2: copy 'Target grids (2)', one per pair

Lesson 3: prepare a copy/drawing of a phone keyboard for display

Lesson 4: copy 'Great pyramids', one per child

You will need

Photocopiable sheets
'Great pyramids'

General resources
'Target grids (2)'

Equipment
Individual whiteboards; tape measure

Further practice

Photocopiable sheets
'Add and difference'

Oral and mental starters for week 2

See bank of starters on pages 167 and 168. Oral and mental starters are also on the CD-ROM.

25 Rounding round

29 Place value additions and subtractions

14 Measurement facts

Overview of progression

During this week children will consolidate and extend their abilities to use column methods of addition and subtraction. They will use inverses to check their calculations and will make and use estimates to check whether answers are sensible. They are given opportunities to decide when a particular calculation approach is best and they will work with measurement problems in lesson 5.

Watch out for

Ensure that children are confident in place value ideas and that they understand the value of each digit in four-digit numbers. This will help them with written methods of addition and subtraction, as it can help them appreciate the place value implications of why we carry and exchange.

Creative context

Use written addition and subtraction in other areas of the curriculum, such as in science or cooking activities.

Vocabulary

add, altogether, carry, column, difference, digit, equals, exchange, fewer, **inverse,** leave, less, make, minus, more, partition, plus, sign, subtract, sum, take away, total

Curriculum objectives

● To add and subtract numbers with up to four digits using the formal written methods of columnar addition and subtraction where appropriate.
● To estimate to check answers to a calculation.

Success criteria

● I can add numbers, using a column method of addition.
● I can estimate to check answers.

You will need

General resources

'Target grids (2)'

Differentiation

Less confident learners

Ask children to select numbers from the first grid on photocopiable page 'Target grids (2)' to add.

More confident learners

These children should select numbers from the third grid on the photocopiable sheet. Challenge some children to choose more than two numbers to add each time.

Lesson 1

Oral and mental starter 25

Main teaching activities

Whole-class work: Explain that this lesson is about adding four-digit numbers that require a written or mental method. Write the numbers 5647 and 3278 on the board. Ask: *What is the approximate total of these two numbers?* Discuss children's answers, expressing 5647 as less than 6000 or close to 5600, and 3278 as more than 3000 or close to 3300. An approximate answer might be 9000 or 8900. Focus attention on the importance of finding an approximate answer before calculating exactly. Ask: *How could we find the exact total?* Invite two or three children to suggest ways, whether mental with jottings or using a written method. Say that you would like someone to demonstrate how to do it using a column method. Set out the numbers vertically and demonstrate the formal written method involving carrying:

```
  Th  H  T  U
   5  6  4  7
+  3  2  7  8
   8  9  2  5
       |  |
```

Invite children to instruct you as to how to do the written method and to explain in their own words why we carry digits across from a column to the column to its left. Include at least one question that will have a five-digit answer for the more confident learners to demonstrate on the board – for example, 5686 + 6857. Repeat for other pairs of numbers in the same way. Remind children to check their answers using the estimates they made each time.

Independent work: Invite children to choose pairs of numbers from the photocopiable page 'Target grids (2)' from the CD-ROM to add using a written method. The core learners should choose numbers from the second of the three grids. Remind them to make an estimate for each addition and to use the estimate to check that the answer seems sensible.

Progress check: Invite children to discuss their additions. Ask: *What estimates did you make? How many times did you need to carry in this addition? Why was that? What is special about the digits in that column?*

Review

Take feedback. *Why do we need to estimate an answer before we calculate it?* Invite children to share their answers and to demonstrate their written methods, explaining how they checked their answers using their estimates.

Curriculum objectives
● To subtract numbers with up to four digits.
● To estimate and use inverses to check answers to a calculation.

Success criteria
● I can use a written column method of subtraction and can check by adding.

You will need
General resources
'Target grids (2)'

Differentiation
Less confident learners
Ask children to select numbers from the third and the first grids to find the difference between (these will involve fewer occasions of exchange).

More confident learners
These children can select numbers from any of the three grids.

Lesson 2

Main teaching activities

Whole-class work: Revise the column method of subtraction with the class, including more than one exchange, making an estimate first (for example, 7493 − 4957 is about 7500 − 5000 = 2500).

Th	H	T	U
6		8	
X̶	¹4	9̶	¹3
− 4	9	5	7
2	5	3	6

Compare the answer with the estimate. *In what other ways could we check whether our answer is exactly correct?* Remind children that the answer can be added to the number subtracted to see whether this gives the first number (4957 + 2536 = 7493). Repeat for other written subtraction examples involving exchange once, twice or three times.

Paired work: Give each pair the photocopiable page 'Target grids (2)' from the CD-ROM. Ask them to choose a number each, from different grids (for example, one child chooses a number from the third grid and one chooses from the second grid). Together they should estimate the difference between the numbers and then calculate using a written method. They then use addition to check the answer before repeating for other pairs of numbers.

Progress check: Invite children to explain how they subtracted each time and ask them to say the inverse calculation they used to check.

Review
Take feedback and discuss solutions.

Curriculum objectives
● To add and subtract numbers with up to four digits using written methods of columnar addition and subtraction.

Success criteria
● I can add and subtract numbers, using column methods.

You will need
Equipment
Individual whiteboards

Differentiation
Less confident learners
Ask these children to create three-letter words only.

More confident learners
Encourage children to see if they can find words for the answers they make. They could also choose five-letter words to explore.

Lesson 3

Whole-class work: Introduce the following context by displaying this picture of a phone keypad. Point out that some phones have numbers and letters together on the same keys. Write on the board:

rain + snow = ?   wind − sun = ?

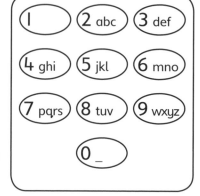

Ask children to say which numbers you would key in for the words rain and snow (7246 + 7669). Invite a child to add the numbers using a column written method and give the answer (14,915). Now ask children to say which numbers you would key in for the words wind and sun (9463 − 786). Invite a child to find the difference between the numbers using a column method of subtraction (8677).

Paired work: Ask children to choose three- and four-letter words, represent them as numbers using the keypad and then find the sums and differences between them.

Progress check: Invite children to discuss their calculations. *How did you work this out? How could you check this answer?*

Review
Ask some true or false questions such as: tent − rope = owl (true); goat + cow = huts (false). Invite children to demonstrate the calculations using written methods and to say whether the statements are true or false.

Curriculum objectives
● To add and subtract numbers with up to four digits using written methods of columnar addition and subtraction.

Success criteria
● I can add and subtract numbers, using column methods.

You will need
Photocopiable sheets
'Great pyramids'

Differentiation
Less confident learners
Ask children to draw a pyramid containing three-digit numbers to work on before tackling photocopiable page 'Great pyramids'.

More confident learners
Ask children to create their own larger pyramids with ten bricks (four in the bottom row), using four- or five-digit numbers.

Lesson 4
Oral and mental starter 29

Main teaching activities

Whole-class work: Draw six 'bricks' in a pyramid arrangement, and write three small four-digit numbers in the bottom three bricks, as shown here.

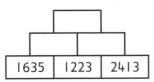

Explain that the remaining bricks should contain numbers that are the sums of the two numbers from the adjoining bricks below, e.g. the sum of 1635 + 1223 fits in the left-hand brick immediately above. Invite children to demonstrate written addition to complete the pyramid. Repeat with larger four-digit numbers in the bottom row.

Now draw a blank pyramid with three of the other bricks given. For example:

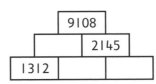

Encourage children to explain how the missing number can be found (by subtracting 2145 from 9108). Complete the pyramid, asking children to use written methods of subtraction.

Independent work: Give children photocopiable page 169 'Great pyramids' to complete. Remind them to use estimates to see whether answers seem sensible and to use inverse operations to check.

Progress check: Invite children to explain how they found the missing numbers and ask them to say the inverse calculations they used to check.

Review

Take feedback and discuss solutions. Identify the written methods used to calculate each sum.

Curriculum objectives
● To solve addition and subtraction two-step problems in contexts.

Success criteria
● I can solve two-step measurement problems involving addition and subtraction.

You will need
Equipment
Tape measure

Differentiation
Less confident learners
Suggest questions for these children to answer.

More confident learners
Invite children to write questions that involve multiple steps.

Lesson 5
Oral and mental starter 14

Main teaching activities

Whole-class work: Write *Robert Wadlow, height 272cm – world's tallest man.* Measure the heights of children in centimetres. Ask: *How much taller was Robert Wadlow than Emily is? Was Robert Wadlow taller than both Jack and Emily put together?* Discuss suitable mental or written methods.

Now draw the following diagram showing flight distances between some cities. Explain that the children will write questions to form a quiz. For example: *How much further is it to fly from London to Istanbul than from Vienna to Madrid? A pilot flies from Vienna to Madrid and then to London. How far did he fly?*

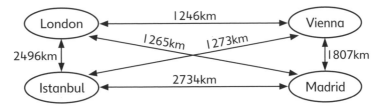

Group work: Ask each group to write at least five questions using the information in the diagram and answer them, using written methods.

Whole-class work: Set a quiz using questions from each group, scoring points for correct answers. Remind children to use inverse operations to check.

Progress check: Say: *Ask me a question that uses subtraction/addition.*

Review

Pose this problem: *A pilot flew from London to all three other cities. Which order should he visit them to ensure the shortest distance and how far would that be?* (London to Madrid, then to Vienna and then to Istanbul = 4345km).

Time

Expected prior learning

Children should be able to:

- give the number of seconds in a minute and the number of days in each month, year and leap year
- read and write times on analogue and 12-hour digital clocks.

Topic	Curriculum objectives	Expected outcomes
Measurement	**Lesson 1**	
	To read, write and convert time between analogue and digital 12- and 24-hour clocks.	Read, write and convert analogue and digital 12-hour times. Use am and pm and can work out time intervals.
	Lesson 2	
	To solve problems involving converting from hours to minutes; minutes to seconds; years to months; weeks to days.	Solve problems involving time (12-hour times).
	Lesson 3	
	To read, write and convert time between analogue and digital 12- and 24-hour clocks.	Read and write times on a digital 24-hour clock.
	Lesson 4	
	To read, write and convert time between analogue and digital 12- and 24-hour clocks.	Give times as 24-hour digital times.
	Lesson 5	
	To solve problems involving converting from hours to minutes; minutes to seconds; years to months; weeks to days.	Solve problems involving time (24-hour times).

Preparation

Lesson 1: prepare sets of cards cut out from 'Time after time cards', one set per pair

Lesson 2: copy 'Time problems', one per child

Lesson 4: prepare sets of cards cut out from 'Time dominoes', one set per pair

You will need

Photocopiable sheets

'Time after time cards'; 'Time problems'; 'Time dominoes'

General resources

Interactive activity 'Time pairs'

Equipment

Individual whiteboards; clock-faces with moving hands; 0–9 number cards

Further practice

Use the interactive teaching resource 'Clocks' to give further practice of reading and converting times between analogue and digital 12- and 24-hour clocks. In option, select both clocks and ask children to convert one given time (such as analogue) to the other (such as digital).

Oral and mental starters for week 3

See bank of starters on pages 168 and 169. Oral and mental starters are also on the CD-ROM.

21 Follow me

32 Time trials

33 What's the time, Mr Wolf?

36 Time for conversion

Overview of progression

During this week the children will revise, consolidate and extend their knowledge of telling the time in digital and analogue form and will explore time intervals between pairs of times. In lessons 1 and 2 they will revise telling times in analogue and digital 12-hour form and will calculate intervals and solve related problems. In lesson 3 children will be introduced to 24-hour times and will begin to explore the relationship between 12-hour and 24-hour times. In lessons 4 and 5 they will explore these ideas further and will solve problems involving time intervals using 24-hour times.

Watch out for

It is important that children are confident in telling the time to the nearest minute on analogue and on 12-hour digital clocks before beginning work on 24-hour time. Provide such children with geared analogue clocks to help them relate between 12-hour and 24-hour times.

Creative context

Link this time work to science work, cooking, athletics and other sporting activities.

Vocabulary

analogue, clock, digital, hour, minute, second, time, 12-hour time, **24-hour clock**, 24-hour time

Curriculum objectives
● To read, write and convert time between analogue and digital 12-hour clocks.
Success criteria
● I can read, write and convert time between analogue and digital 12-hour clocks.
● I can use am and pm and can work out time intervals.

You will need
Photocopiable sheets
'Time after time cards'
General resources
Interactive activity 'Time pairs'
Equipment
Small clock-faces with moving hands

Differentiation
Less confident learners
Let children start with only the cards showing times from 1 am to 2am and work in hour, quarter, half and three-quarter hour steps.
More confident learners
Include the cards on the photocopiable sheet that are labelled 'Extension set', which give some later times.

Lesson 1   Oral and mental starter 21

Main teaching activities

Whole-class work: Use the interactive activity 'Time pairs' on the CD-ROM to revise matching 12-hour times on digital and analogue clocks. As you are working together with the class ask children to suggest things that they might be doing at these times (at school, watching TV, having lunch...) and invite them to say whether the time would then be an am or a pm time.

Give each child a small clock-face with moving hands and write pairs of digital times on the board, such as 5:45 and 6:10. Ask children in pairs to show these times on their small clock-faces and to suggest what they might be doing if these were am or pm times. *How many minutes are there between these two times?* Discuss time intervals and help children to use counting-on strategies to work out the lengths of time between pairs of times. Demonstrate how a diagram can be used to work out wider intervals, using 'o'clock' times as stepping stones. For example:

4:05 ⟶ *55 mins* ⟶ <u>5:00</u> ⟶ *2 hours* ⟶ <u>7:00</u> ⟶ *25 mins* ⟶ 7:25

Show how all the minutes can be combined and converted to hours and minutes to find the total time interval:

55 mins + 25 mins = 80 mins = 1 hour 20 mins

1 hour 20 mins + 2 hours = 3 hours 20 mins

Paired work: Give each pair a set of cards cut out from photocopiable page 'Time after time cards' from the CD-ROM. Ask them to shuffle the cards and to take turns to pick two cards. Suggest that they put the earlier time on the left-hand side of a sheet of paper and the later time on the right-hand side, in a line. They must show both times on their clock-faces and then work out the time interval between them. The two times and the interval should be recorded.

Progress check: As children are using the cards ask: *If this time was an am/pm time what might you be doing then? Will it be morning, afternoon, evening or night? How did you work out this time interval?*

Review

Discuss the children's work. Invite children to demonstrate their methods for particular questions they recorded. Ask: *How could you check that the answer is correct?* Invite others to count on given time intervals from the earlier time to check.

Curriculum objectives
- To solve problems involving time.

Success criteria
- I can solve problems involving time (12-hour times).

You will need

Photocopiable sheets
'Time problems'

Equipment
Clock faces

Differentiation

Less confident learners

Provide children with clock-faces with moving hands to support them.

More confident learners

Ask children to write their own problems for others to solve.

Lesson 2 — Oral and mental starter 32

Main teaching activities

Whole-class work: Explain that this lesson is about time problems. On the board revise how to find time intervals by counting on using 'o'clock' times as stepping stones. For example, to find the time interval between 1:25pm and 9:50am:

9:50am ⟶ *10 mins* ⟶ <u>10:00am</u> ⟶ *3 hours* ⟶ <u>1:00pm</u> ⟶ *25 mins* ⟶ 1:25pm

10 mins + 25 mins = 35 mins

3 hours + 35 mins = 3 hours 35 mins

Remind children that, if the total of the minutes is greater than 60, they must convert this time to hours and minutes.

Independent work: Provide children with photocopiable page 'Time problems' from the CD-ROM to complete. Ask them to use counting on to find the time differences.

Progress check: Ask children to describe how they solved a problem from their sheet: *How did you work out this time interval? Did you make any jottings?*

Review

Take feedback. Invite children to share some of their questions and answers from the sheet and to explain how they worked out the answers. Check that they write the time in digital form and use am and pm appropriately.

Curriculum objectives
- To read, write and convert time between analogue and digital 12- and 24-hour clocks.

Success criteria
- I can read and write times on a digital 24-hour clock.

Differentiation

Less confident learners

Ask these children to give o'clock times.

More confident learners

Challenge this group to choose times to the nearest minute, such as 4:33pm = 16:33.

Lesson 3 — Oral and mental starter 32

Main teaching activities

Whole-class work: Draw a long line on the board showing midnight at the left-hand end and midnight at the right-hand end. Invite a child to mark on noon or midday (in the middle of the line). Under the line in the appropriate positions write the 'o'clock' 12-hour digital times, 12:00am, 1:00am, 2:00am, 3:00am... all the way to 11:00pm and then 12:00am again. Discuss events that happen at the different times of day as you write them. Explain that we call these times 12-hour digital times because we only ever write the hour as a number up to 12.

Now write 13:00 on the board. *Has anyone ever seen this written as a time? What does it mean? Why might we use numbers greater than 12?* Explain that rather than using am and pm which can sometimes cause confusion for important situations, such as on bus or train timetables, we use a 24-hour clock rather than a 12-hour clock. Above the line write 24-hour times, each using four digits: 00:00, 01:00, 02:00, 03:00... all the way to 23:00.

Paired work: Pairs take turns to give each other a 12-hour time which they then convert to a 24-hour time (for example, 6:00pm = 18:00 or 3:15pm = 15:15).

Progress check: Ask: *Say a quick way of changing a pm time to a 24-hour time?* (Add 12 to the hour.)

Review

Invite each pair to call out pairs of times from their sheet, but present them as 'true or false' questions. For example: *16:00 is the same as 6:00pm – true or false?*

Curriculum objectives
● To read, write and convert time between analogue and digital 12- and 24-hour clocks.

Success criteria
● I can give times as 24-hour digital times.

You will need
Photocopiable sheets
'Time dominoes'

Differentiation
Less confident learners
Let these children work together in pairs to match the times into one long line rather than playing this as a game of dominoes.

More confident learners
When children have finished the game they can make additional cards showing other pairs of matching times.

Lesson 4
Oral and mental starter 33

Main teaching activities

Whole-class work: Call out times in words and ask children to say the times as 24-hour times, using the words morning, evening, night, afternoon. For example: *half past 7 in the evening; twenty-four minutes past seven in the morning; quarter to eleven at night.* Revise the work introduced in the previous lesson and draw the timeline from midnight to midnight again if necessary.

Paired work: Give each pair a set of cards cut out from photocopiable page 'Time dominoes' from the CD-ROM. Ask them to deal out the cards and then play dominoes, positioning the cards to make touching pairs that match.

Progress check: During the paired work ask: *Which hour times would you say are in the afternoon? In the evening? At night? Which times are easiest to write in 24-hour time?*

Review

Invite children to put the following times in order, starting from midnight, and then give each of the times in 24-hour digital form: half past seven in the evening; quarter to six in the morning; ten past four in the afternoon; six minutes to nine in the evening; quarter past midday; five past two at night.

Curriculum objectives
● To solve problems involving time.

Success criteria
● I can solve problems involving time (24-hour times).

You will need
Equipment
0–9 number cards

Differentiation
Less confident learners
Provide children with only the 0–5 digit cards to make times such as 10:25, 12:30, 13:45, 21:30 and so on.

More confident learners
Encourage children to make all the possible times that can be made using four of the digits 0, 1, 3, 5 and 8 (without repeating digits) – for example, 01:35, 01:38, 01:53, 01:58, 03:15, 03:18... They should then choose pairs of times to find the difference between them.

Lesson 5
Oral and mental starter 36

Main teaching activities

Whole-class work: Demonstrate how a diagram can be used to work out time intervals involving 24-hour times, using 'o'clock' times as stepping stones. For example, the interval time between 09:13 and 16:53:

09:13 → 47 *mins* → 10:00 → 6 *hours* → 16:00 → 53 *mins* → 16:53

Show again how the whole minutes can be combined and converted to hours and minutes to find the total time interval:

47 mins + 53 mins = 100 mins = 1 hour 40 mins

6 hours + 1 hour 40 mins = 7 hours 40 mins

Paired work: Give each pair a set of 0–9 number cards. Players turn the cards face down and take turns to pick four cards and see if they can be made into a real 24-hour time (say, 23:59 or 06:34). If it can, the time is recorded. If not, the cards are replaced and four more chosen. When both players have recorded a time they should work together to find the time interval between them, starting with the earlier time and counting on to the later time.

Progress check: Ask: *How do you know if the digits can be made into a 24-hour time? Which digits must the time have? Is it easier to work out time differences for 12-hour times or for 24-hour times? Why do you think that?*

Review

Take feedback on the week's lessons on time. *What have you learned about 24-hour times? Why do we use 24-hour time?*

 SCHOLASTIC

Multiplication and division: written methods

Expected prior learning

Children should be able to:

- recall and use multiplication facts for the 1, 2, 3, 4, 5, 6, 8 and 10 multiplication tables and related division facts
- write and calculate mathematical statements for multiplication and division, using mental methods.

Topic	Curriculum objectives	Expected outcomes
Multiplication and division	**Lesson 1** To recall multiplication and division facts for multiplication tables up to 12 × 12. To use place value, known and derived facts to multiply and divide, including: multiplying by 0 and 1; dividing by 1; multiplying together three numbers.	Multiply three numbers together and use written methods.
	Lesson 2 To use place value, known and derived facts to multiply and divide, including: multiplying by 0 and 1; dividing by 1; multiplying together three numbers. To multiply two-digit and three-digit numbers by a one-digit number using formal written layout.	Perform short multiplication for multiplying using multi-digit numbers.
	Lesson 3 To recall multiplication and division facts for multiplication tables up to 12 × 12. To use place value, known and derived facts to multiply and divide, including: multiplying by 0 and 1; dividing by 1; multiplying together three numbers.	Perform short division with exact answers when dividing by a one-digit number.
	Lesson 4 To use place value, known and derived facts to multiply and divide, including: multiplying by 0 and 1; dividing by 1; multiplying together three numbers.	Perform short division with exact answers when dividing by a one-digit number.
	Lesson 5 To solve problems involving multiplying and adding, including using the distributive law to multiply two-digit numbers by one digit, integer scaling problems and harder correspondence problems such as which n objects are connected to m objects.	Solve one- and two-step problems involving multiplication.

Preparation

Lesson 3: copy 'Written division (2)', one per child

Lesson 4: copy 'Shape clues', one per pair

Lesson 5: copy 'Problem puzzles', one per child

You will need

Photocopiable sheets

'Written division (2)'; 'Shape clues'; 'Problem puzzles'

General resources

Interactive activity 'Multiplication and division'; interactive activity 'True or false'

Equipment

Individual whiteboards; large dice; 3–9 number cards

Further practice

Use the interactive activity 'True or false' to check children's understanding of 6-, 8-, 9-, 11- and 12-times tables facts.

Oral and mental starters for week 4

See bank of starters on pages 85, 167 and 168. Oral and mental starters are also on the CD-ROM.

17 True or false

20 Bingo

8 Function machine

31 Factor fun

Overview of progression

During this week the children will consolidate and extend their abilities to use formal written methods of multiplication and division. In lesson 1 they multiply three small numbers together using recall of tables facts and short multiplication. This is developed further in lesson 2 where they create their own multiplication questions to solve. In lesson 3 the formal written method of short division is explored further, and in lessons 4 and 5 children solve problems and puzzles using both short multiplication and short division.

Watch out for

It is vital that children are able to recall multiplication and division facts related to the times tables in order to successfully master short multiplication and division. Where children lack confidence in this, they can initially be provided with a multiplication table square to refer to when learning the written methods. Where children struggle with using the condensed forms of short multiplication and short division they can continue to work on the expanded form until they are ready to move on.

Creative context

Look out for opportunities to perform multiplication in real contexts, such as getting into teams in PE, sitting on benches in the hall, giving out items such as coloured pencils to children, cooking situations, and so on.

Vocabulary

column method, condensed method, expanded method, **factor**, facts, groups of, lots of, multiple, multiply, **product**, short division, short multiplication, tables, times

Curriculum objectives
• To recall multiplication and division facts for multiplication tables up to 12 × 12.
• To multiply together three numbers.

Success criteria
• I can multiply three numbers together and use written methods.

You will need

Equipment
Individual whiteboards

Differentiation

Less confident learners
Ask children to answer the questions using the expanded method of multiplication, if more appropriate than short multiplication.

More confident learners
Several extension questions can be given (such as 12 × 12 × 8 or 9 × 12 × 7) where there is a three-digit number to be multiplied rather than a two-digit number.

Lesson 1 — Oral and mental starter 17

Main teaching activities

Whole-class work: Introduce the following context: *Connor has four full sticker books; each has 12 pages and each page holds six stickers. How could we find how many stickers he has?* Discuss how this problem could be presented as a number sentence, inviting each child to show what they would do on their individual whiteboard and to hold it up. Show how this could be recorded as the number sentence $4 \times 12 \times 6 = ?$ Ask: *How could we find the answer to this question?* Remind children that the numbers can be arranged in any order and ask them to try to work out the answer on their whiteboards. Take feedback on their attempts to work it out. Draw attention to any known facts used, such as: *I knew that 4 × 12 was 48 so then I had to multiply 48 by 6.* Discuss ways of multiplying a two-digit number by a single digit number, such as by partitioning: $48 \times 6 = 40 \times 6 + 8 \times 6$. Revise how this can be shown in a written form, either expanded or condensed:

```
    H T U        or      H T U       or       H T U
      4 8                  4 8                   4 8
  ×     6            ×       6           ×         6
    2 4 0                  4 8                 2 8 8
      4 8                2 4 0                   4
    2 8 8                2 8 8
```

Explain to the children that you would like them to try to use the short condensed written method today, known as short multiplication. Provide several other examples to work through together, drawing a simple table to present each question, describing them in the context of sticker books introduced at the start of the lesson:

Number of sticker books	Number of pages	Number of stickers on each page
4	8	8
3	8	9
6	12	8

Independent work: Write further numbers into the table above for children to work on individually, using the numbers 3, 4, 6, 7, 8, 9, 11 and 12 (using 11 and 12 as the number of pages). These can include $6 \times 8 \times 4$; $9 \times 8 \times 4$; $3 \times 9 \times 6$; $7 \times 12 \times 7$; $7 \times 8 \times 9$; $6 \times 11 \times 6$ (and so on). Remind children to use short multiplication, where possible, having done one multiplication using known tables facts.

Progress check: As children are using short multiplication ask: *Why do you need to carry this digit into the next column? How can you check this answer? Do it again in a different order?*

Review

Choose several questions from the table and invite children to show their workings on the board. Show that answers can be checked by multiplying in a different order. For example, for $4 \times 12 \times 6$ you could first multiply 48 by 6 and could then check it by multiplying 4 by 72 where 72 is made by multiplying 12 by 6.

Curriculum objectives
● To use place value, known and derived facts to multiply.
● To multiply two-digit and three-digit numbers by a one-digit number using formal written layout.
Success criteria
● I can perform short multiplication for multiplying using multi-digit numbers.

You will need
Equipment
Large dice; 3–9 number cards

Differentiation
Less confident learners
Give children a dice to roll three times to create three-digit numbers, focusing on multiplying them by 3, 4 or 5.
More confident learners
Children can try picking five cards to create four-digit × one-digit multiplications.

Lesson 2

Main teaching activities

Whole-class work: Explain that in today's lesson the children will be doing short multiplication with larger numbers. Ask them to roll a large dice three times to create a three-digit number (say, 354) and to multiply this number by 3. Demonstrate written forms for the question 354 × 3:

```
  H T U     or        H T U     or        H T U
  3 5 4               3 5 4               3 5 4
×     3             ×     3             ×     3
─────────           ─────────           ─────────
  9 0 0                 1 2             1 0 6 2
  1 5 0               1 5 0               ¹ ¹
    1 2               9 0 0
─────────           ─────────
1 0 6 2             1 0 6 2
```

Roll the dice three more times to create a different three-digit number and multiply by 4, 6, 7 (and so on). Invite children to the front to work through the examples and encourage them to attempt the condensed form (short multiplication), describing the process in their own words.

Independent work: Provide each child with a set of 3–9 digit cards. Ask them to pick four to create a three-digit by one-digit multiplication (for example, 735 × 6). They use short multiplication to answer each question.

Progress check: Say: *Describe what you did to reach this answer?*

Review

Take feedback on multiplications the children have written and ask them to demonstrate their working to the rest of the class.

Curriculum objectives
● To use place value, known and derived facts to divide.
Success criteria
● I can use short division with exact answers when dividing by a one-digit number.

You will need
Photocopiable sheets
'Written division (2)'
Equipment
Individual whiteboards

Differentiation
Less confident learners
Before copying, alter the questions to: 66÷3, 72÷6, 84÷4, 55÷5, 70÷7.
More confident learners
Before copying, add the digits 1 or 2 before each number being divided to make a three-digit number.

Lesson 3

Main teaching activities

Whole-class work: Revise short division as follows. Write:

```
3 | 8  4
```

Ask children to say what question we are trying to solve: *84 divided by 3.* Say: *Look at the tens digit. How many threes in 8? There are 2 threes with 2 left over. Write 2 above in the tens column and carry the 2 left over.*

```
    2
3 | 8 ²4
```

Look at the units. We now have 24. How many threes in 24? There are 8 threes so we write 8 above to complete the answer.

```
    2 8
3 | 8 ²4
```

Remind children that they can use short multiplication to multiply 28 by 3 to give 84 as a means of checking their answer. Demonstrate other examples in the same way (92 ÷ 4, 96 6, 91 ÷ 7...), asking children to work out answers on their whiteboards.

Independent work: Provide each child with photocopiable page 'Written division (2)' from the CD-ROM. They should use short division to work out each answer and use the second box to multiply using short multiplication to check their answers.

Progress check: Say: *Describe what you did to reach this answer?*

Review

Invite children to write some of their divisions on the board and describe strategies they used to work out each answer.

Curriculum objectives
● To use place value, known and derived facts to multiply and divide.

Success criteria
● I can use short multiplication and short division.

You will need
Photocopiable sheets
'Shape clues'
Equipment
Individual whiteboards

Differentiation
Less confident learners
These children should focus on the first two sets of shapes on photocopiable page 'Shape clues'. They do not need to find the total of the shapes in the set.
More confident learners
Children can focus on the later sets of shapes which include multiplication and division of three-digit numbers.

Lesson 4   Oral and mental starter 8

Main teaching activities

Whole-class work: Draw the following shapes and symbols on the board, explaining that each stands for a different two-digit number:

Ask the children the following questions and invite them to use short division or short multiplication to answer them on their whiteboards.

1. *When the triangle is multiplied by 4 the answer is 96. What is the triangle worth?* (24)

2. *If the pentagon's value is three times greater than the triangle, what is the pentagon worth?* (72)

3. *The heart's value is one sixth the value of the pentagon; what is the heart worth?* (12)

4. *When the cross is multiplied by 6 the answer is 84. What is the cross worth?* (14)

Record the values of the shapes and ask: *What is the total value of the four shapes?* (122)

Paired work: Provide children with photocopiable sheet 171 'Shape clues'. Ask them to work together in pairs to find the value of each shape in a set, using the clues given. Explain that the shapes might stand for two- or three-digit numbers. Remind children to use short multiplication or division and to check using the inverse operation. They could also then find the total value of the shapes in each set.

Progress check: Say: *Describe what you did to reach this answer?*

Review

Take feedback on the activity. Invite children to demonstrate their workings and solutions on the board.

Curriculum objectives
● To solve problems involving multiplying and adding.

Success criteria
● I can solve multiplication and division problems using written methods.

You will need

Photocopiable sheets
'Problem puzzles'

General resources
Interactive activity 'Multiplication and division'

Equipment
Individual whiteboards

Differentiation

Less confident learners

Let children undertake this work in pairs to encourage peer tutoring, where more confident learners help those who are less confident.

More confident learners

Ask children to make up their own puzzles for others to solve.

Lesson 5 Oral and mental starter 31

Main teaching activities

Whole-class work: Work together with the class through both screens of the interactive activity 'Multiplication and division' on the CD-ROM. Discuss appropriate strategies for solving word problems involving multiplication and division. Talk about how money and measurements given as decimals can be thought of as whole numbers – for example, £4.20 can be thought of as 420p, or 3.2 litres as 3200 millilitres. Give children opportunities to work with a partner and decide how each problem could be solved, recording workings and solutions on their whiteboards.

Independent work: Provide each child with photocopiable page 'Problem puzzles' from the CD-ROM to complete.

Progress check: Ask: *How did you work out each problem puzzle? Did you use multiplication or division? Show me the method you used to work out this solution. How could you check it?*

Review

Mark the work together, inviting children to explain their decision-making and to demonstrate the methods they used. Encourage them to check their answers using inverse operations. Identify any common misconceptions and review in particular the use of the short and long forms of multiplication and division.

2D shapes, angles and coordinates

Expected prior learning

Children should be able to:

- identify and name shapes according to the numbers of sides
- identify and recognise right angles in shapes
- understand the nature of parallel sides.

Topic	Curriculum objectives	Expected outcomes
Geometry: properties of shapes	**Lesson 1**	
	To identify acute and obtuse angles and compare and order angles up to two right angles by size.	Identify acute and obtuse angles. Compare and order angles.
Geometry: position and direction	**Lesson 2**	
	To describe positions on a 2D grid as coordinates in the first quadrant. To plot specified points and draw sides to complete a given polygon.	Describe positions and plot points on a coordinates grid.
	Lesson 3	
	To describe movements between positions as translations of a given unit to the left/right and up/down.	Translate shapes up/down and left/right.
Geometry: properties of shapes	**Lesson 4**	
	To compare and classify geometric shapes, including quadrilaterals and triangles, based on their properties and sizes.	Know the names and properties of quadrilaterals.
	Lesson 5	
	To compare and classify geometric shapes, including quadrilaterals and triangles, based on their properties and sizes.	Describe and identify regular and irregular shapes.

Preparation

Lesson 1: prepare 'Angles' for display on the interactive whiteboard

Lesson 2: prepare 'Coordinate grid' for display on the interactive whiteboard; copy 'Coordinate grids', one per child

Lesson 3: prepare 'Coordinate grid' for display on the interactive whiteboard; copy a few spare answer sheets from lesson 2

Lesson 4: copy 'Coordinate grids', one per child; prepare 'Coordinate grids' for display on the interactive whiteboard

Lesson 5: copy '2D shapes – polygons', one per pair, and 'Venn diagram', several per pair

You will need

Photocopiable sheets
'Angles'

General resources
'Coordinate grid'; 'Coordinate grids'; '2D shapes – polygons'; 'Venn diagram'

Equipment
Individual whiteboards; blank cards; rulers

Further practice

Give the children further practice of comparing and classifying geometric shapes with specified properties, for example 'a parallelogram that isn't a rectangle'

Oral and mental starters for week 5

See bank of starters on page 168. Oral and mental starters are also on the CD-ROM.

15 Twenty questions

34 I spy

Overview of progression

During this week the children will consolidate and extend their knowledge of the properties of 2D shapes, angles and coordinate grids. Lesson 1 explores angles, including acute and obtuse angles. In lessons 2 and 3 children are given opportunities to plot and identify points on a coordinate grid and they begin to make simple translations of the shapes. In lesson 4 they revise the properties and names of quadrilaterals and in the final lesson of the week they compare and classify 2D polygons according to a range of mathematical criteria.

Watch out for

Common errors made by children include the following:
- identifying rectangles as regular (they do not have equal sides)
- identifying a rhombus as regular (the angles are not equal)
- looking at a square twisted round and thinking it is a rhombus (the angles are still right angles)
- thinking a parallelogram that is not a rectangle or a rhombus is symmetrical (show that it isn't by folding).

Creative context

Link this shape work to art activities, including creating patterns and angles using colour and shapes.

Vocabulary

acute, angles, equal, equilateral, horizontal, irregular, isosceles, **line of symmetry**, names of quadrilaterals, **obtuse**, pair of coordinates, parallel, perpendicular, **regular polygon**, right, scalene, shape, sides, translate, Venn diagram, vertex, vertical, vertices

Curriculum objectives
- To identify acute and obtuse angles.
- To compare and order angles up to two right angles by size.

Success criteria
- I can identify acute and obtuse angles.
- I can compare and order angles.

You will need

Photocopiable sheets

'Angles'

Equipment

Individual whiteboards

Differentiation

Less confident learners

Provide pairs with only four or five cards to order.

More confident learners

Invite children to draw shapes rather than just angles on their cards and to mark one of the angles in each shape, to be ordered in the same way.

Lesson 1   Oral and mental starter 15

Main teaching activities

Whole-class work: Explain that today's lesson is about angles. Display photocopiable page 'Angles' from the CD-ROM as a revision of previous work. Ask children to identify the letters of the angles that are acute and obtuse angles, revising the fact that acute angles are less than one right angle (90 degrees) and that obtuse angles are larger than one right angle but smaller than two right angles (between 90 and 180 degrees). In pairs, ask children to look at the angles and to put them in order of size, recording their answers on their individual whiteboards. Ensure that they remember that *angle* is the amount of turn and is not related to the lengths of the lines or to the distance between the end points of the lines.

Paired work: Provide each pair with a set of six blank cards. Explain that you would like them to make an angle game. On each card they should draw an angle, using a ruler, each labelled with a letter. Angles should be marked with an arc and each should be different. They should be able to put the angles in order of size themselves and when in the correct order, the letters should spell out a six-letter word when arranged from smallest to largest. Once completed, the set of cards can be swapped with another pair who must work out the six-letter word.

Progress check: Ask: *What type of angle is this? How do you know? Is it smaller or larger than a right angle? What do we call this angle?*

Review

Draw an irregular shape on the board with a range of acute, right and obtuse angles. Ask children to identify the type of each angle. *How do you know whether these angles are acute, right or obtuse angles? Find an example of each of these angles in the classroom?*

Curriculum objectives
● To describe positions on a 2D grid as coordinates in the first quadrant.
● To plot specified points and draw sides to complete a polygon.

Success criteria
● I can describe positions and plot points on a coordinate grid.

You will need
General resources
'Coordinate grid'; 'Coordinate grids'

Differentiation
Less confident learners
Support children in identifying which coordinate comes first in a pair of coordinates.

More confident learners
Ask children to measure and find the perimeters of the shapes they have drawn.

Lesson 2
Oral and mental starter 15

Main teaching activities

Whole-class work: Display photocopiable page 'Coordinate grid' from the CD-ROM. *Who can show me where I would plot the point (3, 2) on this grid?* To remind children which coordinate comes first, use phrases such as *In the house and up the stairs* or *along the corridor and up the stairs* and *× is across, x is a cross.* Invite children to come to the front and plot and join the points (3, 2), (6, 2) and (6, 5) on the grid to form a shape. Ask: *What shape is this? How many sides does it have? What angles does it have? Is it symmetrical? What do we call this shape?* Discuss the word *scalene* and explain that this triangle has one right angle and two acute angles.

Independent work: Give each child the photocopiable page 'Coordinate grids' from the CD-ROM. Ask them to plot the following points on each grid and join them in order to make shapes. Grid 1: (2, 2) (4, 2) (2, 5). Grid 2: (4, 4) (5, 5) (4, 7) (3, 6). Grid 3: (3, 3) (5, 3) (5, 5) (2, 5). Grid 4: (6, 0) (8, 2) (6, 4) (4, 2). Grid 5: (1, 4) (3, 3) (5, 3) (7, 4). Grid 6: (4, 8) (2, 4) (6, 4). They should then describe the shape, giving its name and describing its angles. Note that their answer sheets will be used again in lesson 3.

Progress check: Ask: *Which coordinate comes first? What other coordinates are along the same vertical/horizontal line as this point?*

Review

Invite children to read out their descriptions of each of the shapes drawn. Discuss any differences of opinion.

Curriculum objectives
● To describe movements between positions as translations of a given unit to the left/right and up/down.

Success criteria
● I can translate shapes up/down and left/right.

You will need
Photocopiable sheets
'Coordinate grid'
Equipment
Rulers

Differentiation
Less confident learners
Enlarge a completed answer sheet from lesson 2 onto A3 for less confident children to work with.

More confident learners
Encourage children to predict the new coordinates of the translated shapes before plotting them.

Lesson 3
Oral and mental starter 34

Main teaching activities

Whole-class work: Explain that today's lesson is about translating or sliding shapes. Display photocopiable page 'Coordinate grid' from the CD-ROM and plot a point on it. Ask children to describe the position as a pair of coordinates say (6, 4). *Where would this point move to if I slid it two squares up? What would be its new pair of coordinates?* (6, 6) *What if I slid the original point two squares down* (6, 2) *or two squares to the right* (8, 4) *or two squares left?* (4, 4) Repeat for other points, including combinations of movements left/right and up/down (for example, 4 squares right and 3 squares up). Demonstrate how a whole shape can be translated (slid), where each of the vertices moves in the same way.

Independent work: Give each child their answer sheet (or a copy of a completed sheet) from lesson 2, with each grid showing a shape drawn on it. Ask them to redraw each shape in a new position, translating each as follows:

Grid 1: 3 squares right 2 squares up   **Grid 2:** 2 squares left 3 squares down

Grid 3: 1 square right 1 square down   **Grid 4:** 3 squares left 3 squares up

Grid 5: 1 square left 3 squares up   **Grid 6:** 0 squares right 2 squares down

Progress check: While children are translating the shapes ask: *How many across to the left/right are you translating the shape? How many up/down?*

Review

Choose one of the completed grids. Ask children to give the coordinates of the vertices of the original shape and then to give them for the translated shape. *Which numbers have changed? By how many?*

 SCHOLASTIC

Curriculum objectives

● To compare and classify geometric shapes based on their properties and sizes.

Success criteria

● I know the names and properties of quadrilaterals.

You will need

General resources

'Coordinate grids'; 'Coordinate grid'

Equipment

Rulers

Differentiation

Less confident learners

Provide children with a set of examples of each of the quadrilaterals, such as those explored in autumn 2, week 5, lesson 2.

More confident learners

Encourage children to describe each of their quadrilaterals in more detail, considering angles, symmetries, diagonals and so on.

Lesson 4

Oral and mental starter 15

Main teaching activities

Whole-class work: Revise the names and properties of quadrilaterals and give examples of them, using the following criteria:

- Parallelogram: A quadrilateral with two pairs of parallel sides.
- Rhombus: A rhombus is a special parallelogram as it has four equal sides.
- Rectangle: A quadrilateral with four right angles; a rectangle is a type of parallelogram.
- Square: A square is a special rectangle as it has four equal sides.
- Kite: A kite has two pairs of equal sides but no parallel sides.
- Trapezium: A quadrilateral with exactly one pair of parallel sides.

Invite children to the front to sketch pictures of each type of quadrilateral and talk about them. Discuss the symmetrical properties of those drawn.

Independent work: Provide each child with the photocopiable page 'Coordinate grids' from the CD-ROM. Ask them to draw a different quadrilateral on each grid, making sure that the vertices of each quadrilateral lie on the grid lines so that the coordinates of the shapes can be given. They should draw:

- Grid 1: a parallelogram that isn't a rectangle
- Grid 2: a kite
- Grid 3: a square
- Grid 4: a trapezium that has one line of symmetry
- Grid 5: a rectangle with no horizontal or vertical sides
- Grid 6: a trapezium that is not symmetrical

Progress check: Ask children to describe the different shapes they have drawn. *What are the differences between these two shapes?*

Review

Display photocopiable page 'Coordinate grid' on the whiteboard. Ask children to call out a set of coordinates of the vertices of a quadrilateral from one of their grids without saying what it is. The other children should try to visualise the shape and say its name. Then draw it correctly on the board.

Curriculum objectives
● To compare and classify geometric shapes based on their properties and sizes.
Success criteria
● I can describe and identify regular and irregular shapes.

You will need
General resources
'2D shapes – polygons'; 'Venn diagram'

Differentiation
Less confident learners
Ask children to focus on specific criteria, such as *Is a triangle, Has a right angle*. Those experiencing difficulty in knowing where to place shapes could begin by sorting shapes into one Venn ring initially.
More confident learners
Encourage these children to cover as many different sorting criteria as possible in the time available.

Lesson 5

Main teaching activities

Whole-class work: Display the photocopiable page '2D shapes – polygons' from the CD-ROM on the interactive whiteboard and ask the children to name each of the shapes shown. Discuss that some of the shapes are regular (all their sides and angles are equal). Ask children to identify those that are regular and irregular. Point to the equilateral triangle, name it and explain that all the sides are equal and all the angles are the same size. Then point to the isosceles triangle and ask the children to describe what is special about this triangle (two sides are equal and two angles are equal). Ask: *How many lines of symmetry do these shapes have?*

Now tell the children that they are going to sort some shapes according to certain criteria. Ask them to suggest some criteria and write them on the board (number of sides, number of angles, regular/irregular, number of lines of symmetry, number of right angles). Ensure that the criteria are mathematical and based on properties of shape. Spend some time defining each criterion.

Draw a Venn diagram on the board:

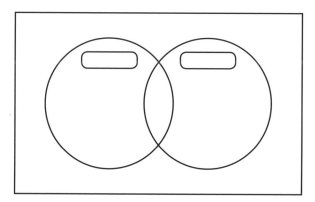

Explain to the children that they can use a diagram like this to sort their shapes. Demonstrate how the intersection involves shapes with both criteria and that shapes outside the rings have neither.

Paired work: Give each pair photocopiable page '2D shapes – polygons', along with several copies of the photocopiable page 'Venn diagram' from the CD-ROM. Explain that they should sort all the shapes on the sheet by any criteria they like from the list on the board. After each sort, they should draw their shapes in the correct places on the Venn diagram, labelling each diagram appropriately.

Progress check: During the paired work ask: *How have you decided to sort the shapes? What would go into this section of the Venn diagram? How can you be sure? Draw one more shape to go in each section?*

Review

Ask the children to explain their sorting of the shapes. Ensure they are using correct mathematical vocabulary for the names of shapes and their properties. Ask questions such as: *How many sides has a pentagon/hexagon/heptagon? What is a quadrilateral? What is another name for a regular quadrilateral? Is an isosceles triangle regular or irregular? Why?*

Statistics and measurement

Expected prior learning

Children should be able to:

- know metric units of measure
- read simple scales (such as 2, 5, 10 units) in pictograms and bar charts.

Topic	Curriculum objectives	Expected outcomes
Statistics	**Lesson 1**	
	To interpret and present discrete and continuous data using appropriate graphical methods, including bar charts and time graphs.	Collect data in a tally chart.
	Lesson 2	
	To interpret and present discrete and continuous data using appropriate graphical methods, including bar charts and time graphs.	Collect data and display it in a bar chart.
	Lesson 3	
	To solve comparison, sum and difference problems using information presented in bar charts, pictograms, tables and other graphs.	Solve problems about data in bar charts.
Statistics; Measurement	**Lesson 4**	
	To interpret and present discrete and continuous data using appropriate graphical methods, including bar charts and time graphs. To convert between different units of measure [for example, kilometre to metre; hour to minute]. To estimate, compare and calculate different measures, including money in pounds and pence.	Estimate masses of objects. Convert grams to kilograms. Organise data and display it in a line graph.
Measurement	**Lesson 5**	
	To estimate, compare and calculate different measures, including money in pounds and pence.	Estimate, measure and compare masses, including reading scales.

Preparation

Lesson 1: copy 'Capacity for tallies', one per group

Lesson 3: copy 'Speed typing', one per child

Lesson 4: collect together weighing equipment and a range of items to weigh

Lesson 5: collect together weighing equipment and a range of items to weigh

You will need

Photocopiable sheets

'Capacity for tallies'; 'Speed typing'

General resources

Interactive teaching resource 'Data handling'

Equipment

Individual whiteboards; range of empty drinks containers; large sheets of squared paper; rulers; several sets of kitchen/bathroom scales (ones with arrows and electronic ones); other spring balance scales (if available); range of light and heavy objects to weigh

Further practice

Photocopiable sheets

'Comparing mass'

Oral and mental starters for week 6

See bank of starters on pages 167 and 168. Oral and mental starters are also on the CD-ROM.

30 Counting on and back

35 Mass facts

Overview of progression

In lessons 1 and 2 of this week the children will revise, consolidate and extend their knowledge of tally charts and bar charts and will collect data and represent them in different forms. In lesson 3 they will interpret bar charts and answer questions about them involving sums and differences. In lessons 4 and 5 children will explore units of mass and will estimate them in grams and kilograms, converting between them as appropriate. They will also display information about mass in a line graph and will estimate and measure masses of common and familiar objects, reading scales on a range of weighing equipment.

Watch out for

The most common error in interpreting charts such as bar charts and line graphs is that children fail to notice and use the scales on the axes appropriately.

Creative context

Link this time work to science activities, cooking, athletics and other sporting activities and draw attention to bar charts and pictograms used in real-life life situations.

Vocabulary

bar chart, data, frequency, interpret, key, line graph, pictogram, scale, statistics, tally

Curriculum objectives
• To interpret and present discrete and continuous data.

Success criteria
• I can collect data in a tally chart.

You will need

Photocopiable sheets
'Capacity for tallies'

Equipment
Range of empty drinks containers

Differentiation

Less confident learners

If children are ability grouped, give them containers with capacities that are to the nearest 100ml already.

More confident learners

More confident groups could draw their own tally chart and choose how to group the data.

Lesson 1 — Oral and mental starter 30

Main teaching activities

Whole-class work: A few days prior to this lesson, ask the children to collect a range of used drinks containers (washed) which they should bring into school. Explain that in today's lesson the children will be exploring the following statement to see whether it is true or not: *Most drinks in a supermarket are sold in litre containers.* Invite children to say whether they think initially that this statement might be true, but stress the importance of collecting accurate data to check their predictions.

Group work: Organise the children into groups of four or five. Share out the drinks containers and provide each group with photocopiable page 'Capacity for tallies' from the CD-ROM. Ask them to sort the containers and discuss how they could round capacities to the nearest 100ml to make them easier to sort and classify. They should then fill in the tally chart on the photocopiable sheet.

Whole-class work: Now collect together all the information from each group's tally chart and create one large tally chart for the whole-class. Ask questions about the data, such as: *How many containers held less than one litre... one litre... more than one litre? What does this mean about the original statement (Most drinks in a supermarket are sold in litre containers)? Do you think that statement is true or false?* Take feedback and show how the data can be grouped into three groups:

Capacity	Number of bottles, cans and packets
Less then 1 litre	
1 litre	
More than 1 litre	

Independent work: Ask children to draw a simple pictogram of the information gained from the whole-class data, choosing and using an appropriate scale. If time, they should write several statements about the information in the pictogram.

Progress check: As children are completing their tally charts ask: *How can you check your tallies? Could you use the total number of containers as a means of checking? How?*

Review

Discuss the scale used on each of the children's pictograms. *Why did you choose to have one symbol standing for ten containers? Why did you choose 2?* Invite children who chose different scales to show their pictograms. *What are the differences you can see between these two pictograms? Do they still show the same information?* Invite children to say the advantages and disadvantages of each.

Curriculum objectives
● To interpret and present discrete data in a bar chart.

Success criteria
● I can collect data and display it in a bar chart.

You will need
Equipment
Squared paper; rulers

Differentiation
Less confident learners
Provide children with a set of axes already drawn and give support in helping them to choose an appropriate scale.

More confident learners
Encourage children to draw a bar chart with horizontal rather than vertical bars.

Lesson 2 — Oral and mental starter 30

Main teaching activities

Whole-class work: Display or describe the following personality quiz and ask children to say which of the types they think best describes them.

Type 1	Type 2	Type 3	Type 4	Type 5	Type 6
Thoughtful	Cheerful	Adventurous	Hard-working	Independent	Crazy

Are you:

- *thoughtful, kind and considerate to others?*
- *cheerful, always trying to make people smile?*
- *adventurous, you love to try new things?*
- *hardworking, you like to do things well?*
- *independent, you prefer doing things on your own?*
- *crazy, other people often describe you as mad?*

As a whole-class, work together to decide how to collect the data about the most common personality types in the class and mark tallies on a chart to show each child's preference. Note: be sensitive to children who are hesitant to choose a personality type – stress that everyone is likely to be a bit of everything and that no one category is 'better' than another. Describe people that you know (such as other teachers) in these terms to make them realise that each category is a good one. A favourite teacher of theirs, perhaps, could be described as Hardworking to remove any stigma or teasing.

Independent work: Provide squared paper for each child. Ask them to draw a bar chart of the information on the personality types and to choose an appropriate scale for the vertical axis.

Progress check: Ask children to describe the information in their bar chart: *How did you decide what scale to use?*

Review

Invite children to make statements about the information in their bar chart. Ask further questions, such as: *How many more children in our class were described as Crazy than Cheerful?*

■SCHOLASTIC

Curriculum objectives

● To solve comparison, sum and difference problems using information presented in bar charts.

Success criteria

● I can solve problems about data in bar charts.

You will need

Photocopiable sheets

'Speed typing'

General resources

Interactive teaching resource 'Data handling'

Equipment

Rulers

Differentiation

Less confident learners

Support children in reading the scales of the bar charts.

More confident learners

Challenge children to write a report on the information.

Lesson 3   Oral and mental starter 35

Main teaching activities

Whole-class work: Display screen 3 of interactive teaching resource 'Data handling' on the CD-ROM. Establish that this bar chart relates to 'eye colour'. Ask questions about the data, such as: *How many children in this survey had [   ] coloured eyes? How many more children had [   ] coloured eyes than [   ] coloured eyes? Work out the number of children in this survey altogether.* Explain that a grey-eyed child had been away the day the survey had been done. Invite a child to modify the data table accordingly. Ask similar questions and discuss the impact of modifying the data table further.

Paired work: Provide each pair with photocopiable page 'Speed typing' from the CD-ROM to complete. Establish that children understand that the two bar charts relate to improvements in five children's typing speeds over a period of three weeks.

Progress check: Ask: *What do you notice about the two scales on the bar charts?*

Review

Invite each pair to present their findings and discuss the answers together.

Curriculum objectives

● To interpret and present continuous data using line graphs.

Success criteria

● I can estimate masses of objects and convert grams to kilograms.

● I can organise data and display it in a line graph.

You will need

Equipment

Individual whiteboards; items to estimate mass; kitchen weighing scales; large sheets of squared paper; rulers

Differentiation

Less confident learners

Provide children with axes already drawn. Support them in writing the scale.

More confident learners

Ask children to write statements about their completed line graph.

Lesson 4   Oral and mental starter 35

Main teaching activities

Whole-class work: Pass round a range of objects and ask children to estimate the mass of each of them (for example, a large book, a calculator, a brick, a mug). Ask them to record their estimates of each on their whiteboards and then each item is weighed to see how close their estimates were. After each weighing, say that they can revise their other estimates accordingly. Discuss the link between grams and kilograms and remind children how to convert from one to the other (by multiplying or dividing by 1000).

Explain that you have a friend with a young child and every three months its mass is weighed. Display this information:

	Birth	3 months	6 months	9 months	12 months	15 months	18 months
Mass	3000g	6500g	8kg	9kg	9.5kg	10.5kg	11kg

Paired work: Pairs draw a line graph of the data on large squared paper. Tell them that the vertical scale should show the mass in kilograms from 0–12 and the ages of the child should be written along the horizontal axis on each vertical line. They should plot the data on the graph and then draw straight lines linking the points.

Progress check: Ask: *Which part of drawing the line graph did you find most difficult?*

Review

Invite children to show their line graphs and discuss any difficulties. Ask questions such as: *By how much did the baby grow between 9 months and 18 months?*

Curriculum objectives
• To estimate, compare and calculate different measures.

Success criteria
• I can estimate, measure and compare masses, including reading scales.

You will need

Equipment
Several sets of kitchen/bathroom scales (ones with arrows and electronic ones) Other spring balance scales (if available); range of light and heavy objects to weigh

Differentiation

Less confident learners
When reading scales children may find it easier to give readings to the nearest 100g or even to the nearest half or whole kilogram.

More confident learners
Encourage children to measure to the nearest 10 grams or even to the nearest gram, where possible.

Lesson 5 Oral and mental starter 35

Main teaching activities

Whole-class work: Explain that today's lesson is about estimating and measuring the masses of objects using grams and kilograms. Look at the different sets of scales that you have, including electronic scales where a reading is given, and those with arrows. Draw some simple scales on the board and point to various positions, asking children to estimate the mass. For example:

Ask children to give readings in both grams and kilograms and to discuss items that they think might weigh each amount (such as a heavy book or a bag of potatoes).

Group work: Give each group a range of items and scales and ask them to estimate and measure the mass of each. For example: myself, my school bag, a tin of beans, several books, a bag of sugar, a bag of potatoes, a shoe, my PE kit. Ask children to estimate, then measure, and write the masses in both grams and kilograms.

Progress check: Ask: *How close was your estimate? Why do you think this was heavier than you estimated? About how many shoes would weigh the same as this book?*

Review

Write some items that children have weighed and their masses on the board. Ask questions involving their masses. For example: *If this book weighs 1.2kg and I placed it on the balance scales, how many mugs each weighing 500g would balance the scales?*

7-times table facts

Most children should be able to recall the multiplication facts for the 7-times table.

Some children will not have made such progress and will require further practice in learning the multiples and then recalling the multiplication facts.

1. Check

40 7-times table revision

Encourage the children to recall the facts quickly by keeping the pace sharp. Observe which children are confident and which need further practice. Extend to division facts for multiples of 7 for the more confident children. Ask questions such as:

- *What are eight sevens?*
- *Which multiple of 7 is 84?*
- *What is the product of 7 and 4?*

2. Assess

Provide photocopiable page 47 'Multiple questions' with 7 written into the blank space at the top. Observe the children at work, and note those who work quickly and accurately. Give children lacking confidence a multiplication square to refer to. For the more confident, when they have finished the activity ask them to write a word problem which uses multiplying by 7. They can then swap word problems with their partner to find the solution. Record the outcomes.

3. Further practice

The recommended oral and mental starter activities, photocopiable sheets and interactive activity provide further practice in recall of multiplication facts for the 7-times table and other multiplication facts.

Curriculum objectives
- To recall multiplication facts for multiplication tables up to 12 × 12.

You will need
1. Check

Oral and mental starter

40 7-times table revision

2. Assess
'Multiple questions'; multiplication squares

3. Further practice

Oral and mental starters

8 Function machine

11 Magic square (1)

20 Bingo

Photocopiable sheets
'Multiples grid game'; 'Missing numbers'; Multiplication grid

General resources
Interactive activity 'Colour by numbers'

Time conversions

Most children should be able to convert from hours to minutes, minutes to seconds, years to months and weeks to days, multiplying by 60, 60, 12 or 7 respectively.

Some children will be less confident in multiplying by 60, 12 and 7 or may not know the relationships between the units of time.

1. Check

36 Time for conversion

Observe which children know the relationships between units of time and who can easily multiply to convert from the larger unit to the smaller one. Ask children to explain the link between multiplying by 6 and 10 when multiplying by 60.

- *How many minutes in four hours? How can you find out?*
- *Tell me how many days in a week? Minutes in an hour? Months in a year?*

2. Assess

Provide photocopiable page 170 'Converting time'. Observe the children at work, and note those who work quickly and accurately. Children lacking confidence could be given the list of relationships as shown in the oral and mental starter. For the more confident, when they have finished the activity ask them to write other equivalent pairs of units of time. Record the outcomes.

3. Further practice

The recommended oral and mental starter and photocopiable activities provide further practice in converting between units of time, including solving time-related problems.

Curriculum objectives
- To solve problems involving converting from hours to minutes; minutes to seconds; years to months; weeks to days.

You will need
1. Check

Oral and mental starter

36 Time for conversion

2. Assess

Photocopiable sheets
'Converting time'

3. Further practice

Oral and mental starters

33 What's the time, Mr Wolf?

Photocopiable sheets
'Multiples of numbers to 10'; 'Present problems'

Curriculum objectives
● To multiply two-digit and three-digit numbers by a one-digit number using formal written layout.

You will need
I. Check
Oral and mental starter
8 Function machine

2. Assess
2–9 digit cards; dice

3. Further practice
Oral and mental starters
11 Magic square (1)

Photocopiable sheets
'Merry-go-round'

Short multiplication

Most children should be able to set out the multiplication vertically and multiply, using carrying.

Some children will not have made such progress and will require further practice in recalling multiplication facts and using the carrying process.

I. Check
8 Function machine

Write a function such as × 6, × 7, × 8 or × 9 on the board, and list some two-digit numbers as input numbers. Ask children to use a written method to find each output. Observe which children are confident and which need further practice. Extend to three-digit numbers. Ask questions such as:
- *How could you find 37 × 6?*
- *Set it out vertically using a written method?*
- *Which digit do you carry?*

2. Assess

Children turn three 2–9 digit cards to make a multiplication of a two-digit number × one-digit number and solve each using a written method. Observe the children at work, and note those who work quickly and accurately and whether they set questions out correctly. Children lacking confidence could select two number cards and roll a dice to create the two-digit × one-digit multiplication, which would involve recall of simpler times tables facts. Observe when carrying is carried out correctly. Record the outcomes.

3. Further practice

The recommended oral and mental starter and photocopiable sheets provide further practice in the written method of short multiplication.

Curriculum objectives
● To estimate, compare and calculate different measures, including money in pounds and pence.

You will need
I. Check
Oral and mental starter
28 Money matters

2. Assess
Individual whiteboard

3. Further practice
Oral and mental starters
30 Counting on and back

Photocopiable sheets
'Money problems'

Money calculations

Most children should be able to calculate with money in pounds and pence.

Some children will not have made such progress and may mix pounds and pence when calculating.

I. Check
28 Money matters

Observe whether children can identify amounts of money that are equivalent, such as 35p and £0.35. Extend this to including more than 100p (say, 125p is £1.25). Ask them to add two or three numbers from the grid in the OMS – for example, 8p, £1 and £0.50. Note whether children convert easily from pence to pounds or vice versa before adding.
- *How can you write 73p in pounds?*
- *What is £0.08 in pence?*
- *What is the total of £6 and 7p?*

2. Assess

Write this list of prices on the board: 45p, £13, £2.20, 100p, £5. Ask children to choose pairs of prices and find the sum or difference between them. Observe the children at work, and note those who work confidently, converting between pounds and pence appropriately. More confident learners can choose sets of three or four prices and find the total. Record the outcomes.

3.Further practice

The recommended oral and mental starter and photocopiable sheet provide further problem-solving practice in working in both pounds and pence, converting between them where necessary.

Oral and mental starters

Number and place value

23 Place value chains (2)

Begin to write a chain of numbers involving adding or subtracting 1, 10, 100 or 1000 to four-digit numbers. For example, write:

3246 — +10 ➞   3256 —+100 ➞   3356 — − 1   ➞   3355 — +1000 ➞   ....

Ask the children to continue the chain with other numbers in this way or to identify what has been added or subtracted to give a new number in the chain.

Extension
Use multiples of 1, 10, 100 or 1000.

24 Secret numbers

Provide each child with a number fan. Tell the children that you have chosen a secret number that lies somewhere between two numbers (say, between 5000 and 6000). Children take turns to ask questions that you can only answer 'yes' or 'no' to in order to narrow down the options, such as: *Is it an even number? Is it greater than 5500? Does it round to 5000 to the nearest 100?* Children have ten questions to ask before guessing the number.

Extension
A child can choose the secret number and answer the questions. Questions could also involve Roman numerals, measurements or fractions, as appropriate.

25 Rounding round

Rehearse rounding two-, three- and four-digit numbers to the nearest 10, 100 and 1000 by calling out numbers and encouraging the children to show you the rounded number on their number fans.

Addition, subtraction, multiplication and division

26 Magic square (2)

Copy a magic square onto the board:

2   7   6
9   5   1
4   3   8

Explain that the sum of each row, column and diagonal is the same (15).

Choose a times table (say, 9 or 12), and multiply each number in the magic square by that number to create a new grid of numbers. Ask children to check to see if the numbers still form a magic square and to say what the total is.

Fractions

27 Run-around fractions

Around the walls of the classroom (or hall) pin pieces of paper showing a variety of fractions. Call out a fraction that is equivalent to one shown and ask the children to point to (or move to) that fraction. This can be played as a game where children who make a mistake are 'out'.

Extension

Questions could be called out instead, such as: *Which fraction is one half of one third?* Or *Which fraction is one quarter more than one half?* Equivalent decimals could also be called out.

Measurement

28 Money matters

Draw a 4 × 5 rectangle on the board, mainly with prices less than a pound written in pounds and in pence in each section. For example:

55p	£0.72	8p	£0.30	£1
50p	30p	£0.35	72p	£0.20
720p	£0.50	£0.20	100p	£0.75
35p	92p	£7.20	75p	45p

Ask children to find equivalences. You could also ask them to add pairs of prices or find differences between them. It can be useful to draw the template on card and laminate it. New numbers can then be written whenever required.

■SCHOLASTIC

Name: _____   Date: _____

Great pyramids

- The number on each brick is the total of the numbers in the two bricks supporting it.
- Fill in the missing numbers, using written methods of addition and subtraction.

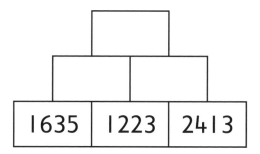

| 1635 | 1223 | 2413 |

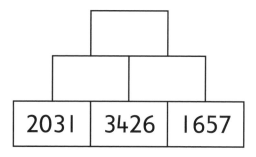

| 2031 | 3426 | 1657 |

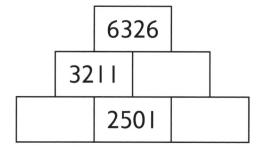

6326
3211
2501

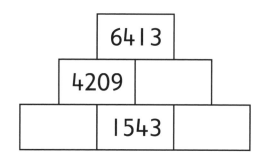

6413
4209
1543

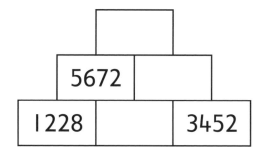

5672
1228 3452

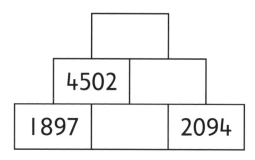

4502
1897 2094

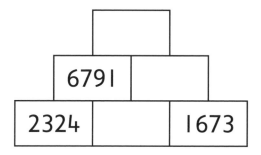

6791
2324 1673

Now make up one of your own.

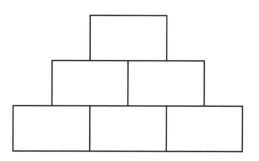

Converting time

- Fill in the missing numbers.

1. 9 weeks = _____ days

2. 7 years = _____ months

3. 3 hours = _____ minutes

4. 2 minutes = _____ seconds

5. 8 weeks = _____ days

6. 10 years = _____ months

7. 4 hours = _____ minutes

8. 11 weeks = _____ days

9. 4 years = _____ months

10. 7 hours = _____ minutes

11. 9 minutes = _____ seconds

12. 20 minutes = _____ seconds

- Now write some equivalent pairs of measurements using different units of time.

I can convert minutes to seconds, hours to minutes, weeks to days and years to months.

How did you do?

Shape clues

- Use the clues to work out the value of each shape in these sets.

Set 1

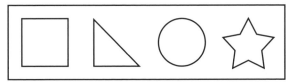

☐ × 4 = 64

☐ × 3 = ◯

◯ ÷ 4 = ◺

◺ × 6 = ☆

Set 2

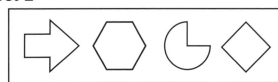

14 × 6 = ◇

◇ ÷ 7 = ⇨

⇨ × 8 = ◔

◔ ÷ 6 = ⬡

Set 3

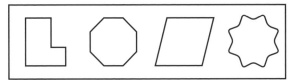

▱ × 7 = 98

▱ × 6 = ⌐

⌐ ÷ 3 = ◯

◯ × 9 = ✿

Set 4

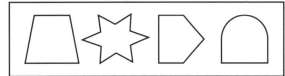

28 × 6 = ⬠

⬠ ÷ 3 = ✶

✶ × 8 = ▽

▽ ÷ 4 = ⌂

I can use short multiplication and short division to solve problems.

How did you do?

Number, place value and rounding

Expected prior learning

Children should be able to:

- recognise the place value of each digit in a three-digit number (hundreds, tens, ones)
- round small numbers to the nearest 10 and 100
- read and write, compare and order numbers up to 1000.

Topic	Curriculum objectives	Expected outcomes
Number and place value	**Lesson 1**	
	To recognise the place value of each digit in a four-digit number (thousands, hundreds, tens, and ones). To order and compare numbers beyond 1000.	Name, compare and order four-digit numbers.
	Lesson 2	
	To identify, represent and estimate numbers using different representations.	Identify, position and estimate four-digit numbers on number lines. Begin to extend their knowledge of the number system to include decimal numbers and fractions.
	Lesson 3	
	To round any number to the nearest 10, 100 or 1000.	Round four-digit numbers to the nearest 10, 100 or 1000.
	Lesson 4	
	To count in multiples of 6, 7, 9, 25 and 1000. To count backwards through zero to include negative numbers.	Read and understand negative numbers.
	Lesson 5	
	To solve number and practical problems that involve all of the above and with increasingly large positive numbers.	Solve number and practical problems.

Preparation

Lesson 2: copy 'Blank number lines', one per child (modified before copying, see lesson plan)

Lesson 3: copy 'Target grids (2)', one per pair

Lesson 4: copy 'Negative numbers', one per child

You will need

Photocopiable sheets
'Negative numbers'

General resources
'Blank number lines'; 'Target grids (2)'

Equipment
Individual whiteboards; dice

Further practice

Provide further practice of identifying four-digit numbers by completing 'Target grids template' with numbers between 1000 and 9000.

Oral and mental starters for week 1

See bank of starters on page 208. Oral and mental starters are also on the CD-ROM.

23 Place value chains (2)

3 Writing numbers

24 Secret numbers

Overview of progression

During this week the children will consolidate and extend their place value ideas of four-digit numbers, including comparing, ordering, positioning them on number lines and rounding them. In lesson 1 they will order four-digit numbers and will move on to exploring different representations of numbers on number lines in lesson 2. In lesson 3 they will round numbers to the nearest 10, 100 and 1000. Lesson 4 introduces negative numbers and by the end of the week children will be exploring all aspects of four-digit numbers set in a real-life context.

> ### Watch out for
>
> Ensure that children are confident with the place value of four-digit numbers and that they appreciate the different values of the digits. Children often experience difficulty writing in words numbers that include the digit zero, particularly in the middle of the number (such as 6047). Where this mistake occurs provide place value arrow cards and encourage children to place the 40 and 7 cards correctly onto the 6000 card to create the number 6047.

Creative context

Make links between measurement topics in science and technology that involve four-digit numbers.

Vocabulary

compare, digit, estimate, hundreds, **place value**, minus, multiples, negative numbers, ones, order, rounding, sequences, tens, thousands, units

Curriculum objectives
● To recognise the place value of each digit in a four-digit number.
● To order and compare numbers beyond 1000.
Success criteria
● I can name, compare and order four-digit numbers.

Differentiation
Less confident learners
Children can write three-digit numbers to be ordered, if appropriate.
More confident learners
Ask children to use four-digit numbers between a particular range (for example, numbers between 4600 and 4900 or numbers made with the digits 3, 4, 0 and 4).

Lesson 1
Oral and mental starter 23

Main teaching activities

Whole-class work: Explain that today's lesson will involve ordering four-digit numbers. Draw six dots in a 2 × 3 array on the board and write a four-digit number next to each. For example:

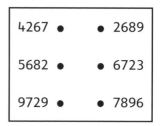

Ask: *Which is the smallest of these numbers? How do you know? What is the thousands/hundreds/tens/units digit of the largest/smallest number? How can we put these numbers in order?* Revise the values of the digits and explain how you can tell by looking at the thousands digits first which numbers are larger or smaller. Invite a child to draw a line from the smallest number to the next smallest (and so on) to order them, such as:

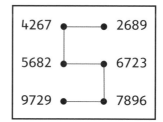

Ask: *What letter is this?* (S) Repeat for other arrays, joining the numbers from smallest to largest and seeing what letter is spelled. Note that lines can already be pre-drawn on the array, such as the dotted one in the letters A and E below and not every dot needs to have a number marked, as in E below.

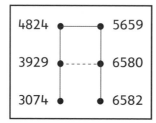 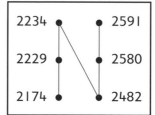 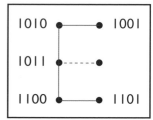

Independent work: Invite each child to make up their own letter quizzes. They should draw dots with four-digit numbers next to them, so that when the numbers are joined in order each spells a letter. Several letters can also spell out a word: SUN, OIL, SCAN, CALL and so on. Some letters may require more dots to be drawn in different positions, as appropriate. Children can then swap their quizzes with a friend.

Progress check: Ask: *Which digit has the largest value in the number 1234?* Watch out for children who incorrectly say 4 as this can indicate that they have failed to grasp the relative values of the digits.

Review

Ask children to call out numbers from their quizzes and ask them questions about them: *How do you write Jamie's number using digits? What is the hundreds digit of the number? What number is one thousand more than it? How could you partition the number into thousands, hundreds, tens and units?*

Curriculum objectives

- To identify, represent and estimate numbers using different representations.

Success criteria

- I can identify, position and estimate four-digit numbers on number lines.

You will need

General resources

'Blank number lines'

Equipment

Dice

Differentiation

Less confident learners

Focus on only one type of number line interval (for example, 0–1000, 1000–2000... to 5000–6000).

More confident learners

These children could use number cards rather than dice to create a wider range of numbers to position.

Lesson 2 — Oral and mental starter 23

Main teaching activities

Whole-class work: Play the game 'Think of a number'. Explain that you are thinking of a multiple of 10 between zero and 9000 (say, 3560). By asking questions that you can only answer 'yes' or 'no' to children should try to guess the number. They should do this in as few questions as possible. Questions could be of the type *Is it higher than 5000? Is it lower than 2500?* Encourage children to ask good questions, those which narrow down the possibilities most effectively. For example, *Is it larger than 5000?* is more helpful than the question *Is it 2610?* Encourage children to keep track of the numbers using a number line: *We know it is between 2500 and 5000. Then Megan's question showed us it is higher than 3000 and Sam's question that it is lower than 4000.* Zoom in on the number as the possibilities are narrowed:

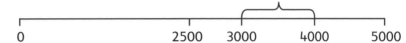

| 0 | | 2500 | 3000 | 4000 | 5000 |

Repeat for another number. Discuss that we could keep zooming in further and further on a number line, including other whole numbers and even decimal or fraction numbers that lie between whole numbers.

Paired work: Before copying photocopiable page 'Blank number lines' from the CD-ROM, mark on the following numbers at each end of the lines: 3000 and 4000, 4000 and 5000, 0 and 5000, 5500 and 5600, 2000 and 2100, 2000 and 2500, 0 and 10,000. Each child in the pair should have their own sheet. Ask children to take turns to roll a dice four times to create four-digit numbers. They should then decide where on one of their number lines the approximate position of the number would be marked with a cross that they should then label. The aim of the game is to be the first to have at least one cross marked on each line.

Progress check: Say: *Split the line into ten equal parts to help you check. What number do you think this might be? How can you be sure?*

Review

Take feedback on the number lines work. Children can copy one of their lines on the board and mark a point for the rest of the class to estimate.

Curriculum objectives
● To round any number to the nearest 10, 100 or 1000.

Success criteria
● I can round four-digit numbers to the nearest 10, 100 or 1000.

You will need
General resources
'Target grids (2)'

Differentiation
Less confident learners

Children can list multiples of 1000 from 1000–6000 only and choose numbers from the first grid to round.

More confident learners

Each player should choose ten four-digit multiples of 100 between 1000 and 9900 to write as a list. They then choose numbers from the grids and round them to the nearest 100.

Lesson 3 Oral and mental starter 3
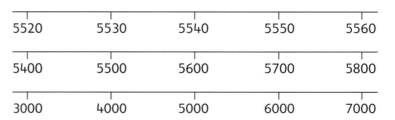

Main teaching activities

Whole-class work: Draw these number lines:

5520	5530	5540	5550	5560

5400	5500	5600	5700	5800

3000	4000	5000	6000	7000

Discuss the nature of multiples of 10, 100 and 1000. Give a four-digit number that appears in the range of each line (say, 5537). Point to the first line and ask children to identify where on the line it would be. *Which multiple of 10 is it closest to? So if we round 5537 to the nearest 10 what is the answer?* (5540) Then ask children to say what the same number would be rounded to the nearest 100. *Where on the second line would 5537 come? Which multiple of 100 is it closest to?* (5500) Finally look at rounding to the nearest 1000. *Which multiple of 1000 is it closest to?* (6000)

Paired work: Give each child photocopiable page 'Target grids (2)' . Each player writes the multiples of 1000 from 1000 to 9000 on a piece of paper. Players take turns to choose a number from one of the grids on the sheet. They round the number to the nearest 1000 and cross off the multiple of 1000 from their list, if they can. The winner is the player who is first to cross off all their multiples of 1000.

Progress check: Ask: *What is this to the nearest 10... 100... 1000?*

Review

Take feedback. Ask children to select some numbers and show how they rounded them.

Curriculum objectives
● To count in multiples of 6, 7 and 9.
● To count backwards through zero to include negative numbers.

Success criteria
● I can read and understand negative numbers.

You will need
Photocopiable sheets
'Negative numbers'

Differentiation
Less confident learners

Give children a number line showing numbers from −20 to 20.

More confident learners

Ask these children to devise their own negative number problems for others to solve.

Lesson 4 Oral and mental starter 24

Main teaching activities

Whole-class work: Begin by counting on from zero in steps of 6 around the room, pointing to a child to say the next number in the sequence. Repeat for steps of 7 and then 9 and then count backwards in similar steps from a multiple of the number (say, back from 49 in steps of 7). When zero is reached, ask: *Could we continue counting back? What numbers would we use?* Show a thermometer presented horizontally with numbers from −10 to 10. Describe the numbers less than zero as negative numbers. *Which do you think is larger? −7 or −2? −8 or 0?* Show that for negative numbers what might seem to be a *larger* number is in fact *smaller*. For example, −8 is *smaller* than −2. Indicate which direction on the scale the temperature is warmer/colder and demonstrate changing temperatures by counting forwards and backwards along the line initially without crossing 0. For example: *It was 6 degrees this morning and it is now 3 degrees warmer. It is now 9 degrees.* Show how we can write this as 6 + 3 = 9. *The temperature rises from −10 to −3. How many degrees does it rise?* (7) Write this as −10 + 7 = −3. Use the vocabulary *minus 10* or *negative 10*.

Independent work: Provide each child with photocopiable page 'Negative numbers' from the CD-ROM to complete.

Progress check: Ask: *How do you say this number? How many less than zero is it?*

Review

Take feedback. Ask: *How many larger is 3 than −3? Which is larger: −1 or −9?*

Curriculum objectives

● To solve number and practical problems that involve increasingly large positive numbers.

Success criteria

● I can solve number and practical problems.

Differentiation

Less confident learners

Give children data from a lower league, such as from the Football Conference North or South League.

More confident learners

Provide these children with data from a higher league.

Lesson 5

Main teaching activities

Whole-class work: Discuss the average attendance at some lower level football league teams, such as those in the Football Conference League. Display the following data (alternatively you can take real data directly from a website by typing *UK football attendance* into a search engine and using one of the many statistics sites available).

Team	Average attendance over the season
Layton Town	5914
Gatsby Town	3813
Stanley County	3555
Bridgehome	3543
Beverly Town	2764
Hart County	2376
Newhamton United	2236
Kampton Harriers	2197
Dursley City	2181
Prestbury Town	1694
Coralford	1390
Whitestone Rovers	1187
Hamwick	1033

Ask questions about the data such as:

● *Which team has an average attendance that is about 3800? Rounds to 1700? Is about 1000 more than the attendance at Whitestone Rovers?*
● *Which teams have an attendance that, when rounded to the nearest 1000, is 1000? Is 2000?*
● *How many teams have an average attendance between 2500 and 3800?*

Independent work: Explain that each of the children is a newspaper sports journalist. You would like them to write a report on the attendances of these teams, comparing them, rounding them and describing differences between them.

Progress check: Ask questions such as: *What is the thousands/hundreds/tens/ units digit of this number?* Encourage children to explain how they are rounding the numbers. For example: *I have rounded this number to the nearest 100* (and so on).

Review

Invite children to read out their newspaper reports to the class. They could leave out the names of some of the teams and the other children could work out which team they are referring to by the descriptions. Draw together the ideas explored during this week and remind children of the importance of knowing the values of the digits in large numbers.

Addition, subtraction, money and measures

Expected prior learning

Children should be able to:

- rapidly recall and use addition and subtraction facts to 20
- accurately add and subtract numbers mentally including one-, two- and three-digit numbers
- know the relationships between metric units of length and mass.

Topic	Curriculum objectives	Expected outcomes
Addition and subtraction	**Lesson 1**	
	To solve addition and subtraction two-step problems in contexts, deciding which operations and methods to use and why.	Solve money problems involving mental addition and subtraction.
	Lesson 2	
	To solve addition and subtraction two-step problems in contexts, deciding which operations and methods to use and why.	Solve measurement problems involving mental addition and subtraction.
	Lesson 3	
	To solve addition and subtraction two-step problems in contexts, deciding which operations and methods to use and why. To estimate and use inverse operations to check answers to a calculation.	Solve money problems involving mental addition and subtraction.
	Lesson 4	
	To solve addition and subtraction two-step problems in contexts, deciding which operations and methods to use and why.	Solve problems involving mental addition, subtraction, multiplication and division involving one and two steps.
Measurement	**Lesson 5**	
	To estimate, compare and calculate different measures, including money in pounds and pence.	Use measuring equipment appropriately. Create and solve measurement problems involving mental addition, subtraction, multiplication and division.

Preparation

Lesson 1: copy 'Money puzzles', one per pair

Lesson 2: copy 'Weighing problems', one per pair

Lesson 3: copy 'Totally different shopping', one per child

Lesson 4: copy 'Party planning', one per child

You will need

Photocopiable sheets
'Money puzzles'; 'Weighing problems'; 'Totally different shopping'; 'Party planning'

General resources
Interactive teaching resource 'Weighing scales'

Equipment
Individual whiteboards; metre stick; height measurer; tape measures; trundle wheels; rulers

Further practice

Offer further practice of calculating two-step measure problems by giving children different combinations of items to estimate, calculate then weigh using the interactive teaching resource 'Weighing scales'.

Oral and mental starters for week 2

See bank of starters on pages 208 to 210. Oral and mental starters are also on the CD-ROM.

25 Rounding round

9 Story time

24 Secret numbers

14 Measurement facts

Overview of progression

This week has a strong problem-solving focus and each day children will be solving problems set in real-life money and measurement contexts. Some activities will require mathematical reasoning and deduction skills and most activities require mental and addition strategies to be used to solve them. Lessons 1, 3 and 4 have money contexts and lessons 2 and 5 involve measurement problems. In lesson 5 the children will be involved in estimating and using appropriate equipment to measure lengths, widths and heights.

Watch out for

Children often make mistakes in money and measurement problems when they fail to notice the correct units used. For example, the mass of an item may be given in kilograms while a total mass of it and another may be given in grams. Similarly, money problems involving pounds and pence can also be incorrectly answered.

Creative context

Look out for opportunities to perform calculations in real-life measurement and money contexts, such as prices of items at a tuck shop or school fete, dinner money collection, cooking situations, science activities and so on.

Vocabulary

centimetres, grams, **inverse**, kilograms, length, mass, measuring equipment, metres, millimetres, pence, pounds, problem, strategy

Lesson 1 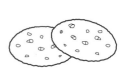 Oral and mental starter 25

Main teaching activities

Whole-class work: Present the following problem: *Three cups of tea and two biscuits cost £2.17. If one cup of tea cost 45p, what does one biscuit cost?*

Ask: *How could we work out the answer to this problem?* Give children time in pairs to use appropriate strategies to work out this problem on their whiteboards. Take feedback and invite children to show their working to the class. Discuss different approaches, such as: *James subtracted 45p three times, Zoe added together three lots of 45p and then took that from £2.17, Claire multiplied 45p by 3*, and so on. Remind the class of the link between pounds and pence and discuss any difficulties that might occur because of this. You could suggest to some children that they change the total in the question to 217p and work with pence. Stress the importance of checking their answers, by adding together the prices of the items shown (including their own answer) and checking whether the total is the one that was given initially.

Provide another similar puzzle to solve, for example: Two ice creams and a lolly cost £3.90 in total. If each ice cream costs £1.25, how much do two lollies cost?

   = £3.90

Discuss strategies and give children time to talk together in pairs and present their solutions. (Each lolly is £1.40 so two are £2.80.) Again stress the importance of checking by adding together the prices of the original items to check that it gives the correct total.

Provide further puzzles of the same type as practice before children begin their work in pairs.

Paired work: Provide each pair with photocopiable page 'Money puzzles' from the CD-ROM. Ask them to work out the prices of the items shown, using the information given on the sheet. Encourage them to show their working.

Progress check: Invite children to explain how they are working out the price of each item. *How did you work this out? What information were you given? How could you check this?*

Review

Ask children to give their answers, to describe their working and to explain how they checked their solutions.

Curriculum objectives

● To solve addition and subtraction two-step problems in contexts, deciding which operations and methods to use and why.

Success criteria

● I can solve measurement problems involving mental addition and subtraction.

You will need

Photocopiable sheets

'Weighing problems'

General resources

Interactive teaching resource 'Weighing scales'

Differentiation

Less confident learners

Children can focus on the earlier questions on the photocopiable sheet.

More confident learners

Invite children to use the information they have to give the masses of several of the items (for example, for question 4 to give the price of two cartons of orange juice and three packs of cheese).

Lesson 2   Oral and mental starter 9

Main teaching activities

Whole-class work: Sketch three items on the board: a carton of milk, a piece of cheese and an apple. Say that the mass of the three items is 1 kilogram, and no two items are the same mass. *How much could each item weigh?* Give children time in pairs to record some possibilities on their whiteboards. Take feedback and revise the relationship with grams and kilograms. Then present a new piece of information, such as *one apple weighs 400g*. Ask: *Can we work out what everything weighs now?* Give children time to investigate different possibilities.

Now display the interactive teaching resouce 'Weighing scales' on the CD-ROM showing the three items on the scale. Add an extra carton of milk to the pan and watch the display adjust to 1.5kg. *What does this tell you about the mass of the milk and of the cheese?* (The milk must be 500g and the cheese must be 300g.) *Given what you now know, how much would three pieces of cheese and a carton of milk weigh?* (1400g or 1.4kg.) Show this on the scales to check answers. Create further similar questions based on the masses of the other items available for weighing.

Paired work: Provide pairs with photocopiable page 'Weighing problems' from the CD-ROM to complete.

Progress check: Invite children to explain how they are working out the mass of each item. *How did you work this out? What are the possibilities? How could you check this?*

Review

Ask children to give their answers, to describe their working and to explain how they checked their solutions.

Curriculum objectives

● To solve addition and subtraction two-step problems in contexts.
● To estimate and use inverse operations to check answers to a calculation.

Success criteria

● I can solve money problems involving mental addition and subtraction.

You will need

Photocopiable sheets

'Totally different shopping'

Differentiation

Less confident learners

Provide place value cards for support.

More confident learners

Ask children to make up their own questions for others to solve.

Lesson 3   Oral and mental starter 9

Main teaching activities

Whole-class work: Write the following on the board: [ ] + [ ] = £1.48. Ask: *If two different items together cost £1.48, what prices could they be?* Encourage children to realise that there are lots of different possible solutions. Explain that, if you know the price of one item, you can work out the other price: *If one item is 36p, we can subtract 36p from £1.48 to find the price of the other.* Discuss that addition and subtraction are *inverses* and talk about how to find the missing number in other addition statements (using subtraction or counting on) – for example, [ ] + 15 = 31 or £1.12 + [ ] = £2.01. Invite children to show strategies for finding the missing numbers mentally.

Repeat for a missing number subtraction statement, such as [ ] − 46p = 64p. *How could we find the missing number?* Discuss how addition can be used to find the first number in the subtraction and stress the importance of checking that the statement is true at the end, using inverse.

Independent work: Provide children with photocopiable page 'Totally different shopping' from the CD-ROM. Ask them to use appropriate addition and subtraction strategies to solve each problem.

Progress check: Ask: *How did you solve this problem? Did you work mentally or with a written method? How did you check this answer?*

Review

Take feedback and ask children to show their strategies on the board.

Curriculum objectives
● To solve addition and subtraction two-step problems in contexts, deciding which operations and methods to use and why.
Success criteria
● I can solve problems involving mental addition, subtraction, multiplication and division involving one and two steps.

You will need
Photocopiable sheets
'Party planning'

Differentiation
Less confident learners
Mask and alter the prices on the photocopiable sheet to provide easier calculations. Provide place value cards for support.
More confident learners
Ask children to write their own problems for others to solve.

Curriculum objectives
● To estimate, compare and calculate different measures.
Success criteria
● I can create and solve measurement problems involving mental addition, subtraction, multiplication and division.

You will need
Equipment
Metre stick; height measurer; tape measures; trundle wheels; rulers

Differentiation
Less confident learners
Children could focus on making only four or five of the measurements and could be given support with this.
More confident learners
Encourage children to include questions that combine different units of length.

Lesson 4 — Oral and mental starter 24

Main teaching activities

Whole-class work: Draw a football on the board with a price tag of £2.37. Ask children to work out the cost of two footballs on their whiteboards and to hold them up. *How many of you did an addition? How many of you did a multiplication? Which was quicker to do?* Show several of the approaches used and invite children to explain how they worked it out in their own words. Now ask them to find the cost of three footballs. Again, take feedback on the strategies used. *Did anyone just add on the price of another football to the previous total? Did anyone multiply by 3? Which approach was quicker?* Now ask children to find the cost of five footballs. Again take feedback. Draw attention to the fact that multiplication is useful when we have larger numbers of the same item. Ask several one- or two-step problems such as:

● What is the maximum number of footballs could I buy for £10?
● How much change from £5 would I get it I bought two footballs?

Invite children to discuss the problems in pairs and write their answers on their whiteboards. Remind them to make estimates and then use them to check.

Independent work: Provide children with photocopiable page 'Party planning' from the CD-ROM. Ask them to use appropriate addition, subtraction or multiplication and division strategies to solve each problem.

Progress check: Ask: *How did you solve this problem? Did you work mentally or with a written method? How did you check this answer?*

Review
Take feedback and discuss solutions.

Lesson 5 — Oral and mental starter 14

Main teaching activities

Whole-class work: Explain to the children that today they will make and use measurements to create problems to solve. Working in groups, they will measure a range of lengths, widths and heights in millimetres, centimetres or metres, using suitable measuring equipment (if appropriate, these activities could be done in the hall or outside). The children will then make up problems about the information to form a class quiz.

Group work: Organise the class into groups of four. Each group should estimate, measure and record the following five measurements for each child in the group: (1) their height; (2) the length of their shoe; (3) the width of their outstretched hand; (4) the width of their little fingernail; (5) how far they walk in ten strides. The children should then write some statements about the different measurements, and make them into word problems, such as:

● *James is 14cm taller than Zoe. If Zoe is 110cm tall, how tall is James?*
● *How many pigeon-steps would Hannah make to go the same distance as she makes in ten strides?*
● *How much wider is Kim's little fingernail than Adam's, if hers is 13mm and Adam's is 9mm?*

Progress check: Ask: *What questions can you think of that would use subtraction/addition?*

Review
Do a quiz using questions from each group. Points can be scored for correct answers. Remind children that inverse operations can be used to check answers.

■SCHOLASTIC

Addition and subtraction: written methods

Expected prior learning

Children should be able to:
- rapidly recall and use addition and subtraction facts to 20
- recognise the place value of each digit in four-digit numbers
- accurately add and subtract numbers mentally including one-, two- and three-digit numbers.

Topic	Curriculum objectives	Expected outcomes
Addition and subtraction	**Lesson I**	
	To add and subtract numbers with up to 4-digits using the formal written methods of columnar addition and subtraction where appropriate. To estimate and use inverse operations to check answers to a calculation.	Add numbers with up to four-digits using columnar addition. Estimate and use inverse operations to check.
	Lesson 2	
	To add and subtract numbers with up to 4-digits using the formal written methods of columnar addition and subtraction where appropriate. To estimate and use inverse operations to check answers to a calculation.	Subtract numbers with up to four-digits using columnar subtraction. Estimate and use inverse operations to check.
	Lesson 3	
	To add and subtract numbers with up to 4-digits using the formal written methods of columnar addition and subtraction where appropriate.	Add and subtract numbers with up to four-digits using columnar addition and subtraction.
	Lesson 4	
	To add and subtract numbers with up to 4-digits using the formal written methods of columnar addition and subtraction where appropriate.	Add and subtract numbers with up to four-digits using columnar addition and subtraction.
	Lesson 5	
	To solve addition and subtraction two-step problems in contexts, deciding which operations and methods to use and why.	Solve two-step money problems involving addition and subtraction, choosing an appropriate and effective calculation method.

You will need

Equipment
Individual whiteboards; 0–9 number cards

Further practice

Photocopiable sheets
'Simply subtraction'

Oral and mental starters for week 3

See bank of starters on pages 208 and 209. Oral and mental starters are also on the CD-ROM.

13 Targets

25 Rounding round

29 Place value additions and subtractions

Overview of progression

During the week children will be given extensive opportunities to practise written methods of addition and subtraction, involving many instances of carrying or exchange/borrowing. They will use inverses to check their calculations and will make and use estimates to check whether answers are sensible. Lessons 1, 2, 3 and 4 are designed to encourage children to examine the nature of the digits that result from carrying or borrowing in each column. In lesson 5 children create and solve measurement problems by adding or subtracting four-digit numbers.

Watch out for

Ensure that children are confident in place value ideas and that they understand the value of each digit in four-digit numbers. This will help them with written methods of addition and subtraction, as it can help them appreciate the place value implications of why we carry and exchange.

Creative context

Use written addition and subtraction in other areas of the curriculum – for example, in science or cooking activities.

Vocabulary

add, altogether, carry, column, difference, digit, equals, exchange, fewer, **inverse**, leave, less, make, minus, more, partition, plus, sign, subtract, sum, take away, total

Curriculum objectives

• To use a written column method of addition.
• To estimate and use inverses to check answers to a calculation.

Success criteria

• I can add numbers, using a column method of addition.
• I can estimate and use inverses to check answers.

You will need

Equipment

Individual whiteboards

Differentiation

Less confident learners

Invite children to try to find the numbers with the lower totals in the list.

More confident learners

Encourage these children to try to find the numbers with the higher totals in the list.

Lesson 1   Oral and mental starter 13

Main teaching activities

Whole-class work: Explain that this lesson is about finding totals of pairs of four-digit numbers. Ask: *What four-digit numbers can I make if I can use the digits 1 and 4?* Build a list of numbers such as 1111, 4444, 1414, 1114, 1441, 4414, 4441 (and so on). Select 1111 and 4444: ask children to write the total on their whiteboards and hold them up. *How did you work out the answer? Why was it so easy?* Choose other pairs from the list to add, asking children to write the total each time on their whiteboards (for example, 1141 + 1441 = 2582, 1414 + 4444 = 5858). *With which pair of numbers from the board could you make the total 8858?* Invite children to say how they can predict which numbers have been used by looking at the digits 8858 in turn. After several similar questions (*How could you make the total 8582... 2588...*) ask children what numbers could be made from the digits 1 and 9 (1111, 1919, 1119, 9191, 1911, 9999...). *What is the total of 1111 + 1119?* Invite children to write the answer on their whiteboards and hold them up. *Why is this question more difficult than the previous ones?* (It requires exchange/ carrying.) Demonstrate how a written method can be used to add the numbers to give the answer 2230.

Ask the following questions: 1191 + 1111, 1111 + 1911, 1919 + 1111, 9191 + 1119, 9911 + 9119, 1119 + 1119, 1111 + 9999. Demonstrate the formal written method involving carrying for each:

```
   Th  H  T  U
    9  9  1  1
 +  9  1  1  9
 1  9  0  3  0
       1     1
```

Invite children to instruct you as to do how to do the written method and to explain in their own words why we carry digits across from a column to the column to its left. Include at least one question that requires carrying in adjacent columns (for example, for 1999 + 1919). Remind them that answers can be checked using subtraction.

Paired work: Ask children to write a range of four-digit numbers using the digits 1, 4 and 9 – for example, 1149, 1411, 9944, 4911, 1419, 4499 and so on. They should choose pairs and find the total. Encourage them to use estimating and to find pairs of numbers that have the following totals:

2568	(1149 + 1419)
2640	(1149 + 1491)
2910	(1491 + 1419)
5530	(1411 + 4119)
6408	(4494 + 1914)
9905	(4911 + 4994)
14,322	(9411 + 4911)
14,443	(9944 + 4499)
19,355	(9944 + 9411)

Progress check: Invite children to discuss their additions. *What estimates did you make? How many times did you need to carry in this addition? Why was that? How could you check this answer using subtraction?*

Review

Take feedback. Invite children to share their answers and to demonstrate their written methods, explaining how they can check their answers using subtraction.

Curriculum objectives
● To subtract numbers with up to four digits.
● To estimate and use inverses to check answers to a calculation.

Success criteria
● I can use a written column method of subtraction and can check by adding.

You will need
Equipment
Individual whiteboards

Differentiation
Less confident learners
Encourage children to choose one number made with larger digits (say, 8855) and one number made with mainly smaller digits (say, 1151) to ensure easier subtractions.

More confident learners
Encourage these children to support some of the other children through peer tutoring by explaining the written method in their own words.

Lesson 2

Main teaching activities

Whole-class work: Explain that this lesson is about finding the difference between pairs of four-digit numbers. *What four-digit numbers can I make if I can use the digits 5 and 8?* Build a list of numbers such as 8888, 5555, 8558, 5858, 5558, 8855. Select 8888 and 5555 and ask children to write the difference on their whiteboards and hold them up. *How did you work out the answer? Why was it so easy?* Choose the following pairs to find the difference between: 8888 − 5558, 8885 − 5858, 8855 − 5855, 5888 − 5555. Ask children to write the answer each time on their whiteboards.

Now choose the numbers 8885 and 5558 and ask: *Why is the difference between these two numbers so much harder than the previous ones?* Demonstrate that, if using a written method, this question requires exchange:

```
Th  H  T  U
            7
 8  8  8  ¹5
−  5  5  5  8
   3  3  2  7
```

Similarly invite children to show the written method you would use for 8858 − 5585, 8558 − 5855 and so on.

Ask the following questions including more difficult subtractions requiring exchange in two or more columns: 8555 − 5885, 8558 − 5888, 8855 − 5885 and so on. Invite children to instruct you as to how to do the written method and to explain in their own words why we need or exchange. Include examples where exchange takes place in adjacent columns, such as:

```
Th  H  T  U
    7  ¹7
 8  8  ¹5  5
−  5  8  7  5
   2  9  8  0
```

Remind them that answers can be checked using addition and give several examples.

Paired work: Ask children to write a range of four-digit numbers using the digits 1, 5 and 8 – for example, 1155, 1811, 1815, 8855, 8851, 5858 and so on. They should choose pairs and find the difference between them. Encourage them to use estimating and to find pairs of numbers that have the following differences:

4233   (5818 − 1585)
3733   (8851 − 5118)
3726   (8881 − 5155)
4264   (5815 − 1551)
3996   (5811 − 1815)
7656   (8811 − 1155)

Children should check each of their answers using a written method of addition.

Progress check: Invite children to discuss their subtractions. *Which did you find easy? Which did you find more difficult? Why was that? How could you check this answer using addition?*

Review

Take feedback. Invite children to share their answers and to demonstrate their written methods, explaining how they can check their answers using addition.

Curriculum objectives
- To add and subtract numbers with up to four digits using columnar addition and subtraction.

Success criteria
- I can add and subtract numbers, using column methods.

You will need

Equipment
Individual whiteboards

Differentiation

Less confident learners
Ask children to attempt the earlier questions in the list first.

More confident learners
Ask these children to work on the later questions and then make up their own problems of this type.

Lesson 3   Oral and mental starter 25

Main teaching activities

Whole-class work: Write: XXXX + YYY = 6332 and XXXX − YYY = 4778 on the board. Tell the children that XXXX is a four-digit number with all its digits the same and YYY is a number with three identical digits. Invite children in pairs to discuss what the digits X and Y could represent. Allow time for discussion and for recording answers on whiteboards. Take feedback, then write the questions vertically:

```
  X  X  X  X          X  X  X  X
+     Y  Y  Y       −     Y  Y  Y
──────────          ──────────
  6  3  3  2          4  7  7  8
```

Invite children to explain what they noticed. For example: *X must be 5 or 6 if the total is 6332 and that the subtraction suggests it must be 5. Then if X was 5, Y must be 7 in order to get the units digit 2 in the addition.*

Paired work: Ask pairs to find the value of each letter in these additions and subtractions:

AAAA + BBBB = 7777, AAAA − BBBB = 3333   [Ans: A = 5, B = 2]

CCCC + DDDD = 14,443, DDDD − CCCC = 1111   [Ans: C = 6, D = 7]

EEEE + FFFF = 15,554, EEEE − FFFF = 2222   [Ans: E = 8, F = 6]

GGGG + HHHH = 14,443, GGGG − HHHH = 5555   [Ans: G = 9, H = 4]

JJJJ + KKKK = 16,665, KKJJ − JJKK = 1089   [Ans: J = 7, K = 8]

LLLL + MMM = 18,887, MMMM − LLL = 7889   [Ans: L = 9, M = 8]

Progress check: Ask: *How did you work this out? How could you check that you answered this correctly?*

Review

Discuss the problems and the strategies used to solve them.

Curriculum objectives
- To add and subtract numbers with up to four digits using columnar addition and subtraction.

Success criteria
- I can add and subtract numbers, using column methods.

You will need

Equipment
0–9 number cards; individual whiteboards

Differentiation

Less confident learners
Ask children to turn over 6 or 7 cards to make two three-digit numbers.

More confident learners
Invite children to turn over 9 or 10 cards to make two four-digit numbers.

Lesson 4   Oral and mental starter 29

Main teaching activities

Whole-class work: Ask children to choose any digit from 0 to 9 and write it on their whiteboards. Write on the board: 2553 + 5735 = [ ] and 6724 − 3448 = [ ]. Invite a child to answer each on the board, giving answers 8288 and 3276. Explain that any child who wrote 8 on their board scores 3 points as the digit 8 appears three times, those who wrote 2 score two points (and so on). Repeat for other pairs of addition and subtraction, with children keeping their initially chosen digit.

Paired work: Give each child a set of 0–9 number cards. Each child chooses a particular digit to score points throughout the length of the game. Players shuffle the two sets of cards together and then take turns to pick eight cards, arranging them to form a four-digit + four-digit addition or a four-digit − four-digit subtraction. Both players answer the question and they both score points if any digits in the answer are their chosen digit. The player who picks the cards can choose to arrange them in any way they like and also to say whether to add or subtract the two numbers. The winner is the first player to score 10 points.

Progress check: Invite children to explain any strategies they used to decide how to arrange the digits and whether to add or subtract.

Review

Take feedback. Invite children to show some of their calculations on the board.

Curriculum objectives

● To solve addition and subtraction two-step problems in contexts, deciding which operations and methods to use and why.

Success criteria

● I can solve two-step measurement problems involving addition and subtraction, choosing an appropriate and effective calculation method.

You will need

Equipment

Individual whiteboards

Differentiation

Less confident learners

Give children suggestions for questions they could answer.

More confident learners

Invite children to write questions that involve multiple steps.

Lesson 5 Oral and mental starter 29

Main teaching activities

Whole-class work: Discuss the written methods of addition and subtraction explored this week. Now draw and label six different-sized parcels on the board, giving their masses (or display this picture):

A	B	C	D	E

5258g	1245g	3184g	1098g	6731g

Explain that, in groups, you would like the children to write a range of different questions about these parcels to form part of a quiz. Give examples of the sort of questions they could write, such as:

- *How much heavier is parcel E than parcel A?*
- *What is the total mass of parcels B and C?*
- *How much heavier are parcels A and C together than parcel E on its own?*
- *How much less than 2 kilograms is parcel D?*
- *What is the total mass of all the parcels?*

Group work: Ask each group to write at least five questions using the information in the diagram and answer them, using written methods.

Whole-class work: Do a quiz using questions from each group. Points can be scored for correct answers. Remind children that inverse operations can be used to check answers.

Progress check: Ask: *What questions can you think of that would use subtraction/addition?*

Review

Discuss the following problem and ask children to suggest how they would solve it: *If we weighed three of one of the parcels, the total mass would be 3735g. Which parcel is it?* Remind children of the importance of making an estimate to save time by ruling out many of the possibilities.

Multiplication and division: mental and written methods

Expected prior learning

Children should be able to:

- recall and use multiplication facts for the 1, 2, 3, 4, 5, 6, 8 and 10 multiplication tables and related division facts
- write and calculate mathematical statements for multiplication and division, using mental methods.

Topic	Curriculum objectives	Expected outcomes
Multiplication and division	**Lesson 1**	
	To recall multiplication and division facts for multiplication tables up to 12 × 12. To recognise and use factor pairs and commutativity in mental calculations.	Write statements about the equality of expressions such as associative law (2 × 3) × 4 = 2 × (3 × 4).
	Lesson 2	
	To use place value, known and derived facts to multiply and divide, including: multiplying by 0 and 1; dividing by 1; multiplying together three numbers.	Perform mental multiplication and division.
	Lesson 3	
	To multiply two-digit and three-digit numbers by a one-digit number using formal written layout.	Perform short multiplication for multiplying using multi-digit numbers.
	Lesson 4	
	To use place value, known and derived facts to multiply and divide, including: multiplying by 0 and 1; dividing by 1; multiplying together three numbers.	Perform short division with exact answers when dividing by a one-digit number.
	Lesson 5	
	To solve problems involving multiplying and adding, including using the distributive law to multiply two-digit numbers by one digit, integer scaling problems and harder correspondence problems such as which n objects are connected to m objects.	Write statements about the equality of expressions (for example, use the distributive law 39 × 7 = 30 × 7 + 9 × 7).

Preparation

Lesson I: prepare eight long thin strips of cards for each pair

Lesson 4: copy 'Short division', one per pair

You will need

Photocopiable sheets

'Short division'

Equipment

Individual whiteboards; 0–9 number cards; long thin strips of card; dotty paper; counters; Blu-Tack®

Further practice

Give children regular practice of short division of three-digit by single digit numbers with and without remainders

Oral and mental starters for week 4

See bank of starters on page 209. Oral and mental starters are also on the CD-ROM.

12 9-times table

20 Bingo

37 Inverses

31 Factor fun

Overview of progression

During this week the children will develop their understanding of the nature of multiplication and division and will extend their abilities to mentally multiply and divide and use short multiplication and division. In lesson I they explore the commutative nature of multiplication and begin to write statements about the equality of expressions. In lesson 2 they are given opportunity to multiply and divide mentally. Lessons 3 and 4 involve practising short multiplication and short division respectively and in lesson 5 children will use arrays to further explore the distributive nature of multiplication and addition.

Watch out for

It is vital that children are able to recall multiplication and division facts related to the times tables in order to successfully master short multiplication and division. Where children lack confidence in this, they can initially be provided with a multiplication table square to refer to when learning the written methods. Where children struggle with using the condensed forms of short multiplication and short division they can continue to work on the expanded form until they are ready to move on.

Creative context

Look out for opportunities to perform multiplication in real-life contexts, such as getting into teams in PE, sitting on benches in the hall, giving out items such as coloured pencils to children, cooking situations and so on.

Vocabulary

brackets, column method, condensed method, equivalent, expanded method, expression, **factor**, facts, groups of, lots of, multiple multiply, **product**, short division, short multiplication, times, tables

Curriculum objectives
● To recall multiplication and division facts for multiplication tables up to 12 × 12.
● To recognise and use commutativity in mental calculations.

Success criteria
● I can write statements about the equality of expressions, for example (2 × 3) × 4 = 2 × (3 × 4).

You will need
Equipment
Long thin strips of card

Differentiation
Less confident learners
Provide children with a range of statements and support them in trying to identify whether the expressions on either side of the equals sign have the same answers.

More confident learners
Encourage children to write more complex statements (for example, where expressions are identical apart from the brackets). They could also include both multiplication and addition in a statement (14 x 2 = 10 x 2 + 4 x 2).

Lesson 1 — Oral and mental starter 12

Main teaching activities

Whole-class work: Write 24 in the centre of the board. Invite children to the front to draw spokes around the number and write some multiplication questions that have the answer 24 (2 × 12, 24 × 1, 3 × 8 and so on). When children begin to run out of expressions, discuss how more than two numbers can be used in each expression (for example, 2 × 3 × 4). When you have a wide variety, select two and write them either side of an equals sign: 2 × 12 = 4 × 2 × 3. Remind children that the equals sign is not an 'answer giver' as in the case of 3 x 4 = 12, but is actually something that shows when two expressions have the same answer or are equivalent. *Is the statement I have written true or false? Do both expressions have the same answer?* Discuss that the statement is true since 2 × 12 is equivalent to 4 × 2 × 3 as they both have the same answer. Write several more statements of this type using pairs from the board and ask children to say whether they are true or false (for example, 4 x 1 x 6 = 2 × 2 × 2 × 3). Include some false ones by adjusting the numbers slightly (4 × 2 × 3 = 3 × 2 × 8).

When children are confident in saying whether statements are true or false, write two identical expressions either side of the equals sign, such as 2 × 3 × 4 = 2 × 3 × 4. *If I draw some brackets into one of these expressions to show which part of the multiplication I do first, will it make a difference to whether the expressions are equal?* Write brackets into both sides in different positions and discuss that brackets can be used to show which calculation you do first, such as (2 × 3) × 4 = 2 × (3 × 4).

Encourage children to notice that whichever part you do first, the expressions are still equal and so the overall statement is still true. Stress that this is not true for every operation – for example, (12 ÷ 6) ÷ 2 does not equal 12 ÷ (6 ÷ 2). It is just that multiplication (and addition) have this special property.

Now write 28 on the board and begin to write multiplications around the number with the answer 28 as a lead into the paired activity.

Paired work: Ask the children to write further multiplication expressions with the answer 28 on a sheet of paper. Then provide each pair with eight long thin strips of card and ask them to write six true and two false statements on them using pairs of expressions on either side of an equals sign. Explain that this will form a class quiz.

Progress check: As children are writing their statements encourage them to use brackets in some of their expressions: *What is special about multiplication? Which of your statements are true? How do you know?*

Review

Use the questions generated by the children to form a class quiz. Choose children to stand and hold up their statements and invite the rest of the class to say whether each is true or false. Include questions with brackets and discuss any statements that children disagree about.

Curriculum objectives
● To use place value, known and derived facts to multiply and divide.
Success criteria
● I can perform mental multiplication and division.

You will need
Equipment
Counters; Blu-Tack®

Differentiation
Less confident learners
Alter the calculations to include simpler steps (more multiplications) and give children a smaller start number.
More confident learners
Children can use a different start number (say, 24).

Lesson 2   Oral and mental starter 20

Main teaching activities

Whole-class work: Display this pentangle on the board.

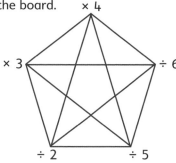

Tack a counter at one of the corners (say, on the ×4). *We are going to start with the number 20 and move this counter to different positions, always following the instruction we move to. We must try to keep going so that each answer is a whole number. Move to ÷5 [20 ÷ 5 = 4], then to ÷2 [4 ÷ 2 = 2], then to ×3 [2 x 3 = 6], and then to ÷6 [6 ÷ 6 = 1].* Show that with the multiplication you can keep going, making the number larger and larger. Repeat, starting with 20 again and beginning with the counter on a different position to start.

Paired work: Ask children to copy the diagram and play the game in pairs. Explain that they must stop if their answer goes over 100. The winner is the player who has the last turn before it is impossible to go without giving a whole number up to 100. They should record their steps. Encourage them to find the longest chain of turns that they can. If time, the calculations could be altered – for example, to ×8, ÷4, ×7, ÷3.

Progress check: Ask: *What was your longest chain of steps?*

Review

Take feedback. Invite children to recreate their longest chain of steps.

Curriculum objectives
● To multiply two-digit and three-digit numbers by a one-digit number using formal written layout.
Success criteria
● I can perform short multiplication for multiplying using multi-digit numbers.

You will need
Equipment
0–9 number cards

Differentiation
Less confident learners
If necessary, let children answer the questions using the expanded method of multiplication.
More confident learners
Give these children further multiplications in the list, such as 285 × 7, 334 × 6, 222 × 9. (Note that the answer will then change to 222 × 9.)

Lesson 3   Oral and mental starter 37

Main teaching activities

Whole-class work: Explain that the focus of today's lesson is short multiplication. Ask children to pick four digits from a set of 0–9 number cards to create a three-digit × one-digit multiplication (say, 476 × 8). Demonstrate the expanded and condensed form:

```
Th H  T  U      or      Th H  T  U
    4  7  6                  4  7  6
 ×        8              ×        8
       4  8              3  8  0  8
    5  6  0                 6  4
 3  2  0  0
 3  8  0  8
```

Pick further sets of number cards and invite children to the front to work through the examples. Encourage them to attempt the condensed form (short multiplication) and to describe the process in their own words.

Independent work: Ask children to answer the following multiplications using short multiplication and see which of them has the answer closest to 2000: 661 × 3, 548 × 4, 417 × 5, 356 × 6, 274 × 7, 328 × 8, 224 × 9. (Answer: 224 × 9)

Progress check: Ask: *Describe what you did to reach this answer?*

Review

Take feedback on multiplications the children have written. Ask them to demonstrate their working to the class.

Lesson 4 — Oral and mental starter 31

Curriculum objectives
● To use place value, known and derived facts to divide.
Success criteria
● I can use short division with exact answers when dividing by a one-digit number.

You will need
Photocopiable sheets
'Short division'
Equipment
Individual whiteboards

Differentiation
Less confident learners
Where children experience difficulties, invite a more confident child to explain their methods to the less confident learner (peer tutoring).
More confident learners
Ask children to focus on answering the last few questions of the sheet.

Main teaching activities

Whole-class work: Revise short division for three-digit numbers. Write on the board:

$$3\overline{)846}$$

Ask: *What question are we trying to solve?* (846 divided by 3) *Look at the hundreds digit. How many 3s in 8? There are two 3s with 2 left over. We write 2 above the hundreds column and carry the 2 left over. Look at the tens. We now have 24. How many 3s in 24? There are eight 3s so we write 8 and then move to the units. How many 3s in 6? There are two 3s in 6 so we write 2 to complete the answer.*

$$3\overline{)8\,^24\,6}\quad=\quad282$$

Remind children that they can multiply 282 by 3 as a means of checking their answer. Show how short multiplication can be used to check this. Demonstrate other examples in the same way (928 ÷ 4, 966 ÷ 6, 917 ÷ 7), asking children to work out the answers each time on their whiteboards.

Independent work: Give each child 'Short division' from the CD-ROM. Ask them to use short division to calculate, and short multiplication to check answers.

Progress check: Ask: *Describe what you did to reach this answer?*

Review

Invite children to write some of their divisions on the board, describing strategies they used to work each out.

Lesson 5 — Oral and mental starter 31

Curriculum objectives
● To solve problems involving multiplying and adding.
Success criteria
● I can write statements about the equality of expressions.

You will need
Equipment
Dotty paper

Differentiation
Less confident learners
Suggest children draw rectangles for smaller numbers, such as three rows of 8 or four rows of 7.
More confident learners
Ensure that children draw rectangles with more than 10 in each row, such as 17, 14, 18 and so on.

Main teaching activities

Whole-class work: Show a grid of dotty paper and draw a rectangle around eight rows of 14 dots. *How could we work out how many dots are inside this rectangle?* Ask children to suggest ways, including counting the number in each row and column.

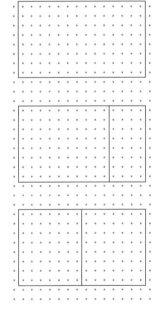

Explain that we can split the dots into groups to make them easier to count. Draw a vertical line in different positions and show how the multiplication 8 × 14 can be found by adding 8 × 10 and 8 × 4.

Discuss other ways that this could be found, such as using 8 × 7 + 8 × 7. Show that these can be written as equivalent expressions:
8 x 14 = 8 × 10 + 8 × 4 = 8 × 7 + 8 × 7. Show that the total of each expression is 112.

Paired work: Provide each pair with dotty paper. Ask them to draw a rectangle around some dots and write different expressions that could be used to find the total number of dots. For example, four rows of 12 could be
4 × 12 = 4 × 10 + 4 × 2 or 4 × 6 + 4 × 6.

Progress check: Ask: *How do you know your statement is true? Show me how you used the dots to work this out.*

Review

Take feedback. Invite children to demonstrate their findings on the board.

Fractions

Expected prior learning

Children should be able to:

- know the role of the numerator and denominator
- recognise and use fractions as numbers: unit fractions and non-unit fractions with small denominators
- recognise, find and write fractions of a discrete set of objects: unit fractions and non-unit fractions with small denominators.

Topic	Curriculum objectives	Expected outcomes
Fractions (including decimals)	**Lesson 1**	
	To solve problems involving increasingly harder fractions to calculate quantities, and fractions to divide quantities, including non-unit fractions where the answer is a whole number.	Find unit fractions of a set or quantity. Find non-unit fractions of a set or quantity.
	Lesson 2	
	To recognise and show, using diagrams, families of common equivalent fractions.	Identify pairs of equivalent fractions using multiplication or division.
	Lesson 3	
	To recognise and show, using diagrams, families of common equivalent fractions.	Identify fractions equivalent to a given fraction using division. Simplify fractions.
	Lesson 4	
	To recognise and write decimal equivalents of any number of tenths or hundredths. To add and subtract fractions with the same denominator.	Count up and down in tenths. Add and subtract fractions with the same denominator.
	Lesson 5	
	To count up and down in hundredths; recognise that hundredths arise when dividing an object by one hundred and dividing tenths by ten. To recognise and write decimal equivalents of any number of tenths or hundredths. To add and subtract fractions with the same denominator.	Count up and down in hundredths. Add and subtract fractions with the same denominator.

Preparation

Lesson 4: copy 'Tenths maths', one per child

Lesson 5: copy 'Hundredths maths', one per child

You will need

Photocopiable sheets
'Tenths maths'; 'Hundredths maths'

Equipment
Individual whiteboards; number fans; 1–10 number cards; large sheets of paper; coloured pencils

Further practice

Photocopiable sheets
'Fraction shapes'

Oral and mental starters for week 5

See bank of starters on page 210. Oral and mental starters are also on the CD-ROM.

22 Fraction action

27 Run-around fractions

38 Decimal divisions

Overview of progression

Lesson 1 includes problems that involve finding unit and non-unit fractions of quantities using division and multiplication. Lessons 2 and 3 focus on finding and identifying equivalent fractions and simplifying fractions. Lessons 4 and 5 explore tenths and hundredths and provide practice in adding and subtracting fractions with the same denominator. The link between fractions and decimals is also developed further.

Watch out for

Children develop many misconceptions about fractions that result from assuming that things that work for whole numbers will also work for fractions (for example, a fraction with a bigger number on the bottom is smaller than one with a smaller number on the bottom). It is important that children are given opportunity to talk about the differences between whole numbers, fractions and decimals to challenge these misconceptions.

Creative context

Take opportunities to link this fraction work to real-life situations, such as by asking children to describe sets of the class: *19 out of the 28 children in our class are girls* or *three quarters of our class have school dinners.*

Vocabulary

decimal, denominator, equal parts, **equivalent fraction**, **factor**, hundredth, integer, numerator, set, simplify, tenth

Curriculum objectives
- To solve problems involving increasingly harder fractions to calculate quantities, and fractions to divide quantities.

Success criteria
- I can find unit fractions of a set or quantity.
- I can find non-unit fractions of a set or quantity.

You will need

Equipment

Individual whiteboards

Differentiation

Less confident learners

Ask children to work on the first few problems in the list.

More confident learners

Ask children to work on the later, more complex, problems in the list.

Lesson 1

Oral and mental starter 22

Main teaching activities

Whole-class work: Explain that today's lesson is about finding unit fractions of sets of amounts. Explain that a man is giving his three children some money, shared equally between them. *What fraction of the money will each child get?* Establish that each will receive one third. Ask a child to write one third using fraction notation: ⅓. Ask: *How can we find one third of an amount of money?* Help children to see the link between fractions and division and show that to find one third you would divide by 3. *How much is one third of £27?* Show that one third of 27 is 9 and write ⅓ of 27 = 9. Call out similar problems: *What is one quarter of £36? What is one fifth of 60 Euros?* Ask children to write the questions and answers on their whiteboards. Emphasise that the denominator of the fraction (the bottom number) is the number you divide by as it shows how many equal groups the money is divided into.

Then revise finding non-unit fractions: *What is ¾ of £32?* Remind children that you divide to find one quarter and then multiply to find three quarters. Revise the saying *Divide for one part, then multiply for many.*

Group work: Provide each group with two or more of the following problems (which are written in order of difficulty). Ask children to work together to solve the problems and to record clearly their working and solutions so that they can show them to others.

Which is more: ¼ of 28p or ⅙ of 36p?

What is the difference between ¼ of 100cm and ⅓ of 33cm?

Omar has 60 sweets. He gave ¼ to his brother, ⅓ to his friend and ⅙ to his father. How many has he left for himself?

What is ½ of ⅕ of 250g?

What is the total of ½, ⅓ and ¼ of £24?

32 people are in a room. ¾ are adults. Of those that are not adults, ⅓ are girls. How many are boys?

I spend ⅓ of a day sleeping, 1/12 of a day eating, ⅙ of a day shopping, ¼ of a day working and the rest is leisure time. How many hours of leisure time do I have?

Progress check: Discuss the problems and solutions and ask each group to show their working. Encourage them to describe any difficulties experienced and to explain the problem-solving strategies they used.

Review

Write the following list on the board. Ask children to work out mentally which measurement is the longest and to explain why.

⅗ of 100cm   ¾ of 80cm   ⅚ of 30cm   ⅔ of 90cm   ⅝ of 40cm   7/9 of 90cm

(The solutions are 60cm, 60cm, 25cm, 60cm, 25cm, 70cm.)

Go through the questions, encouraging children to describe how they found each solution. Remind them to use estimating to check the answers. For example: *Five eighths is a bit more than one half so five eighths of 40cm must be a bit more than 20cm, so my answer of 25cm is about right.*

Curriculum objectives

● To recognise and show, using diagrams, families of common equivalent fractions.

Success criteria

● I can identify pairs of equivalent fractions using multiplication or division.

You will need

Equipment

1–10 number cards

Differentiation

Less confident learners

If necessary, provide a fraction wall to help children compare the fractions.

More confident learners

Ask children to give a third equivalent fraction when an equivalent pair is found.

Lesson 2 — Oral and mental starter 27

Main teaching activities

Whole-class work: Remind children that two fractions are equivalent when they stand for the same amount (for example, two quarters is the same as one half). Play *Snap*. Write a range of simple fractions less than 1 and their equivalents on the board. Point to two fractions at a time. Ask children to say *Snap* and snap their fingers if they are equivalent fractions. If they are not they should remain quiet. *How can you be sure when two fractions are equivalent?* Remind them that if they can multiply or divide the numerator and denominator by the same number to give the other fraction, then they are equivalent. For example, the numerator and denominator of $^{12}/_{16}$ can be divided by 4 to give the equivalent fraction ¾. Draw a 0–1 number line, and ask children to estimate the position in which each pair of equivalent fractions would go.

Paired work: Provide each pair with 1–10 number cards. Each child turns over two cards to form a fraction with the larger number on the bottom and writes it down. The positions of both fractions on a 0–1 number line are determined. A point is scored for the larger fraction. If they are equivalent, both children score a point.

Progress check: Ask: *How do you know these are equivalent? Which number can you multiply or divide both the numerator and denominator by to get this equivalent fraction?*

Review

Play *Snap* game but this time, if the fractions are not equivalent, ask children to say which of the two fractions is closer to one half/one whole/zero.

Curriculum objectives

● To recognise and show, using diagrams, families of common equivalent fractions.

Success criteria

● I can identify fractions equivalent to a given fraction using division.
● I can simplify fractions.

You will need

Equipment

Large sheets of paper; coloured pencils

Differentiation

Less confident learners

Support children by suggesting which number to divide by for the first few fractions in the paired work.

More confident learners

Ask children to choose more difficult non-unit fractions as the starting point for their pairs of equivalent fractions.

Lesson 3 — Oral and mental starter 22

Main teaching activities

Whole-class work: Ask children to imagine that there are 120 people in the school building and that 24 of them are adults. *How could we write this as a fraction?* ($^{24}/_{120}$). Point out that this fraction uses quite large numbers and it might be possible to write an equivalent fraction with smaller numbers. Remind the children that we can do this by dividing the numerator and denominator by the same number. Ask: *How can we simplify this fraction by writing an equivalent one that uses smaller numbers?* Invite children to suggest what number the numerator and denominator could be divided by.

Establish that when the numerator and denominator cannot be divided by the same factor the fraction is said to be in its *simplest form*.

Paired work: Invite children to make up a puzzle for other pairs to solve. Ask pairs to write a fraction made from two of the following numbers: 15, 20, 25, 50, 60, 75, 100, 120, 150, 200, 250, 500 (for example, $^{20}/_{60}$, $^{15}/_{150}$ or $^{75}/_{200}$). They should then simplify the fraction, writing an equivalent one that uses smaller numbers (⅓, ¹⁄₁₀ or ⅜). They do this five times and copy the ten fractions into a mixed-up arrangement on a large sheet of paper. Pairs then swap sheets and, using five different-coloured pencils, they circle those fractions that are equivalent in the same colour.

Progress check: Ask. *How can you be sure these are equivalent? What did you divide the numerator and denominator by to get this fraction?*

Review

Look at the completed puzzles and invite children to check each other's answers.

Curriculum objectives
● To recognise and write decimal equivalents of any number of tenths or hundredths.
● To add and subtract fractions with the same denominator.

Success criteria
● I can count up and down in tenths and hundredths.
● I can add and subtract fractions with the same denominator.

You will need
Photocopiable sheets
'Tenths maths'
Equipment
Individual whiteboards

Differentiation
Less confident learners
Provide children with a number line marked in tenths as fractions and as decimals to refer to.
More confident learners
Invite children to add tenths for totals greater than 1 (for example, $\frac{7}{10} + \frac{7}{10} = \frac{14}{10}$).

Main teaching activities

Whole-class work: Explain that today's lesson explores tenths. Sketch a number line from 0 to 1 with ten intervals. Point to the first interval. *What fraction of the whole line is this?* Establish that this is one tenth. *How can we write this as a fraction?* Continue in the same way for other tenths and discuss equivalent fractions for the intervals.

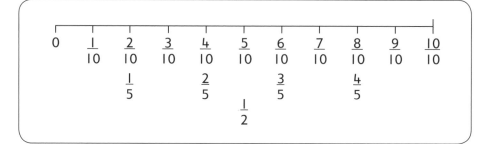

Ask the class to count on and back with you in tenths from zero. Call out addition and subtraction questions for fractions with totals up to one whole. Ask children in pairs to write their answers on their whiteboards and hold them up.

$\frac{1}{10} + \frac{1}{10} =$ $\frac{3}{10} + \frac{5}{10} =$ $\frac{4}{10} + \frac{6}{10} =$

$\frac{3}{10} - \frac{1}{10} =$ $\frac{7}{10} - \frac{2}{10} =$ $\frac{8}{10} - \frac{6}{10} =$

Draw a square and use it to demonstrate each addition and subtraction as a fraction of a square. Then ask: *Can we count in tenths in a different way?* Identify the decimal equivalents of tenths, mark them on the line, and count on and back:

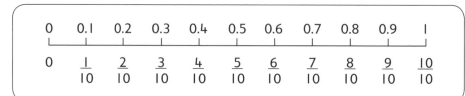

Similarly, ask questions involving adding and subtracting decimals (1dp) with totals to 1, such as 0.4 + 0.2, 0.9 − 0.3 and so on.

Independent work: Provide each child with photocopiable page 'Tenths maths' from the CD-ROM to complete.

Progress check: Ask: *When adding and subtracting fractions, what do you notice about the denominator of the answer?*

Review

Remind children that hundredths are ten times smaller than tenths. Show a number line divided into hundredths and ask: *Can you see how ten hundredths is the same as one tenth?* Count on and back in hundredths. Ask some additions and subtractions with hundredths, such as:

$\frac{8}{100} + \frac{5}{100} =$ $\frac{9}{100} + \frac{31}{100} =$

$\frac{15}{100} - \frac{6}{100} =$ $\frac{100}{100} - \frac{1}{100} =$

Explain that this decimal work will be explored further in the following lesson.

Curriculum objectives

● To count up and down in hundredths.
● To recognise and write decimal equivalents of any number of tenths or hundredths.
● To add and subtract fractions with the same denominator.

Success criteria

● I can count up and down in hundredths.
● I can add and subtract fractions with the same denominator.

You will need

Photocopiable sheets
'Hundredths maths'

Equipment
Individual whiteboards

Differentiation

Less confident learners
Provide children with a number line marked in hundredths as fractions and as decimals to refer to.

More confident learners
Ask children to simplify any fraction answers that can be written in a simpler form.

Main teaching activities

Whole-class work: Explain that today's lesson explores hundredths. Begin by reminding children how a whole square can be split into tenths, as explored in the previous lesson. Then use it to demonstrate each hundredth as a fraction of a square.

Ask the class to count on and back with you in hundredths as you point to each new section: *twenty-two hundredths, twenty-three hundredths* and so on. Record these using fraction notation ($\frac{23}{100}$).

Call out addition and subtraction questions for fractions with the denominator of 100 for with totals up to one whole. Ask children in pairs to write their answers on their whiteboards and hold them up.

$\frac{22}{100} + \frac{3}{100} =$ $\frac{13}{100} + \frac{9}{100} =$ $\frac{16}{100} + \frac{6}{100} =$

$\frac{28}{100} - \frac{1}{100} =$ $\frac{70}{100} - \frac{40}{100} =$ $\frac{100}{100} - \frac{5}{100} =$

Then ask: *Can we count in hundredths in a different way?* Identify the decimal equivalents of hundredths and show counting on in hundredths on a number line:

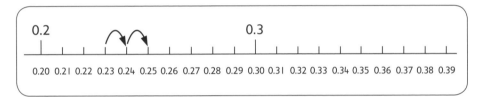

Similarly, ask questions involving adding and subtracting decimals (2dp) with totals to 1, such as 0.04 + 0.02, 0.94 − 0.03 and so on.

Independent work: Provide each child with photocopiable page 212 'Hundredths maths' to complete.

Progress check: Ask: *When adding and subtracting fractions, what do you notice about the denominator of the answer?*

Review

Discuss the work covered this week, including equivalent fractions and adding and subtracting fractions. Ask children to talk to a partner about what they have learned.

Measurement: area, perimeter and capacity

Expected prior learning

Children should be able to:

- give the common units of measure for capacity
- measure the perimeters of rectangles
- multiply and divide numbers by 1000.

Topic	Curriculum objectives	Expected outcomes
Measurement	**Lesson 1**	
	To estimate, compare and calculate different measures, including money in pounds and pence. To convert between different units of measure [for example, kilometre to metre; hour to minute].	Know metric units of capacity. Convert millilitres to litres and vice versa.
	Lesson 2	
	To estimate, compare and calculate different measures, including money in pounds and pence. To convert between different units of measure [for example, kilometre to metre; hour to minute].	Estimate and measure capacities and read scales accurately. Convert millilitres to litres and vice versa.
	Lesson 3	
	To measure and calculate the perimeter of a rectilinear figure (including squares) in centimetres and metres.	Calculate perimeters of rectilinear shapes, including sides with lengths not given.
	Lesson 4	
	To find the area of rectilinear shapes by counting.	Find the area of rectangles by counting.
	Lesson 5	
	To find the area of rectilinear shapes by counting.	Find the area of rectilinear shapes.

Preparation

Lesson 1: copy and prepare the cards from 'The witch's cauldron', per group

Lesson 2: copy 'A problem of scale', one per child

Lesson 3: copy 'Rectilinear shapes', one per child

Lesson 5: copy 'Rectilinear areas', one per child

You will need

Photocopiable sheets

'The witch's cauldron'; 'A problem of scale'; 'Rectilinear shapes'; 'Rectilinear areas'

General resources

Interactive teaching resource 'Measuring jug'; interactive teaching resource 'Pattern square'

Equipment

Individual whiteboards; one-litre measuring cylinder; variety of measuring cylinders and containers with different scales; string; scissors; rulers; squared paper

Further practice

Photocopiable sheets

'A capacity for questions'

Oral and mental starters for week 6

See bank of starters on pages 127, 208 and 209. Oral and mental starters are also on the CD-ROM.

16 Multiply by 10 and 100

24 Secret numbers

20 Bingo

12 9-times table

Overview of progression

During the first part of the week the children will be given opportunities to estimate and measure capacities, read scales and convert between litres and millilitres. In lesson 3 they will revise work on perimeters and will find perimeters of rectilinear shapes. The final two lessons of the week focus on finding areas of rectangles and rectilinear shapes, beginning initially with counting squares. Links will be made with multiplication as a means of quickly counting squares in an array.

Watch out for

The most common error in measurement topics is that children fail to write a unit at all (for example, 6 rather than 6ml or 6cm^2). Watch out for children doing this or giving the wrong unit, and draw attention to the fact that we do *not* put an s on the end of the abbreviated unit (as in 5cms).

Creative context

Link this measurement work to science activities, cooking, food products, athletics and sports fields and other areas found in real life.

Vocabulary

area, capacity, cm^2, length, litre (l), measurement, millilitre (ml), perimeter, rectangle, rectilinear, unit, width

Curriculum objectives
● To estimate, compare and calculate different measures.
● To convert between different units of measure.

Success criteria
● I know metric units of capacity.
● I can convert millilitres to litres and vice versa.

You will need

Photocopiable sheets
'The witch's cauldron'

Equipment
One-litre measuring cylinder; individual whiteboards

Differentiation

Less confident learners
If necessary, after a few minutes this group could lay the cards down and look at them.

More confident learners
When finished, ask children to answer question 2 at the top of the record sheet.

Lesson 1

Oral and mental starter 16

Main teaching activities

Whole-class work: Hold up a one-litre measuring cylinder and ask: *How many millilitres are there in a litre?* Write on the board 1 litre = 1000 millilitres. *How many millilitres are there in two litres? Three litres? How many in half a litre? Quarter of a litre? A tenth of a litre?*

Focus on a tenth of a litre. Point to the 100ml mark on the measuring cylinder and ask a child to count up in tenths from one tenth to one whole as you point to 100ml, 200ml, 300ml and so on. *If I had three tenths of a litre, how much would I need to add to make 1 litre?* Repeat with ⁴⁄₁₀, ⁵⁄₁₀ (making the link with one half), ⁶⁄₁₀, ⁷⁄₁₀, ⁸⁄₁₀ and ⁹⁄₁₀. Make the link with last week's work on fractions and decimals and show that ⁷⁄₁₀ of a litre = 0.7 litres or 700ml.

How many millilitres in 2½ litres? 3½ litres? 4½ litres? Discuss and record the answers in millilitres and then discuss different ways of recording the capacities: 2½ litres, 2.5l, 2500ml. Call out similar capacities and ask children to record each in three ways on their whiteboards and hold them up.

Group work: Arrange the children into groups of three or four. Give each group photocopiable page 'The witch's cauldron' from the CD-ROM. Ask children to use clues to find how much potion the witch is making. Within their groups the children shuffle the clue cards and deal them out, without looking at them. Once the children have been dealt their cards they can look at them but they may not show them to anyone else in the group. Explain that the children can talk about the information on the cards with other members of their group but they must not show anyone their cards or they will be out of the game. The first group to correctly find how much potion the witch is making wins.

Progress check: As children are comparing the measurements ask: *Are all the measurements the same unit? Why did you decide to do it that way? How could you change this amount into millilitres?*

Review

Go through the photocopiable sheet together. Ask: *How successfully did you work together? What did you discover about the witch's potion? Did you make sure all the units of measurement were the same?*

Curriculum objectives
● (As lesson 1).

Success criteria
● I can estimate and measure capacities accurately.
● I can convert millilitres to litres and vice versa.

You will need

Photocopiable sheets
'A problem of scale'

General resources
Interactive teaching resource 'Measuring jug'

Equipment
Variety of measuring cylinders and containers with different scales

Differentiation

Less confident learners
Children can work in pairs.

More confident learners
Challenge children to find the total capacity of the liquid shown on the sheet.

Lesson 2 — Oral and mental starter 16

Main teaching activities

Whole-class work: Pass round a range of measuring cylinders with scales on them. Ask children to look at the different types of scales and tell you the intervals between marked numbers. For example: *This scale shows every 100 millilitres from 0 to 1000 millilitres. This container holds two litres and every half litre is marked. This scale only has one litre numbered but there are ten intervals marked.*

Now display the interactive teaching resource 'Measuring jug' on the CD-ROM. Fill the jug to different levels for children to read (in steps of 500ml, 100ml or 200ml). Discuss the importance of knowing what each interval stands for. Count up in equal steps. For example: *The marks on this scale represent 50ml so to read the scale we can count in 50s from zero to the water level.*

Independent work: Give each child photocopiable page 'A problem of scale' from the CD-ROM to complete. Explain that they must read each of the three smaller scales and find the total, before marking this on the fourth scale in each set. If time, ask children to write each of the total amounts in millilitres and in litres.

Progress check: Ask: *What are the numbers in each interval? How do you know? How could you check? Count up again from zero. Do you still agree with your reading?*

Review

Fill the jug to a variety of levels on the interactive teaching resource, giving children time to discuss in pairs the capacities shown. Discuss possible answers and encourage children to convert the measurements from millilitres to litres and vice versa.

Curriculum objectives
● To measure and calculate the perimeter of a rectilinear figure in cm and m.

Success criteria
● I can calculate perimeters of rectilinear shapes, including sides with lengths not given.

You will need

Photocopiable sheets
'Rectilinear shapes'

Equipment
Individual whiteboards; string; scissors

Differentiation

Less confident learners
Provide a range of rectangles, rather than rectilinear shapes.

More confident learners
Ask children to draw their own more complex rectilinear shapes to measure lengths and find perimeters.

Lesson 3 — Oral and mental starter 24

Main teaching activities

Whole-class work: Ask: *What does the word 'perimeter' mean? How can we find the perimeter of a rectangle?* Revise that the perimeter of a rectangle can be found by finding the total of the four sides. Give examples of the dimensions of a rectangle (say, 3cm, 9cm, 3cm and 9cm) and find the perimeter $(3 + 9 + 3 + 9 = 24cm)$. Discuss that a quicker way is by adding the length and the width and then doubling $(3 + 9 = 12, 12 \times 2 = 24)$. Now draw or display a rectilinear shape:

How can we find the perimeter? Measure and mark the lengths of each side and ask children to work out the perimeter and write it on their whiteboards. Use string and scissors to show the dotted lengths along the top are equal to the dotted length below. Similarly demonstrate that the longest vertical line is equal to the two other vertical lines. Use this to find the perimeter. Draw another rectilinear shape and give some but not all of the dimensions. Encourage children to find each missing length using subtraction and then to find the perimeter.

Independent work: Give each child photocopiable page 'Rectilinear shapes' from the CD-ROM to complete.

Progress check: Ask: *How did you work out the length of this unmarked side? How did you find the total of these numbers?*

Review

Take feedback. Ask: *How did you work out the perimeter/length of this side?*

Curriculum objectives
- To find the area of rectilinear shapes by counting squares.

Success criteria
- I can find the area of rectangles by counting squares.

You will need

General resources
Interactive teaching resource 'Pattern square'

Equipment
Individual whiteboards; rulers; squared paper

Differentiation

Less confident learners
Encourage children to draw smaller rectangles and then to write a multiplication showing the number in each row and the number of rows, before finding the area.

More confident learners
Encourage children to draw larger rectangles on the squared paper and then to draw a rectangle on a plain piece of paper, measure its sides and find the area of it, using multiplication.

Lesson 4

Main teaching activities

Whole-class work: Open the interactive teaching resource 'Pattern square' on the CD-ROM. Draw a large rectangle on the grid (say, seven rows of 9), and ask children to work out the perimeter of the rectangle. Children often find this quite difficult to do unless they are given the length and width of the rectangle, as when they just count around the outside of the shape they can often miscount. Give them time to talk to a partner and agree on the perimeter before they write the answer on their whiteboards and hold them up. Discuss the answers and remind them that, as perimeter is a length, they should give an appropriate unit of length with their answer, such as cm.

Then ask: *What is the area of this rectangle? Does anyone know what 'area' is and how we measure it? Think of times when we use the word 'area' in real life?* (Penalty area, art area, dining area and so on.) Establish the meaning of the word *area* (that is, the amount of surface within a boundary or shape) and explain that we measure area by finding the number of squares or part-squares within a shape. We usually use centimetre or metre squares. Write the abbreviation for centimetre squares on the board (cm^2).

Ask children to find the area of the displayed rectangle. Discuss their strategies for finding the total number of squares quickly. For example: *If we know there are nine squares in each row and there are seven rows, what can we do to find the area more quickly than counting each square?* It is not necessary to count the squares as we can find their number by multiplying. Show some further examples of rectangles, asking children to work out the areas and write them on their whiteboards each time.

Independent work: Ask children to draw a range of rectangles on squared paper and to find the area of each shape inside it.

Progress check: During the independent work ask: *How can you find the total number of squares in this rectangle quickly? How many squares are in each row/column?*

Review

Ask: *What have we learned today? What are the different ways we can find the areas of shapes? How could we find the area of the playground? Would we use square centimetres? Or square metres?* Explain that for all rectangles we can multiply the length by the width and find the area. Demonstrate that this can be written as length x width = area (or shortened to l x w = area).

Lesson 5

Curriculum objectives
● To find the area of rectilinear shapes by counting squares.
Success criteria
● I can find the area of rectilinear shapes.

You will need
Photocopiable sheets
'Rectilinear areas'
General resources
Interactive teaching resource 'Pattern square'

Differentiation
Less confident learners
Let children work in pairs to solve the problems.
More confident learners
If time, provide children with photocopiable page 'Rectilinear shapes' and ask them to find the areas of each shape.

Main teaching activities

Whole-class work: Revise the word *area* from lesson 4. Open the interactive teaching resource 'Pattern square' on the CD-ROM. Use one colour to make a rectangle. Ask children to give the area of it and to explain their strategy for doing so. Then, using a different colour, draw a different rectangle that is touching the existing one. Ask children to find the area of the new rectangle and then, changing the colour of the tiles of the new rectangle to match the existing one, ask children to say the area of the whole (rectilinear) shape:

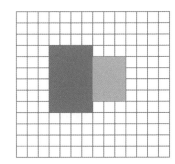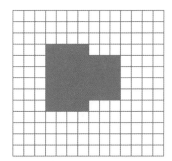

Repeat by drawing new rectilinear shapes. Ask children to think of each as two joined rectangles, to work out the area of each and add them to find the total area. Remind them to use multiplication to find the area of each and to give each area using cm^2 as the unit.

Independent work: Give each child photocopiable page 'Rectilinear areas' from the CD-ROM to complete.

Progress check: During individual work ask: *How did you work out the area of this shape? What is the total area of all the shapes shown on this sheet?*

Review

Draw a rectilinear shape on the board (not on a grid), such as:

Ask: *What is the perimeter of this shape? What is its area? How could we find out?*

Revise that the distance around the edge of a shape is the *perimeter* (cm) and the amount of space inside it is its *area* (cm^2). Say that we can measure the sides of the rectangle and add them to find its perimeter. Give dimensions of the shape in centimetres and ask children to give the perimeter. Ask: *How can we find its area if we do not have squares to count?* Explain that we could overlay a grid of centimetre squares and then count them. *If the length of the top side is 10cm, how many squares will there be in the top row?* Help children to see that we do not need to see the square to be able to work out an area and that, if we know the lengths of the side, we can use multiplication to work it out.

Curriculum objectives
● To count backwards through zero to include negative numbers.

You will need
I. Check
Oral and mental starter
30 Counting on and back

2. Assess
'Blank number lines'

3. Further practice
Oral and mental starters
24 Secret numbers
4 Units digits

Counting backwards through zero

Most children should be able to recognise negative numbers and be able to count backwards through zero and say negative numbers correctly.

Some children will not feel confident in saying negative numbers or understanding which are larger or smaller.

I. Check
30 Counting on and back

Start by counting back in 1s from 20 to beyond zero. Observe who are confident in saying negative numbers and who need further practice.
- *How do you say this number written here (−5)?*
- *Which number is 1 less than minus 3?*

2. Assess

Give children a blank number line sheet and ask them to write zero at the centre and 8 at the right-hand end. They should then write all the other numbers on the line. They should jump in 2s down from 8 to −8, writing the numbers as a sequence. Challenge the more confident to write sequences involving counting back in 3s from 9 or back in 5s from 20, to and beyond zero. If children are unsure provide them with a number line showing the numbers from 10 to −10. Ask them to say the numbers aloud and to continue the sequence further. Record the outcomes.

3. Further practice

Use the suggested OMS (choose numbers less than zero) to provide further reinforcement of counting back.

Curriculum objectives
● To round any number to the nearest 10, 100 or 1000.

You will need
I. Check
Oral and mental starter
25 Rounding round

2. Assess
0–9 number cards; blank number lines

3. Further practice
Oral and mental starters
23 Place value chains (2)
4 Units digits
24 Secret numbers

General resources
'Target grids (2)'

Rounding four-digit numbers to the nearest 1000

Most children should be able to round four-digit numbers to the nearest 1000.

Some children will not have made such progress and will require further practice in estimating and marking numbers on number lines.

I. Check
25 Rounding round

Round four-digit numbers to the nearest 1000. Observe whether children understand that the answer will always be a multiple of 1000 (such as will end in three zeroes). Extend this to rounding five-digit numbers to the nearest 1000. Again observe whether children understand that the answers will be multiples of 1000.
- *If rounding to the nearest 1000, what do we do if a number ends in 500?*
- *What is 5835 rounded to the nearest 1000?*
- *Tell me any numbers that round to 8000, when rounded to the nearest 1000.*

2. Assess

Children take turns to make a four-digit number with four 0–9 number cards and then to round each to the nearest 1000. Challenge the more confident to also round five-digit numbers to the nearest 1000. Encourage those who lack confidence to mark numbers on a number line to help them visualise which multiple of 1000 the number is closest to. Check that all children give answers that are multiples of 1000. Record the outcomes.

3. Further practice

Photocopiable page 'Target grids (2)' from the CD-ROM provides four-digit numbers to round to the nearest 1000.

Curriculum objectives
● To order and compare numbers beyond 1000.

You will need
1. Check
Oral and mental starter
24 Secret numbers

2. Assess
0–9 number cards

3. Further practice
Oral and mental starters
23 Place value chains (2)
General resources
'Target grids (2)'

Comparing and ordering four-digit numbers

Most children should be able to compare and order four-digit numbers.

Some children will not have made such progress and will require further practice in marking numbers on number lines and seeing which is larger or smaller.

1. Check
24 Secret numbers

While playing the OMS game, observe whether children are asking good questions that show an understanding of where four-digit numbers lie in relation to each other. Invite children to show the positions of the numbers in their questions on a number line and to narrow the secret number down.

- *Which is larger: 4611 or 4598? How can you tell?*
- *Tell me some numbers that lie between 5000 and 5200?*
- *Put these numbers in order: 1006, 1600, 6010, 1060?*

2. Assess

Children in a group of four take turns to make a four-digit number with four 0–9 number cards and then to place all four numbers in order, starting with the smallest. Challenge the more confident to write further numbers that lie between pairs of numbers. Let those who lack confidence work in smaller groups or pairs so that they order fewer numbers. Record the outcomes.

3. Further practice

Photocopiable page 'Target grids (2)' from the CD-ROM provides a range of four-digit numbers that can be compared or ordered.

Curriculum objectives
● To add and subtract fractions with the same denominator.

You will need
1. Check
Oral and mental starter
22 Fraction action

2. Assess
'Adding and subtracting fractions'; 'Fraction wall'

3. Further practice
Oral and mental starters
27 Run around fractions
41 Fifths of a metre

Photocopiable sheets
'Tenths maths'; 'Hundredths maths'

Adding and subtracting fractions

Most children should be able to add and subtract fractions with the same denominator.

Some children will not have made such progress and may have a limited understanding of fraction notation and the role of the numerator and denominator.

1. Check
22 Fraction action

Check to see how confident children are in saying what fraction will add to a given fraction to make the total 1. Then provide addition and subtraction questions where totals and differences lie within one whole initially, and then beyond one whole for addition. Observe which children know not to change the denominator and only add or subtract the numerator.

- What would you add to $\frac{3}{10}$ to make one whole?
- What is the sum of $\frac{2}{5}$ and $\frac{2}{5}$?
- What is $\frac{9}{10}$ take away $\frac{2}{10}$?

2. Assess

Ask children to complete photocopiable page 211 'Adding and subtracting fractions'. Children lacking confidence could be given photocopiable page 210 'Fraction wall' to refer to. Give further fractions to more confident learners, asking them to give their answers in their simplest form. Record the outcomes.

3. Further practice

The recommended oral and mental starter activities and photocopiables provide further practice in understanding the nature of fractions and adding and subtracting them.

Oral and mental starters

Number and place value

29 Place value additions and subtractions

Write the following numbers on the board in two lists:

4733	3101
5635	2032
3254	1120
4345	2233

Ask children to choose one number from each list and either add or subtract them. These should be easy calculations as they just involve increasing or decreasing digits without needing to exchange or carry.

30 Counting on and back

Arrange children into a ring and begin with a start number. Each child around the ring should say the next number according to a rule, such as counting on in 7s from zero, counting on in steps of 100g from 2 kilograms, counting back in five-minute intervals from six o'clock, and so on.

Addition, subtraction, multiplication and division

31 Factor fun

Give each child a number fan. Ask them to choose a number between 2 and 12 and to hold it up. Then call out a two-digit number (say, 35). If a child is holding up a number that is a factor of the one you have called out, then they score a point. Children then hold up a new number (or the same one if they choose), you call out another two-digit number and the game continues in this way. The winner is the child with the highest score after ten goes.

Measurement

32 Time trials

Ask true or false questions about the equivalence of pairs of times. For example, 12:15 is the same as *quarter past twelve* or 11:00pm can also be written as 23:00. If children think a statement is true they should put their thumbs up. If not, they should put thumbs down.

33 What's the time, Mr Wolf?

Write a range of times on the board in 24-hour times (16:45, 13:30, 05:15...). Call out times in words to match those on the board, such as *half past one in the afternoon, quarter past five in the morning* and ask children to point to the matching time. Then ask questions for each time: *What time is 45 minutes later than this?*

Geometry

34 I Spy

Describe a polygon that you can see in the classroom, using mathematical terms such as regular, parallel, acute, obtuse. For example: *I spy a shape with two pairs of parallel sides* or *I spy a shape with three acute angles.* Encourage children to look around the room for the shape and to make up their own I spy clues for others.

35 Mass facts

Draw a 4 × 5 rectangle on the board, with a mass in each section. For example:

Ask children to find equivalent pairs showing the same mass (for example, 0.75kg = 750g). It can be useful to draw the template on card and laminate it. New numbers can then be written whenever required.

Fraction wall

1											
$\frac{1}{2}$							$\frac{1}{2}$				
$\frac{1}{3}$			$\frac{1}{3}$			$\frac{1}{3}$					
$\frac{1}{4}$		$\frac{1}{4}$		$\frac{1}{4}$			$\frac{1}{4}$				
$\frac{1}{5}$	$\frac{1}{5}$		$\frac{1}{5}$		$\frac{1}{5}$			$\frac{1}{5}$			
$\frac{1}{6}$	$\frac{1}{6}$	$\frac{1}{6}$		$\frac{1}{6}$		$\frac{1}{6}$			$\frac{1}{6}$		
$\frac{1}{7}$	$\frac{1}{7}$	$\frac{1}{7}$	$\frac{1}{7}$		$\frac{1}{7}$		$\frac{1}{7}$			$\frac{1}{7}$	
$\frac{1}{8}$	$\frac{1}{8}$	$\frac{1}{8}$	$\frac{1}{8}$	$\frac{1}{8}$		$\frac{1}{8}$		$\frac{1}{8}$			$\frac{1}{8}$
$\frac{1}{9}$	$\frac{1}{9}$	$\frac{1}{9}$	$\frac{1}{9}$	$\frac{1}{9}$	$\frac{1}{9}$		$\frac{1}{9}$		$\frac{1}{9}$		$\frac{1}{9}$
$\frac{1}{10}$	$\frac{1}{10}$	$\frac{1}{10}$	$\frac{1}{10}$	$\frac{1}{10}$	$\frac{1}{10}$	$\frac{1}{10}$		$\frac{1}{10}$		$\frac{1}{10}$	$\frac{1}{10}$
$\frac{1}{12}$	$\frac{1}{12}$	$\frac{1}{12}$	$\frac{1}{12}$	$\frac{1}{12}$	$\frac{1}{12}$	$\frac{1}{12}$	$\frac{1}{12}$	$\frac{1}{12}$	$\frac{1}{12}$	$\frac{1}{12}$	$\frac{1}{12}$
$\frac{1}{16}$	$\frac{1}{16}$	$\frac{1}{16}$	$\frac{1}{16}$	$\frac{1}{16}$	$\frac{1}{16}$	$\frac{1}{16}$	$\frac{1}{16}$	$\frac{1}{16}$	$\frac{1}{16}$	$\frac{1}{16}$	$\frac{1}{16}$

Adding and subtracting fractions

■ Find the sums and differences of these fractions.

1. $\frac{1}{10} + \frac{3}{10} =$ ☐

2. $\frac{2}{5} + \frac{1}{5} =$ ☐

3. $\frac{1}{8} + \frac{6}{8} =$ ☐

4. $\frac{3}{7} + \frac{1}{7} =$ ☐

5. $\frac{11}{100} + \frac{6}{100} =$ ☐

6. $\frac{5}{12} + \frac{7}{12} =$ ☐

7. $\frac{10}{10} - \frac{3}{10} =$ ☐

8. $\frac{4}{5} - \frac{3}{5} =$ ☐

9. $\frac{7}{8} - \frac{6}{8} =$ ☐

10. $\frac{3}{7} - \frac{1}{7} =$ ☐

11. $\frac{82}{100} - \frac{7}{100} =$ ☐

12. $\frac{9}{9} - \frac{2}{9} =$ ☐

13. What is the sum of $\frac{22}{100}$, $\frac{9}{100}$ and $\frac{24}{100}$? _____

14. Write four pairs of fractions each with a total of 1.

I can add and subtract fractions with the same denominator.

How did you do?

Hundredths maths

■ Use the square showing hundredths to help you answer these questions.

1. $\frac{1}{100} + \frac{1}{100} =$

2. $\frac{11}{100} + \frac{5}{100} =$

3. $\frac{43}{100} + \frac{6}{100} =$

4. $\frac{73}{100} - \frac{1}{100} =$

5. $\frac{23}{100} - \frac{11}{100} =$

6. $\frac{84}{100} - \frac{16}{100} =$

7. 0.06 + 0.01 =   **8.** 0.44 + 0.03 =

9. 0.72 + 0.09 =   **10.** 0.85 − 0.03 =

11. 0.48 − 0.16 =   **12.** 0.95 − 0.15 =

13. Jo has a ribbon that is $\frac{74}{100}$ of a metre. She cuts off a piece that is $\frac{13}{100}$ of a metre. What fraction of a metre of ribbon is left?

_____

14. Mary has 0.45kg of flour. She uses 0.21kg of it. How much has she now?

_____

I can solve problems by adding and subtracting fractions with the same denominator.

How did you do?

PHOTOCOPIABLE   ■ SCHOLASTIC
www.scholastic.co.uk

Mental calculation

Expected prior learning

Children should be able to:

- rapidly recall and use addition and subtraction facts to 20
- accurately add and subtract numbers mentally, including one- and two-digit numbers
- recall and use multiplication facts for the 1, 2, 3, 4, 5, 6, 8 and 10 multiplication tables and related division facts.

Topic	Curriculum objectives	Expected outcomes
Multiplication and division	**Lesson 1**	
	To recall multiplication and division facts for multiplication tables up to 12 × 12.	Mentally multiply and divide, using knowledge of tables facts.
	To recognise and use factor pairs and commutativity in mental calculations.	
Addition and subtraction	**Lesson 2**	
	To estimate and use inverse operations to check answers to a calculation.	Solve and check mental addition and subtraction using inverses.
Multiplication and division	**Lesson 3**	
	To recall multiplication and division facts for multiplication tables up to 12 × 12.	Use tables and division facts to solve measurement problems, including decimals.
Addition and subtraction Multiplication and division	**Lesson 4**	
	To solve addition and subtraction two-step problems in contexts, deciding which operations and methods to use and why. To solve problems involving multiplying and adding, including using the distributive law to multiply two-digit numbers by one digit, integer scaling problems and harder correspondence problems such as which n objects are connected to m objects.	Solve problems involving mental addition, subtraction, multiplication and division involving one and two steps.
	Lesson 5	
	To solve addition and subtraction two-step problems in contexts, deciding which operations and methods to use and why. To solve problems involving multiplying and adding, including using the distributive law and to multiply two-digit numbers by one digit, integer scaling problems and harder correspondence problems such as which n objects are connected to m objects.	Solve problems including harder multiplication problems such as which n objects are connected to m objects.

Preparation

Lesson 1: copy 'Ten times bingo', one per group; cut out the bingo cards on the sheet, one per child

Lesson 2: copy 'Grid templates', one per child

Lesson 4: copy 'Big Wheel problems', one per child

You will need

Photocopiable sheets

'Ten times Bingo'; 'Big Wheel problems'

General resources

'Grid templates'; interactive activity 'Colour by numbers'

Equipment

Individual whiteboards; Logi-blocks (or a structured set of shapes)

Further practice

Photocopiable sheets

'Word problems'; 'Multiplication breakdown'

Oral and mental starters for week 1

See bank of starters on page 86, 208 and 250. Oral and mental starters are also on the CD-ROM.

31 Factor fun

13 Targets

37 Inverses

Overview of progression

This week, children will consolidate and extend their abilities to mentally add, subtract, multiply and divide numbers using known facts to derive new ones. They will use inverses to check their calculations and will use knowledge of multiplying and dividing numbers by 10 and 100 to solve problems involving larger numbers and decimals. Throughout the week they are given opportunities to solve problems and decide on suitable approaches to calculation.

Watch out for

Children sometimes look for trigger words when solving word problems and fail to fully interpret the situation. For example, they may see the word *times* in the question *I went swimming four times last week and five times this week. How many times did I go?* and may incorrectly give the answer 20. Encourage them to visualise the whole situation and to even sketch pictures where necessary to help them to choose the correct operation (or operations).

Creative context

Look out for opportunities to perform calculations in real-life contexts, such as number of absent children, dinner numbers, cooking situations.

Vocabulary

add, altogether, common factor, difference, divide, equals, **factor**, fewer, **inverse**, leave, less, make, minus, multiple, multiply, plus, **product**, share, sign, subtract, sum, take away, times, total, more

Curriculum objectives
● To recall multiplication and division facts for multiplication tables up to 12 × 12.
● To recognise and use factor pairs and commutativity in mental calculations.

Success criteria
● I can mentally multiply and divide, using knowledge of tables facts.

You will need
Photocopiable sheets
'Ten times bingo'

General resources
Interactive activity 'Colour by numbers'

Equipment
Individual whiteboards

Differentiation
Less confident learners
Ask children to choose questions from the first part of the list on photocopiable page 'Ten times bingo'.

More confident learners
Let children choose questions from the last part of the list.

Lesson 1
Oral and mental starter 31

Main teaching activities

Whole-class work: Open the interactive activity 'Colour by numbers' on the CD-ROM. With the class, go through the activity as a means of recognising multiples of 6, 7, 8 and 9. Discuss features of the multiples of a number (for example, noticing that multiples of 6 and 8 are always even or that the sum of the digits of multiples of 9 always add to make a multiple of 9). Revise the word *factor* and ask children to make statements, such as *72 is a multiple of 8 and 8 is a factor of 72*. Discuss common factors: *a common factor of 27 and 45 is 9 as both numbers have 9 as their factor*. Ask questions such as: *Can you give a common factor of 54 and 72? Is 7 a factor of 54? How many different factors of 64 can you think of?*

Group work: Organise the children into groups of four or five to play a game of bingo, using photocopiable page 'Ten times bingo' from the CD-ROM. Explain that one child should be the caller and should choose questions from the list on the sheet. The other children in the group should each be given one of the grids from the sheet. As questions are called out, children cross off answers on their grid. The winner is the first to get five in a line or with the most crossed off after ten minutes.

Whole-class work: Discuss the questions from the group activity together. *What number is 100 times smaller than 1900? 1000 times larger than 7? How can we use our knowledge of multiplying and dividing by 10, 100 or 1000 to solve these questions?*

Write the following multiplications on the board: 6×800, 80×90, 6000×9. Discuss that we know that 6×800 is 100 times larger than 6×8 and so on. Invite children to call out the answers and explain the tables fact that they used to work each out. Next, write these divisions: $4500 \div 9$, $1400 \div 7$, $6400 \div 8$. Discuss that there are 100 times more lots of 9 in 4500 than there are in 45 and so on.

Independent work: Ask children to choose eight of the following questions and to mentally answer them.

4×70	6×600	40×8	60×70	9×700	90×90
7000×8	120×9	1200×8	600×12	110×70	$5400 \div 6$
$4900 \div 7$	$9600 \div 8$	$6600 \div 6$	$840 \div 7$	$1080 \div 9$	$7700 \div 7$

Progress check: As children are working, ask: *How many times greater than the tables fact will this answer be? How do you know?*

Review
Take feedback and discuss questions and answers, asking children to identify the known tables fact that they used to find each answer.

Curriculum objectives
• To estimate and use inverse operations to check answers to a calculation.

Success criteria
• I can solve and check mental addition and subtraction using inverses.

You will need

General resources
'Grid templates'

Differentiation

Less confident learners
Let children work with grids containing two-digit numbers rather than three-digit multiples of 10.

More confident learners
Ask children to complete grids involving mainly the digits 5, 6, 7, 8 and 9 in the numbers requiring crossing significant boundaries (for example, 590 + 860).

Main teaching activities

Whole-class work: Explain that in this lesson children will revise mental addition and subtraction strategies. On the board draw this grid:

+	270	340	730
510			
350			
490			

Take each cell at a time and find the sum, asking children to describe the mental strategies they used. For example, for 510 + 340: *I added the five hundreds to the three hundreds and added ten to forty, to get 850*, or for 490 + 730: *I counted on 30 from 490 to get 520 and then counted on 700 more to get 1220.* Encourage children to say which methods seem easier for which questions. Add further rows to the table to provide more practice if necessary. Then draw another addition table, with missing numbers that involve using subtraction to find them. For example:

+		360	
520	680		
490			810
		1000	

Give children time in pairs to discuss how they could find the missing column headings, reminding them which numbers add to make the numbers in each cell – for example, 520 + [ ] = 680. Discuss how missing numbers can be found using the inverse of addition, which is subtraction. *So we must subtract or count on from 520 to reach 680 to find the missing number.* Ask: *Will you use addition or subtraction to find this number? Which addition or subtraction facts could you use to help you answer this?* Encourage children to use inverses to check each number: *Is it true that 520 + 160 = 680?*

Independent work: On the board draw grids for children to copy and complete, involving three-digit multiples of 10, where not all the column or row headings are given:

+		660	
	910		
580			1200
470	820		

Provide the children with photocopiable page 'Grid templates' from the CD-ROM to record the numbers and answers.

Progress check: Invite children to select several of the questions from their grids. *Which mental strategy do you think is best for each?*

Review

Ask children to describe the best strategies for finding each missing number. For example: *I used subtraction to find this number and subtracted 580 from 1200 by counting back 500 to 700 and then counting back 80 to 620.*

Curriculum objectives
- To recall multiplication and division facts for multiplication tables up to 12 × 12.

Success criteria
- I can use tables and division facts to solve measurement problems, including decimals.

Differentiation

Less confident learners

Children may require support in thinking up problems. If necessary, give them the questions from the list in the lesson and ask them to solve those.

More confident learners

Encourage these children to write more complex problems involving multi-steps and all four operations.

Lesson 3
Oral and mental starter 31

Main teaching activities

Whole-class work: Introduce the following context on the board: *A shop sells homemade cakes to a range of cafés.* Display the masses of the different cakes they make:

Sponge cake 0.4kg   Madeira cake 0.6kg   Carrot cake 0.5kg
Chocolate cake 0.8kg   Sticky toffee cake 0.7kg   Fruit cake 0.9kg

Ask several one- or two-step problems, such as:
- *A café orders six fruit cakes. What will they weigh in total?*
- *How heavy are one carrot cake and a chocolate cake together?*
- *How much heavier are six Madeira cakes than five sticky toffee cakes?*
- *A delivery of sponge cakes weighs 2.8kg. How many were delivered?*
- *A coffee shop bought one of each type of cake. How heavy was the order?*

Remind children that 0.9kg is 10 times lighter than 9kg and that if you know 9 x 6 is 54 then you know that $0.9 \times 6 = 5.4$. Encourage them to discuss the problems in pairs and to use the tables facts they know to help them work out the answers.

Group work: Ask each group to write at least five questions of their own about the information displayed on the board, and solve them.

Progress check: Invite children to share some of their problems with others. *How would you solve this problem?*

Review

Take feedback on the problems. *Which problem was the most difficult to solve? Why? Which operations did you use?*

Curriculum objectives
- To solve addition and subtraction two-step problems.
- To solve problems involving multiplying and adding.

Success criteria
- I can solve problems involving mental addition, subtraction, multiplication and division involving one and two steps.

You will need

Photocopiable sheets

'Big Wheel problems'

Differentiation

Less confident learners

Let children work in pairs to solve the problems.

More confident learners

Ask children to write at least one problem of their own using several steps.

Lesson 4
Oral and mental starter 37

Main teaching activities

Whole-class work: Discuss the following problems and ask children to say how they might answer them:
- *A train has two carriages. There are 64 seats in each carriage. How many people are on the train if there are 47 empty seats?*
- *An aeroplane has 35 rows of seats. In each row there are three seats at each side and five seats in the middle. How many seats are there in total?*

For the first, discuss whether children would add first and then subtract, double and then subtract or subtract 47 from 64 first and then add 64 to the answer. Ensure that they realise that there isn't just one way to reach a solution.
For the second question draw a simple diagram. Remind children that when multiplying you can split numbers into parts, multiply each part and then add them together. Show how you could find three lots of 35, double it and add five lots of 35, or you could find 11 lots of 35 by finding ten lots of 35 and then adding one more lot of 15. Give children time to discuss solutions with a partner and establish that the answers are 81 and 385.

Independent work: Give each child photocopiable page 'Big Wheel problems' from the CD-ROM to complete.

Progress check: Invite children to describe the approach they used to solve each problem and to say which operations they used (and in what order).

Review

Allow children time in pairs to discuss their approaches to each problem. Invite pairs who chose different approaches to explain them to the class.

Curriculum objectives

● To solve addition and subtraction two-step problems in contexts, deciding which operations and methods to use and why.
● To solve problems involving multiplying and adding, including using the distributive law and harder correspondence problems.

Success criteria

● I can solve problems including harder multiplication problems such as which n objects are connected to m objects.

You will need

Equipment

Individual whiteboards; Logi-blocks (or a structured set of shapes)

Differentiation

Less confident learners

Ask children to make six different cards, each with a number (1, 2 or 3) and each with a triangle or circle on it.

More confident learners

Challenge children to design a set with three shapes rather than two.

Main teaching activities

Whole-class work: Hold up a large yellow triangle from a structured set of shapes (such as Logi-bocks). *I have a set of shapes that come in different shapes and different colours. If there are triangles, squares, rectangles and circles and each comes in three colours, how many shapes have I in total?* Ask children to work in pairs and write the answer on their whiteboards, showing their working, and hold them up. Discuss strategies used for working out the answer - for example, sketching the different shapes and writing the colours next to them or drawing a table, including all the possibilities. *What if I had the four different shapes in four different colours?* Allow children time for discussion and invite them to say what they notice (for example, you can just multiply the two numbers together). Show how this could be written as:

shapes colours total

$4 \times 4 = 16$

Now hold up a small yellow triangle. *What if I have four shapes, four colours and all of them come in two sizes, small or large. How many shapes in total now?* Encourage children to suggest that the answer would be 32 and to explain their reasoning. Again show how this could be recorded as:

shapes colours sizes total

$4 \times 4 \times 2 = 32$

Continue in the same way, changing the numbers and then introducing another criterion such as thickness: *What if I have four shapes, five colours, three sizes and two thicknesses, thin or thick. How many shapes in total now?* Discuss ways of multiplying the numbers together, reminding children that multiplication can be done in any order. For example, $4 \times 5 \times 3 \times 2$ can be solved by multiplying the 5×2 and the 3×4 and then multiplying 10 by 12 to give 120.

Paired work: Ask children to design their own set of playing cards, where no two cards are the same. Each card has the number 1, 2 or 3 on it, each card has a triangle or a circle on it and the shapes are coloured either red or blue. Explain that they must draw each of the possible cards on paper and show, using multiplication, that they have found all the possibilities.

Progress check: Ask: *How do you know you have found all the combinations? How can you be certain? Can you give me a multiplication statement to prove that you have found them all?*

Review

Take feedback on the activity. Invite children to show and compare their cards.

Measurement and decimals

Expected prior learning

Children should be able to:

- give the common units of measure for length, mass and capacity
- count up and down in tenths; recognise that tenths arise from dividing an object into ten equal parts and in dividing one-digit numbers or quantities by 10
- multiply and divide numbers by 10, 100 and 1000.

Topic	Curriculum objectives	Expected outcomes
Fractions (including decimals) Measurement	**Lesson 1**	
	To recognise and write decimal equivalents of any number of tenths or hundredths.	Recognise decimal equivalents of any number of tenths or hundredths.
	To recognise and write decimal equivalents to ¼; ½; ¾.	Recognise and write decimal equivalents to ¼; ½; ¾.
	To convert between different units of measure [for example, kilometre to metre; hour to minute].	Use decimal measurements and convert them to other units.
	Lesson 2	
	To convert between different units of measure [for example, kilometre to metre; hour to minute].	Convert between metric units of measure (smaller to larger units) by dividing by 10 and 100.
	To find the effect of dividing a one- or two-digit number by 10 and 100, identifying the value of the digits in the answer as ones, tenths and hundredths.	
	To solve simple measure and money problems involving fractions and decimals to two decimal places.	
	Lesson 3	
	To convert between different units of measure [for example, kilometre to metre; hour to minute].	Know units of length and their abbreviations. Know relationships between units of length and can convert between them.
	Lesson 4	
	To convert between different units of measure [for example, kilometre to metre; hour to minute].	Convert decimal measurements from a larger metric unit to a smaller one.
	To recognise and write decimal equivalents to ¼; ½; ¾.	Estimate, compare and calculate different measures.
	To solve simple measure and money problems involving fractions and decimals to two decimal places.	
	Lesson 5	
	To estimate, compare and calculate different measures, including money in pounds and pence.	Solve measurement problems with measurements given in different units.
	To solve simple measure and money problems involving fractions and decimals to two decimal places.	Convert between units and compare them.

Preparation

Lesson 1: prepare cards cut out from 'Length cards', one set per pair

Lesson 3: copy 'Length word problems' per pair

You will need

Photocopiable sheets
'Length word problems'

General resources
'Length cards'; interactive activity 'Length'

Equipment
Individual whiteboards; metre stick; place value chart; rulers

Further practice

Photocopiable sheets
'Standard units for length'

Oral and mental starters for week 2

See bank of starters on page 126 and 251. Oral and mental starters are also on the CD-ROM.

16 Multiply by 10 and 100

39 Divide by 10 and 100

Overview of progression

During this week the children will revise, consolidate and extend their knowledge of units of measurement and, in particular, will strengthen their understanding of the use of decimals in measurement. They will estimate and compare decimal measures and will convert from one unit to another in different metric measurement topics. Lesson 1 involves measurements given as fractions, decimals or whole numbers including centimetres and metres. Lesson 2 explores dividing by 10 and 100 to convert metric units of length from a smaller to a larger unit. In Lesson 3 children solve problems involving lengths in different units. Lessons 4 and 5 include other measurement topics, such as mass and capacity, and children are given opportunities to create and solve measurement problems at the end of the week.

Watch out for

Watch out for children whose understanding of place value is not secure, as much of the work during this week involves using known number facts and multiplying or dividing them by a power of ten, hundred or thousand. Such children can be reminded to write multiples of 10, 100 or 1000 as multiplication statements, such as $40 = 4 \times 10$, $6800 = 8 \times 100$ and so on, to reinforce these ideas.

Creative context

Link this measurement work to science activities, cooking, athletics and other sporting activities.

Vocabulary

capacity, centimetres (cm), convert, decimal, gram (g), hundredth, kilogram (kg), kilometre (km), length, litre (l), mass, measurement, metre (m), millilitre (ml), millimetre (mm), tenth, unit

■**SCHOLASTIC**

Curriculum objectives

• To recognise and write decimal equivalents of any number of tenths or hundredths.
• To recognise and write decimal equivalents to ¼; ½; ¾.
• To convert between different units of measure.

Success criteria

• I can recognise decimal equivalents of any number of tenths or hundredths.
• I can recognise and write decimal equivalents to ¼; ½; ¾.
• I can use decimal measurements and convert them to other units.

You will need

General resources

'Length cards'

Equipment

Metre stick

Differentiation

Less confident learners

Provide children with digit cards and a place value chart showing the column headings T U . t. They can make each number and then divide it by 10 to convert it from millimetres to centimetres.

More confident learners

Encourage children to choose two- or three-digit numbers to convert from millimetres to centimetres, or centimetres to metres.

Lesson 1

Oral and mental starter 16

Main teaching activities

Whole-class work: Play the game 'Think of a number'. Explain that you are thinking of a number between zero and 1 (say, 0.75). Invite children to make suggestions as to the nature of the secret number, it could be a fraction or a decimal. By asking questions that you can only answer *yes* or *no* to, they should try to guess the number using as few questions as possible. Encourage them to ask good questions which narrow down the possibilities most effectively. For example, *Is it larger than 0.5?* is more helpful than the question *Is it 0.26?* Gradually get closer to the number until children have found out that it is higher than 0.7 but lower than 0.8. Ask: *What numbers are between 0.7 and 0.8?* Write a list (0.71, 0.72, 0.73... 0.79) or show it on a number line and identify the number chosen for the game.

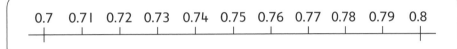

0.7   0.71   0.72   0.73   0.74   0.75   0.76   0.77   0.78   0.79   0.8

Remind children that when we measure, we sometimes need to use decimals including tenths, such as 0.75m. *How long would a line be that is 0.75m?* Show this length on a metre stick and ask children to explain what the digit 7 stands for (seven tenths of a metre) and the digit 5 (five hundredths of a metre). *How can we describe 0.75m in a different way?* (¾m or 75cm) Remind children that, because there are 100cm in each metre, 1cm is one hundredth of a metre or 0.01m. Give other fraction or decimal amounts of a metre, each time asking children to give it in a different way – for example, 0.84m = 84cm.

Paired work: Give each pair a set of cards cut out from photocopiable page 'Length cards' from the CD-ROM. Ask them to arrange the cards into equivalent groups, one showing a fraction of a metre, another showing a decimal in metres and another showing the equivalent length in centimetres. Children could also take turns to pick a card and say its equivalents, in the same way.

Progress check: Invite children to read out the measurement equivalents. For example: *23 centimetres is the same as 0.23m, which is twenty-three hundredths of a metre.*

Review

Take feedback on the activity. Call out simplified fractions of a metre to discuss, such as: *one tenth of a metre, three quarters of a metre, one fifth of a metre, two fifths of a metre* and so on. Invite children to say how each would be written as a decimal in metres (0.1m, 0.75m, 0.2m, 0.4m...) and then to give each length in centimetres. Introduce some lengths greater than one metre, such as 1.13m or 2.99m. Ask children to describe the lengths and give them in centimetres.

Curriculum objectives
● To convert between different units of measure.
● To find the effect of dividing a one- or two-digit number by 10 and 100, identifying the value of the digits in the answer as ones, tenths and hundredths.
● To solve simple measure problems involving decimals.

Success criteria
● I can convert between metric units of measure (smaller to larger units) by dividing by 10 and 100.

You will need
Equipment
Metre stick; place value chart

Differentiation
Less confident learners
Give children digit cards and a place value chart showing the column headings H T U . t h. They can make each number and then divide it by 10 or 100 to convert it from the smaller unit to the larger one.

More confident learners
Children can explore converting lengths in metres to kilometres in the same way, dividing by 1000.

Main teaching activities

Whole-class work: As for lesson 1, play the game 'Think of a number', starting with a number between zero and 100 – but do not say that it is a decimal (say, 34.7). By asking questions that you can only answer *yes* or *no* to, children should try to guess the number using as few questions as possible. Encourage them to ask good questions which narrow down the possibilities most effectively. For example, *Is it larger than 50?* is more helpful than the question *Is it 26?* Gradually get closer to the number until children have found out that it is higher than 34 but lower than 35. *What numbers are between 34 and 35?* Invite children to make suggestions as to the nature of the number: it could involve fractions such as 34½ or a decimal such as 34.5. *Which numbers with tenths lie between 34 and 35?* Write a list: 34.1, 34.2, 34.3... 34.9 and identify the number chosen for the game.

Remind children that when we measure we sometimes need to use decimals including tenths (for example, 34.7cm). *How long would a line be that is 34.7cm?* Show it on a metre stick and ask children to explain what the *point seven* stands for (seven tenths of a cm). *How can we describe seven tenths of a centimetre in a different way?* (7mm)

Remind children that, because there are 10mm in each centimetre, 1mm is one tenth of a centimetre or 0.1cm. Show the following table and explain that we can divide the number of millimetres by 10 to give the number of centimetres:

mm ⟶ ÷ 10 ⟶ cm

1mm	0.1cm
7mm	0.7cm
15mm	1.5cm
347mm	34.7cm

Use a simple place value chart to show how the digits move across to the right one place when dividing by 10.

Repeat for converting from cm into metres, such as:

cm ⟶ ÷ 100 ⟶ m

1cm	0.01m
7cm	0.07m
15cm	0.15m
347cm	3.47m

Again use a simple place value chart to show how the digits move across to the right two places when dividing by 100.

Practise a number of conversions together, reinforcing the units and stating each as an equivalence. For example: 120 *centimetres is the same as* 1.2 *metres*.

Paired work (ability grouped): Ask children to draw simple table headings like those above, mm ⟶ cm, cm ⟶ m. They take it in turns to write a measurement and their partner converts it to the larger unit.

Progress check: Invite children to read out the numbers from their tables as measurement equivalents: *35 centimetres is the same as 0.35 metres*.

Review
Ask children to call out measurements from their tables for others in the class to convert to a larger unit.

Curriculum objectives
● To convert between different units of measure.

Success criteria
● I can identify units of length and their abbreviations.
● I know relationships between units of length and can convert between them.

You will need
Photocopiable sheets
'Length word problems'
General resources
Interactive activity 'Length'
Equipment
Individual whiteboards

Differentiation
Less confident learners
Provide children with a list showing the length relationships.
More confident learners
Give children some three-digit numbers to write problems of length about.

Lesson 3 — Oral and mental starter

Main teaching activities

Whole-class work: Begin the lesson with a revision of all the metric units of length and the relationships between them. Invite children to say how many of one unit make up another and build a list on the board: 10mm = 1cm, 100cm = 1m, 1000m = 1km. Discuss words used to describe length, such as height, width, perimeter, distance, radius, circumference, depth, thickness, diameter, breadth, and discuss the slightly different uses we have for these terms.

Work together through each of the screens of the interactive activity 'Length' on the CD-ROM. Invite children in pairs to write each answer on their whiteboards and hold them up. Revise multiplying and dividing numbers by 10, 100 and 1000, such as 12mm = 1.2cm, 1.4m = 140cm and so on.

Paired work: Give each pair photocopiable page 'Length word problems' from the CD-ROM. Ask them to discuss each problem and solve it, reminding them that some questions include information that is not required for finding the solution.

Progress check: As children are working, ask: *How many millimetres/centimetres/metres make up one centimetre/metre/kilometre? What about half/one quarter/three quarters of a metre/kilometre?*

Review

Ask some children to make up and call out measurements and invite the others to say (a) how you would write it using a different unit and (b) what this might be measuring. For example:

| 0.6 metres | (a) 60 cm | (b) the depth of a bath |
| 160 centimetres | (a) 1.6 cm | (b) the height of teacher |

Curriculum objectives
● To convert between different units of measure.
● To recognise and write decimal equivalents to ¼; ½; ¾.
● To solve simple measure problems involving decimals to two decimal places.

Success criteria
● I can convert decimal measurements from a large metric unit to a smaller one.
● I can estimate, compare and calculate different measures.

Differentiation
Less confident learners
Provide children with measurements such as 2.1km, 3.4kg, 2.5 l and ask them to convert each to metres, grams or millilitres.
More confident learners
Encourage children to write measurements with two decimal places.

Lesson 4 — Oral and mental starter 39

Main teaching activities

Whole-class work: Display a number line from 0 to 4:

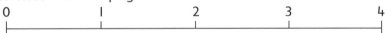

Put an arrow at 2½. *If this line was a scale measuring kilograms, what would the arrow be pointing to?* Discuss that this could be written as 2½kg or 2.5kg. *What if we want to show the mass in grams rather than kilograms?* Revise that 1000g = 1kg and that 2.5kg is 2500g. Now place the arrow at 3.1 and ask: *If this line was a scale measuring centimetres, what would the arrow be pointing to?* Discuss that this could be written as 3.1cm or 31mm.

Draw the same line vertically (with zero at the bottom) and place an arrow at a quarter of the way between two whole numbers (say, at 1¼). *If this line was a scale measuring litres, what would the arrow be pointing to?* Discuss that this could be written as 1¼ l or 1.25 l. *What if we want to show the capacity in millilitres rather than litres?* Revise that 1000ml = 1 l and that 1.25 l is 1250ml. Repeat for other positions of the arrows and using different units (for example, kilometres and metres).

Independent work: Ask children to write at least eight decimals that lie between 0 and 4. They choose one of the following units for each decimal: metres, kilometres, kilograms or litres. They then write each measurement in a different unit (centimetres, metres, grams or millilitres).

Progress check: *Which numbers do you find most difficult to convert? Why?*

Review

Ask children to read out some of their pairs of measurements for others to check.

Curriculum objectives
● To estimate, compare and calculate different measures.
● To solve simple measure problems involving fractions and decimals to two decimal places.

Success criteria
● I can solve measurement problems with measurements given in different units.
● I can convert between units and compare them.

You will need
Equipment
Rulers

Differentiation
Less confident learners
Give children specific problems to solve from the list given.

More confident learners
Encourage children to write problems that involve calculating with the measurements, such as: *I put three of the hockey balls in a bag. What is their total mass?*

Main teaching activities

Whole-class work: Explain that today children will solve measurement problems. Present the following information to the class:

Ball	Diameter	Mass
Tennis ball	64mm	59g
Hockey ball	7.3cm	158g
Football	0.23m	0.5kg
Volleyball	21.4cm	¼ kg
Snooker ball	53mm	121g
Table tennis ball	3.8cm	3g
Cricket ball	7cm	0.156kg
Squash ball	0.04m	25g

Ask: *What information does this show?* Discuss that the diameter means the widest point across a ball from side to side. *What do you notice about the units of measurement?* (They are not all the same.) Discuss several of the diameters and invite children to give them in the same unit of measurement and to compare them. For example:

● the diameter of the snooker ball and the table tennis ball (change both to mm or cm)
● the squash ball and the cricket ball (change both to cm or m)
● the football and the volleyball (change both to cm or m).

Stress that it is very important to do this to enable them to be compared properly.

Repeat for pairs of the masses (for example, the cricket ball and the snooker ball), converting both to g or kg.

Ask: *What questions could we ask about this information?* Invite children to discuss in pairs questions that could be asked about the balls and ask them to suggest them to the class. For example:

● *Which is larger, the tennis ball or the snooker ball? By how much?*
● *How many millimetres larger is the hockey ball than the cricket ball?*
● *Which ball is the heaviest/lightest?*
● *Which ball is the largest/smallest?*
● *Which ball is 2g lighter than the hockey ball?*

Group work: Ask each group to write and solve as many questions as they can about the information. Also ask them to use rulers to draw lines to show some of the diameters of the balls.

Progress check: Ask children to show the methods and checking approaches they used to solve each problem. *How did you decide what to do? Did you need to change the unit of measurement? What did you change it from/to? How did you do that?*

Review

Ask groups to read out their favourite problem for the rest of the class to solve. *Which problem was the most difficult to solve? Why? For which problems did you need to change the unit of measurement?* Encourage children to summarise the strategies used this week and to explain how these were applied in this problem-solving work.

Addition and subtraction: written methods

Expected prior learning

Children should be able to:

- rapidly recall and use addition and subtraction facts to 20
- recognise the place value of each digit in four-digit numbers
- accurately add and subtract numbers mentally including one-, two- and three-digit numbers.

Topic	Curriculum objectives	Expected outcomes
Addition and subtraction	**Lesson 1**	
	To add and subtract numbers with up to 4-digits using the formal written methods of columnar addition and subtraction where appropriate. To estimate and use inverse operations to check answers to a calculation.	Add lists of numbers, using a column method of addition. Estimate to check.
	Lesson 2	
	To add and subtract numbers with up to 4-digits using the formal written methods of columnar addition and subtraction where appropriate. To estimate and use inverse operations to check answers to a calculation.	Add longer lists of numbers, using a column method of addition. Estimate to check.
	Lesson 3	
	To add and subtract numbers with up to 4-digits using the formal written methods of columnar addition and subtraction where appropriate.	Add and subtract numbers with up to four-digits using columnar addition and subtraction.
	Lesson 4	
	To add and subtract numbers with up to 4-digits using the formal written methods of columnar addition and subtraction where appropriate.	Add and subtract numbers with up to four-digits using columnar addition and subtraction.
	Lesson 5	
	To solve addition and subtraction two-step problems in contexts, deciding which operations and methods to use and why.	Solve two-step money problems involving addition and subtraction, choosing an appropriate and effective calculation method.

Preparation

Lesson 3: prepare 'Target grids (2)' for display on the interactive whiteboard

Lesson 5: prepare 'Oceans, seas and rivers' for display on the interactive whiteboard

You will need

Photocopiable sheets
'Oceans, seas and rivers'

General resources
'Target grids (2)'

Equipment
Individual whiteboards

Further practice
Provide further practice of finding differences using real-life data, for example:
- heights of the tallest mountains
- capacities of football grounds
- average weight of different animals.
Information for all of these can be searched on the internet.

Oral and mental starters for week 3

See bank of starters on pages 167, 208 and 286. Oral and mental starters are also on the CD-ROM.

| 13 | Targets |

| 25 | Rounding round |

| 29 | Place value additions and subtractions |

Overview of progression

During the week children will be given extensive opportunity to practise written methods of addition and subtraction and to use the column methods to solve problems involving money and measures. Lessons 1 and 2 involve adding lists of numbers, including estimating to check. In lesson 3 children will add and subtract four-digit numbers and make and use estimates to check whether answers are sensible. During lessons 4 and 5 children solve and create one- and two-step money and measurement problems, involving adding and subtracting four-digit numbers.

Watch out for

Ensure that children are confident in place value ideas and that they understand the value of each digit in four-digit numbers. This will help them with written methods of addition and subtraction, as it can help them appreciate the place value implications of why we carry and exchange.

Creative context

Use written addition and subtraction in other areas of the curriculum, such as in science or cooking activities.

Vocabulary

add, altogether, carry, column, difference, digit, equals, exchange, fewer, **inverse**, leave, less, make, minus, more, partition, plus, sign, subtract, sum, take away, total

■SCHOLASTIC

Curriculum objectives
● To use a written column method of addition.
● To estimate and use inverses to check answers to a calculation.

Success criteria
● I can add lists of numbers, using a column method of addition.
● I can estimate to check.

You will need

Equipment

Individual whiteboards

Differentiation

Less confident learners

Give children a smaller total length and ask them to add fewer numbers in each list.

More confident learners

Give children a higher total length or ask them to check their answers using written methods of multiplication and addition.

Lesson 1 — Oral and mental starter 13

Main teaching activities

Whole-class work: Introduce the context for today's lesson on addition as follows: *A company is putting kerb-stones along the edges of pavements at the sides of roads.* Sketch a simple plan of a road and piece of kerb, as shown here:

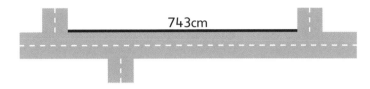

743cm

Explain that kerb-stones come in three different lengths: 95cm, 128cm and 189cm. *Which lengths of kerb-stone could be used for this length? How could we find out?* Remind children to estimate, by rounding numbers first. For example: *If we used just the small kerb-stones we could round 95 to 100 and can estimate that we would use about seven of them because 100cm × 7 = 700cm. If we used just the large kerb-stones we could round 189 to 200 and can estimate that we would use about four of them because 200cm × 4 = 800cm.* Explain that the company do not want to use up all of one type of kerb-stone so they want to have a mix of them. List the vertical additions shown below (without the answers) on the board. Ask children to use estimation to work out which of the sets of kerb-stones would be most appropriate for the length of kerb: 100 + 100 + 130 + 130 + 200 = 660, 100 + 130 + 130 + 200 + 200 = 760, 100 + 130 + 200 + 200 + 200 = 830. Discuss how each of the numbers has been rounded up so the answers will be smaller than each of the estimates. Encourage children to make a prediction and then add the numbers together. They should work out each answer on their whiteboards, using a written method:

H T U	H T U	H T U
9 5	9 5	9 5
9 5	1 2 8	1 2 8
1 2 8	1 2 8	1 8 9
1 2 8	1 8 9	1 8 9
+ 1 8 9	+ 1 8 9	+ 1 8 9
6 3 5	7 2 9	7 9 0
3 3	3 3	3 4

Discuss that the second option is the best, but that there might be a better option. Give children a few minutes to select stone sizes and see if they can get to an answer closer to 743 cm.

Independent work: Explain that the company is changing the kerb-stones it uses and that they now come in the following four sizes: 98cm, 126cm, 157cm and 194cm. List them on the board. Ask children to use a written method to investigate the best option of stones that they should use for a length of kerb that is 832cm long. Ask them to write lists of the stones that could be used and make estimates first as to which option they think will be best. Stress that they should use at least one of each stone in each list.

Progress check: Invite children to discuss their investigation. *What numbers did you try in each list? What estimates did you make? Did you develop any strategies for speeding up your adding?*

Review

Take feedback. Ask children to share their answers and to demonstrate their written methods. Discuss which of the solutions they think was the best option and why they think that.

Curriculum objectives

Curriculum objectives
● To use a written column method of addition.
● To estimate and use inverses to check answers to a calculation.

Success criteria
● I can add longer lists of numbers, using a column method of addition.
● I can estimate to check.

You will need

Equipment
Individual whiteboards

Differentiation

Less confident learners
Give children a smaller total mass (say, 6742g) and ask them which four tins have that total (not every tin type needs to be used).

More confident learners
Give these children a higher total mass (or ask them to check their answers using written methods of multiplication and addition).

Lesson 2 — Oral and mental starter 25

Main teaching activities

Whole-class work: Following on from the previous lesson on adding lists of numbers, introduce the following context: *A hardware store sells tins of paint in different sizes. The tins, when full, weigh 957g, 1348g, 2119g and 3275g.* List these on the board. *A fork-lift truck lifts a box that contains five paint tins. How much might this box weigh?* (Tell the class to ignore the weight of the cardboard box.) Ask children to write the masses of five tins of their choice on their whiteboards and to set them out as a column addition. Remind them to use estimation first to work out the approximate total mass, and then to use the written method to find the total. Take feedback on the different answers and ask: *Which of the total masses that we have found is closest to 9050g?*

Independent work: Using the same masses for the paint tins, ask children to investigate which six tins would have a total mass closest to 12,300g. (Answer: $957g + 1348g \times 2 + 2119g + 3275g \times 2 = 12,322g$.)

Progress check: Invite children to discuss their investigation. *What numbers did you try in each list? What estimates did you make? Did you develop any strategies for speeding up your adding?*

Review

Draw attention to strategies used for making it easier to add digits in each column, for example looking for pairs of numbers that total 10, and ask children to give the estimates they used for each number. Discuss any different estimates used and demonstrate an approach to checking, e.g. using their estimates or adding numbers in a different order.

Curriculum objectives
● To add and subtract four digit numbers using columnar methods.
● To estimate and use inverses to check answers to a calculation.

Success criteria
● I can add and subtract numbers, using column methods.

You will need

General resources
'Target grids (2)'

Equipment
Individual whiteboards

Differentiation

Less confident learners
Let children choose numbers from the first grid.

More confident learners
Ask children to choose pairs of numbers from the third grid to provide a greater challenge.

Lesson 3 — Oral and mental starter 25

Main teaching activities

Whole-class work: Display photocopiable page 'Target grids (2)' from the CD-ROM on the interactive whiteboard. Show the first grid. *Which two numbers from this grid have a total of 7009 and a difference of 1359?* Give children time in pairs to try to solve this puzzle, recording their workings on their whiteboards. Stress the importance of making estimates first rather than just trying different pairs of numbers. If no children have discovered the two numbers, tell them that the numbers are 4184 and 2825. Invite them to demonstrate the written column methods of addition and subtraction that they used on the board and revise carrying and borrowing.

Paired work: Now ask children to choose pairs of numbers from the second grid, to find their sum and difference to create several puzzles of their own. For example: *We have a total of 5863 and a difference of 1901. Which numbers are we?*

Progress check: Invite children to discuss the calculations. *How did you work this out? How could you check that you answered this correctly?*

Review

Invite children to give their own puzzles and give time for the rest of the class to find the solutions. Discuss again how estimation can be used to narrow down many of the possibilities. Encourage children to demonstrate their written methods on the board.

Curriculum objectives
• To add and subtract numbers with up to four digits using columnar addition and subtraction.

Success criteria
• I can add and subtract numbers, using column methods.

You will need

Equipment
Individual whiteboards

Differentiation

Less confident learners
Let these children work in pairs to solve the problems.

More confident learners
Challenge children to also find the totals of the amount that each pair won and the amount that all the people won in total.

Lesson 4   Oral and mental starter 29

Main teaching activities

Whole-class work: Introduce the following problem and ask children to work with a partner to solve it, using addition and or subtraction: *Al and Sal both won over £5000 each in a lottery draw. Al won £2367 more than Sal. Sal won £268 less than £7000. How much did they each win?* Discuss the strategies that could be used to solve the problem (for example, subtracting £268 from £7000, using a mental or written method to find Sal's amount and then adding £2367 to the answer to find Al's amount). Provide similar problems such as those below, but with different numbers. Discuss the methods and solutions and remind children of the importance of estimating and using inverses to check their answers.

Independent work: Display these questions for children to answer:

• Jenny won £1531 less than Benny. Benny won £253 less than £9000. How much did they each win?
• Maisy won £1568 more than Daisy. The amount Daisy won can be written using the digits 3 and 8. The total amount they won altogether was £8244. How much did they each win?
• Jill and Bill together won £11,486, each winning over £5000. Bill won an amount that could be written with four identical digits. How much did they each win?

(Answers: Benny £8747, Jenny £7216, Maisy £4906, Daisy £3338, Jill £5931, Bill £5555.)

Progress check: Invite children to explain the strategies they used to solve the problems.

Review

Take feedback. Invite children to show some of their written calculations on the board.

Curriculum objectives
• To solve addition and subtraction two-step problems in contexts.

Success criteria
• I can solve two-step measurement problems involving addition and subtraction.

You will need

Photocopiable sheets
'Oceans, seas and rivers'

Differentiation

Less confident learners
Give children suggestions for questions they could answer.

More confident learners
Invite children to write questions that involve multiple steps.

Lesson 5   Oral and mental starter 29

Main teaching activities

Whole-class work: Display photocopiable page 'Oceans, seas and rivers' from the CD-ROM on the interactive whiteboard, covering the two rounding columns and just showing the depths and lengths. Explain that, in groups, you would like children to write a range of different questions about these oceans, rivers and seas to form part of a class quiz. Give examples of questions they could write, such as:

- *How much deeper is the Indian Ocean than the Arabian?*
- *Which ocean is 2599m deeper than the Mediterranean Sea?*
- *What is the length of the Nile and the Amazon altogether?*
- *Which river is 724km longer than the Mississippi?*
- *What is the length of the longest three rivers put together?*

Group work: Ask each group to write at least five questions using the information on the sheet and answer them, using written methods.

Whole-class work: Do a quiz using questions from each group. Points can be scored for correct answers. Remind the children that inverse operations can be used to check answers.

Progress check: Ask: *What questions can you think of that would use subtraction? Which would use addition?*

Review

Take feedback on the problems. *Which problem was the most difficult to solve? Why?*

Multiplication and division: mental and written methods

Expected prior learning

Children should be able to:

● recall and use multiplication facts for the 1, 2, 3, 4, 5, 6, 8 and 10 multiplication tables and related division facts

● write and calculate mathematical statements for multiplication and division, using mental methods.

Topic	Curriculum objectives	Expected outcomes
Multiplication and division	**Lesson 1**	
	To recall multiplication and division facts for multiplication tables up to 12 × 12. To recognise and use factor pairs and commutativity in mental calculations.	Recognise and use factors and commutativity in mental multiplication.
	Lesson 2	
	To use place value, known and derived facts to multiply and divide, including: multiplying by 0 and 1; dividing by 1; multiplying together three numbers.	Derive new facts using known facts to multiply by 9, 11, 21 and 19.
	Lesson 3	
	To multiply two-digit and three-digit numbers by a one-digit number using formal written layout.	Perform short multiplication for multiplying by 7.
	Lesson 4	
	To use place value, known and derived facts to multiply and divide, including: multiplying by 0 and 1; dividing by 1; multiplying together three numbers.	Use short division with exact answers when dividing by a one-digit number and can use short multiplication to check.
	Lesson 5	
	To solve problems involving multiplying and adding, including using the distributive law to multiply two-digit numbers by one digit, integer scaling problems and harder correspondence problems such as which n objects are connected to m objects.	Solve one and two-step problems involving multiplication.

■SCHOLASTIC

Preparation

Lesson 5: copy 'Tiling problems', one per child

You will need

Photocopiable sheets
'Tiling problems'
General resources
Interactive teaching resource 'Multiplication square'
Equipment
Individual whiteboards; 0–9 number cards

Further practice

Give regular practice of 12 x 12 table facts using the interactive teaching resource 'Multiplication square'.

Oral and mental starters for week 4

See bank of starters on pages 208, 250 and 251. Oral and mental starters are also on the CD-ROM.

31 Factor fun

40 7-times table revision

37 Inverses

Overview of progression

During this week the children will develop their understanding of the nature of multiplication and division and will extend their abilities to mentally multiply and divide and use short multiplication and division. In lesson 1 they explore the commutative nature of multiplication and use factors to help them multiply mentally. In lesson 2 the focus is on multiplying by 9, 11, 21 and 29 using multiplying by 10 as a first step. Lessons 3 and 4 involve practising short multiplication and short division respectively and in lesson 5 children will solve problems and use arrays to further explore the distributive nature of multiplication and addition.

Watch out for

It is vital that children are able to recall multiplication and division facts related to the times tables in order to successfully master short multiplication and division. Where children lack confidence in this, they can initially be provided with a multiplication table square to refer to when learning the written methods. Where children struggle with using the condensed forms of short multiplication and short division they can continue to work on the expanded form until they are ready to move on.

Creative context

Look out for opportunities to perform multiplication in real-life contexts, such as getting into teams in PE, sitting on benches in the hall, giving out items such as coloured pencils to children, cooking situations, and so on.

Vocabulary

array, equivalent, column method, condensed method, expanded method, **factor,** facts, **inverse**, groups of, lots of, multiple, multiply, **product**, short division, short multiplication, tables, times

Curriculum objectives

● To recall multiplication and division facts for multiplication tables up to 12×12.
● To recognise and use commutativity in mental calculations.

Success criteria

● I can recognise and use factors and commutativity in mental multiplication.

You will need

Equipment
Individual whiteboards

Differentiation

Less confident learners
Ask children to undertake the same activity, using easier numbers such as 6, 9, 15, 14, 21 to multiply together.

More confident learners
Ask children to select any two numbers between 50 and 150, find their factors and multiply in this way.

Lesson 1   Oral and mental starter 31

Main teaching activities

Whole-class work: Explain that today's lesson is about using factors to help us multiply more easily. On the board write:

$$2 \quad 3 \quad 5 \quad 7 \quad \times \quad =$$

Develop the following context with the children: *This calculator was still in my pocket when my trousers were washed. Now the only buttons that work are 2, 3, 5, 7, x and =. Our job is to see which numbers we can make using these buttons. How could we make 18?* ($2 \times 3 \times 3$) Give each of the following numbers and invite children to show ways of making them using the numbers and symbols. For example:

6	(2×3)	12	$(2 \times 3 \times 2)$
15	(3×5)	63	$(3 \times 3 \times 7)$
16	$(2 \times 2 \times 2 \times 2)$	28	$(2 \times 2 \times 7)$
27	$(3 \times 3 \times 3)$	50	$(5 \times 5 \times 2)$
45	$(3 \times 3 \times 5)$	60	$(2 \times 2 \times 3 \times 5)$

Remind children that the numbers that multiply together are factors of the large number and that a factor is a number that will divide into another number without a remainder – for example, 3 is a factor of 6, 7 is a factor of 63. Write a multiplication question using two of the numbers in your list (say, 12 x 15).

How could we use the factors to help us answer this question? Draw attention to the fact that we can rewrite this question to make it easier to solve by using factors of each number and multiplying them in any order. This will produce the same answer:

$$12 \times 15$$
$$2 \times 3 \times 2 \quad \times \quad 3 \times 5$$

Ask: *Which numbers shall we choose to multiply together first?* Encourage children to see that some combination make the calculation easier. This can be demonstrated by drawing loops linking the factors to be multiplied first

$$12 \times 15$$
$$2 \times 3 \times 2 \quad \times \quad 3 \times 5$$ This would give $2 \times 9 \times 10 = 180$.

Repeat this for further pairs of numbers from your list, such as 15 × 28:

$$15 \times 28$$
$$3 \times 5 \quad \times \quad 2 \times 2 \times 7$$ This would give $21 \times 2 \times 10 = 420$.

Invite children to come to the front and draw the loops they would choose. Discuss children's choices, emphasising that any combination will produce the same answer.

Paired work: Ask children to select pairs of numbers from the list to multiply in this way, writing out the factors and indicating with loops how they chose to tackle the calculation.

Progress check: As children are doing this, check their understanding of the nature of multiplication: *What is special about multiplication? Can you do each multiplication in any order and get the same answer? Why?*

Review

Ask children to discuss their multiplications in pairs. Choose an example and ask a child to show their method. *Did anyone solve this in a different order?* List any different methods on the board, again emphasising that the numbers can be multiplied in whichever way is easiest.

Lesson 2 — Oral and mental starter 37

Main teaching activities

Whole-class work: Explain to the children that in today's lesson they will be using facts they already know to solve more difficult multiplication questions. Draw a tin can with a price tag of 35p on the board. *How could you work out what 11 of these cans cost?* Encourage children to suggest strategies including the strategy of finding the cost of ten cans first and adding the price of the extra can (10 x 35p = £3.50 and add 35p = £3.85). *How could you work out what nine of these cans cost?* Revise the strategy of finding the cost of ten cans first and subtracting the price of the extra can: 10 × 35p = £3.50 and subtract 35p = £3.15.

Extend these strategies to include multiplication by 21 and 19. Ask: *How could you work out what 21 of these cans cost?* Show how we can use the strategy of finding the cost of ten cans, then a second lot of ten cans and adding the price of the extra can: 10 × 35p = £3.50 and 10 × 35p = £3.50 making £7.00 and adding 35p = £7.35. Ask children for other suggestions as to how this could be solved, focusing on multiplying by 20 rather than by 10 twice.

Once children are comfortable with this, the following examples can utilise this short-cut. Change the price of the can to 33p and ask: *What is the price of 21 of these cans?* ((10 × 33p) + (10 × 33p) + 33p = £6.93) Repeat for other prices, such as 24p, 45p and so on. *How could you find the price of 19 cans at 44p?* Show how we can use the strategy of finding the cost of ten cans, then a second lot of ten cans and subtracting the price of the extra can: 10 × 44p = £4.40 and 10 × 44p = £4.40 making £8.80 and subtract 44p = £8.36. Find the cost of 19 cans at other prices.

Independent work: Draw several tins on the board with two-digit prices on them in pence, such as 34p, 42p, 28p, 37p. Ask children to first find the cost of ten of them, then 11 of them, then nine of them. They should then find the cost of 20, 21 and 19 in the same way. Encourage them to record their workings and answers clearly.

Progress check: Ask: *When multiplying a number by 9 can you explain in your own words what you do once you know the number multiplied by 10?*

Review

Call out some questions to be solved mentally in this way – for example, 21 × 16, 19 × 33, 21 × 24, 19 × 18. Discuss the strategies used and ask several children to demonstrate their method on the board.

Curriculum objectives

● To multiply two-digit and three-digit numbers by a one-digit number using formal written layout.

Success criteria

● I can perform short multiplication for multiplying by 7.

You will need

Equipment

0–9 number cards

Differentiation

Less confident learners

Ask children to practise multiplying by a different number, such as 3, 4 or 6.

More confident learners

Let children choose four digit cards and begin to multiply four-digit numbers by 7.

Lesson 3   Oral and mental starter 40

Main teaching activities

Whole-class work: Write 584 x 7 on the board. Invite a child to set out the question as a written three-digit x one-digit multiplication on the board. Revise the method of short multiplication, in expanded and condensed form:

```
 Th H  T  U              or      Th H  T  U
     5  8  4                          5  8  4
  ×        7                       ×        7
        2  8                       4  0  8  8
     5  6  0                          5  2
  3  5  0  0
  4  0  8  8
```

Choose further three-digit numbers to multiply by 7. Invite children to the front to work through the different examples, encouraging them to attempt the condensed form (short multiplication) and to describe the process in their own words.

Independent work: Provide each child with a set of 0–9 number cards. Ask them to pick sets of three cards to form three-digit numbers. They should use short multiplication to multiply each number by 7.

Progress check: Ask: *Can you describe what you did to reach this answer?*

Review

Take feedback on multiplications the children have written. Revise the multiples of 7 again and remind children of the importance of knowing all their tables facts by heart.

Curriculum objectives

● To use place value, known and derived facts to divide.

Success criteria

● I can use short division with exact answers when dividing by a one-digit number and can use short multiplication to check.

You will need

Equipment

Individual whiteboards

Differentiation

Less confident learners

Ask children to focus on dividing by 3 or 4 only.

More confident learners

These children should focus on dividing by 6 and 8 only.

Lesson 4   Oral and mental starter 37

Main teaching activities

Whole-class work: Write 855 × 3 = [ ] on the board and ask children to set out the question for short division. Demonstrate the method and discuss how digits are carried to the next column, moving right. For example:

```
            2  8  5
  3 ) 8 5 5     3 ) 8 ²5 ¹5
```

Remind children to multiply 285 by 3 to give 855 as a means of checking their answer. Show how short multiplication can be used to check this. Demonstrate other examples in the same way, including those where digits are carried twice (for example, 936 ÷ 4, 984 ÷ 6, 952 ÷ 7), asking children to work out answers on their whiteboards. Show too an example where the hundreds digit is smaller than the divisor (say, 296 ÷ 4), giving a two-digit answer.

Paired work: Write these numbers on the board: 960, 912, 816, 864, 672, 624, 720, 528, 432, 336, 384. Working in pairs, ask children to each choose a number and divide it by 3, 4, 6 or 8. Each should work out their answers using short division and record them: 528 ÷ 6 = 88, 384 ÷ 3 = 128 (and so on). They should then swap questions and answers and use short multiplication to check each other's calculations.

Progress check: Ask: *Describe what you did to reach this answer?*

Review

Invite children to write some of their divisions on the board and describe strategies they used to work each out.

 SCHOLASTIC

Curriculum objectives
● To solve problems involving multiplying and adding.

Success criteria
● I can solve one- and two-step problems involving multiplication.

You will need
Photocopiable sheets
'Tiling problems'
Equipment
Individual whiteboards

Differentiation
Less confident learners
Children could work in pairs to complete the activity.
More confident learners
Ask children to tackle the challenge question also.

Lesson 5   Oral and mental starter 31

Main teaching activities

Whole-class work: Discuss the following theme: *Jim is a floor-tile layer. He lays rows of tiles across people's kitchen and bathroom floors. He has square tiles that come in different sizes, the lengths and widths as follows:*

Mini tiles 9cm   Small tiles 12cm   Medium tiles 28cm   Large 40cm

Ignoring gaps between tiles, ask questions such as:

- *How long is the line if he lays 12 mini tiles in a line? Six small tiles? 20 medium tiles? Seven large tiles?*
- *How many small or medium tiles would fit in a row if the length of the space is 36cm... 72cm... 1 metre?*

Ask children to show answers to each question on their whiteboards.

Now introduce several two-step problems about the same theme, such as: *In a bathroom Jim laid alternating mini and then small tiles across the floor. He laid eight of each in a line. How long was the line of tiles?* $(9 \times 8 + 12 \times 8)$

Introduce a problem that might involve some pictorial strategies: *In one large room he laid only large tiles. He laid seven rows of 13 tiles. To keep him straight as he laid the tiles he used a piece of string. In different positions, how many tiles are on each side of the string?* With 13 rows of 7 there are 91 tiles altogether. Discuss different positions that the string could be and show that the total number of tiles on each side is always 91. For example:

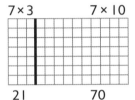
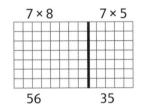
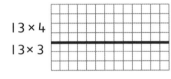

Ask: *What is the width and length of this room?* Give children time in pairs to discuss that $7 \times 40cm = 280cm$ and that $13 \times 40 = 520cm$. Convert these to metres and encourage children to visualise each length.

Independent work: Provide children with photocopiable page 'Tiling problems' from the CD-ROM to complete.

Progress check: Ask: *Why have you decided to record your solutions this way? Why is that?* Encourage children to explain how they know they have found all the solutions.

Review

Invite children to show the rest of the class their recorded solutions and to talk about what they discovered.

Geometry

Expected prior learning

Children should be able to:

- identify and name shapes according to the numbers of sides
- identify and recognise right angles in shapes
- understand the nature of parallel sides.

Topic	Curriculum objectives	Expected outcomes
Geometry: properties of shapes	**Lesson 1**	
	To compare and classify geometric shapes, including quadrilaterals and triangles, based on their properties and sizes. To identify lines of symmetry in 2D shapes presented in different orientations.	Describe and identify regular and irregular shapes. Find the numbers of lines of symmetry of regular and irregular shapes.
	Lesson 2	
	To compare and classify geometric shapes, including quadrilaterals and triangles, based on their properties and sizes.	Describe the properties of polygons, including quadrilaterals and triangles, based on their properties.
Geometry: properties of shapes Geometry: position and direction	**Lesson 3**	
	To identify acute and obtuse angles and compare and order angles up to two right angles by size. To describe positions on a 2D grid as coordinates in the first quadrant. To plot specified points and draw sides to complete a given polygon.	Identify acute, right and obtuse angles. Describe positions and plot points on a coordinate grid.
Geometry: position and direction	**Lesson 4**	
	To describe movements between positions as translations of a given unit to the left/right and up/down.	Translate shapes up/down and left/right.
	Lesson 5	
	To plot specified points and draw sides to complete a given polygon. To compare and classify geometric shapes, including quadrilaterals and triangles, based on their properties and sizes.	Plot points on a grid to draw polygons. Recognise and describe the properties of polygons.

Preparation

Lesson 1: copy 'Regular symmetry', one per child

Lesson 2: prepare 'Visualised shapes' for display on the interactive whiteboard; copy 'Polygon riddles (1)', one per pair

Lesson 3: prepare 'Coordinate grid' for display on the interactive whiteboard; copy 'Coordinate grids', one per child

Lesson 4: as for lesson 3

Lesson 5: copy 'Shape explorers', one per child

You will need

Photocopiable sheets

'Polygon riddles (1) and (2)'; 'Shape explorers'

General resources

'Regular symmetry'; 'Visualised shapes'; 'Coordinate grid'; 'Coordinate grids'

Equipment

Individual whiteboards; rulers; squared paper; coloured pencils

Further practice

Give further practice of classifying shapes using 'Polygon riddles (2)' and 'Visualised shapes' part 2.

Oral and mental starters for week 5

See bank of starters on page 126 and 209. Oral and mental starters are also on the CD-ROM.

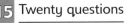

34 I Spy

15 Twenty questions

Overview of progression

During this week the children will consolidate and extend their knowledge of the properties of 2D shapes, angles and coordinate grids. Lesson 1 explores the number of lines of symmetry, including looking for patterns for regular shapes. In lesson 2 children are given opportunities to identify shapes from descriptions of their properties. Later in the week children will plot and identify points on a coordinate grid. In lesson 3 the focus is on plotting shapes and identifying the nature of their angles as to whether they are acute, obtuse or right angles, while lesson 4 explores making simple translations of shapes. In the final lesson of the week the task draws together many of the aspects of the work covered this week.

> ## Watch out for
>
> Common errors made by children include the following:
> - identifying rectangles as regular (they do not have equal sides)
> - identifying a rhombus as regular (the angles are not equal)
> - looking at a square twisted round and thinking it is a rhombus (the angles are still right angles)
> - thinking a parallelogram that is not a rectangle or a rhombus is symmetrical (show that it isn't by folding).

Creative context

Link this shape work to art activities, including creating patterns and angles using colour and shapes.

Vocabulary

acute, angles, equal, **equilateral**, horizontal, irregular, **isosceles**, **line of symmetry**, names of quadrilaterals, **obtuse**, **pair of coordinates** parallel, perpendicular, **regular polygon**, right, **scalene**, shape, sides, translate, triangle, vertex, vertical, vertices

Curriculum objectives
● To compare and classify geometric shapes, including quadrilaterals and triangles, based on their properties and sizes.
● To identify lines of symmetry in 2D shapes presented in different orientations.

Success criteria
● I can describe and identify regular and irregular shapes.
● I can find the numbers of lines of symmetry of regular and irregular shapes.

You will need
General resource
'Regular symmetry'

Differentiation
Less confident learners
Provide children with mirrors and tracing paper to help them work out lines of symmetry. They can also cut out and fold the shapes, if necessary.

More confident learners
Encourage children to support less confident learners in recognising lines of symmetry.

Lesson 1 — Oral and mental starter 34

Main teaching activities

Whole-class work: Explain that this lesson is about regular shapes and finding lines of symmetry. Revise that a line of symmetry separates two reflected halves. Invite a child to the front to sketch a shape that is symmetrical and ask the others to say where the lines of symmetry are. Discuss how lines of symmetry can be identified, by using a mirror, just looking or using tracing paper and folding.

Hold up a cut-out parallelogram made from paper. *Some people sometimes make mistakes about the lines of symmetry of parallelograms.* Distinguish between a diagonal and a line of symmetry by folding the shape from corner to corner. Open it out with the crease vertically.

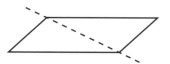

Try other folds too and ensure that children realise that a parallelogram that does not have right angles or equal sides does not have reflective symmetry.

Stress the importance of looking at shapes from all orientations to check how many lines of symmetry they have. Draw or hold up an equilateral triangle and ask children whether this is a regular or an irregular shape. *What is special about regular shapes?* Revise that regular shapes must have equal sides and equal angles to be regular. Now ask how many lines of symmetry the equilateral triangle has. (3) Rotate the shape as children find it much easier to see vertical or horizontal lines of symmetry rather than diagonal ones.

Independent work: Give each child photocopiable page 'Regular symmetry' on the CD-ROM with the shapes on the sheet numbered. Ask them to copy and complete the following table, writing the number of each shape, its name and then listing its properties. Not every shape needs to be examined but encourage children to look at at least three of the regular shapes on the sheets.

Progress check: Ask: *What do you notice about the number of lines of symmetry of regular shapes? Is there a pattern?*

Shape number	Name	Regular or irregular	Number of sides	Number of angles	Number of lines of symmetry

Review

Discuss any patterns that children noticed about the number of lines of symmetry, such as: *For regular shapes, the number of lines of symmetry is always the same as the number of sides and the number of angles.*

Curriculum objectives

- To compare and classify geometric shapes, including quadrilaterals and triangles, based on their properties and sizes.

Success criteria

- I can describe the properties of polygons, including quadrilaterals and triangles, based on their properties.

You will need

Photocopiable sheets

'Polygon riddles (1) and (2)'

General resources

'Visualised shapes'

Equipment

Individual whiteboards

Differentiation

Less confident learners

Pair children appropriately so that less confident learners can discuss the shapes and their descriptions with more confident learners.

More confident learners

Invite children to be more detailed in their descriptions.

Lesson 2 — Oral and mental starter 15

Main teaching activities

Whole-class work: Display photocopiable page 'Visualised shapes' part 1 from the CD-ROM. Call out descriptions of shapes, such as:

- I am a pentagon with two pairs of equal sides and one line of symmetry. (k)
- I have four equal sides and four right angles. I do not have vertical or horizontal sides. (d)
- I am regular and have eight obtuse angles. (p)

Each time, ask children to write the letter of each shape being described on their whiteboards and hold them up. Revise the names and properties of triangles and quadrilaterals. Discuss other names of polygons and describe their properties, including the numbers of sides, angles, right angles, lines of symmetry, the nature of the angles, whether they are regular or irregular, have parallel sides, and so on.

Paired work: Keep the 'Visualised shapes' sheet displayed (or provide copies). Give each child 'Polygon riddles (1)' from the CD-ROM and ask them to write the letter of each shape being described as it is shown on the 'Visualised shapes' sheet. They should then fully describe other shapes from the 'Visualised shapes' sheet so that their descriptions can only apply to that one shape. An additional set of 'Polygon riddles (2)' has also been supplied if time is available.

Progress check: Ask: *What type of angle is this? How many lines of symmetry does this shape have? How do you know? What do you call a quadrilateral with two pairs of parallel sides?*

Review

Invite children to read out their new riddles for the rest of the class to identify the shape being described.

Curriculum objectives

- To identify acute and obtuse angles.
- To describe positions on a 2D grid as coordinates in the first quadrant.
- To plot specified points and draw sides to complete a given polygon.

Success criteria

- I can identify acute, right and obtuse angles.
- I can describe positions and plot points on a coordinate grid.

You will need

General resources

'Coordinate grid'; 'Coordinate grids'

Equipment

Rulers

Differentiation

Less confident learners

Provide children with a right-angle measurer or set square.

More confident learners

Ask children to find the perimeters of the shapes.

Lesson 3 — Oral and mental starter 15

Main teaching activities

Whole-class work: Display photocopiable page 'Coordinate grid' from the CD-ROM. Write A (7, 5) B (1, 2) C (1, 5) on the board, revising which coordinate comes first, and invite a child to plot these positions on the displayed grid. Join the letters to form a shape and label the vertices A, B and C. Ask questions about the shape, including its name (scalene triangle) and whether its angles are acute, right or obtuse.

Independent work: Give each child photocopiable page 'Coordinate grids' from the CD-ROM. Ask them to plot and label the following coordinates on each grid, joining them with straight lines to make polygons. They then write the number of acute, right or obtuse angles each shape has.

	(Answers)	acute	right	obtuse
Grid 1: A(4, 7), B(6, 5), C(6, 2), D(3, 2), E(1, 4)		0	3	2
Grid 2: F(3, 7), G(6, 7), H(7, 4), I(7, 1), J(3, 1)		0	3	2
Grid 3: K(2, 8), L(5, 8), M(7, 7), N(3, 1), O(0, 4)		2	0	3
Grid 4: P(5, 8), Q(8, 4), R(8, 1), S(2, 1), T(3, 7)		1	1	3
Grid 5: U(1, 7), V(5, 6), W(7, 3), X(6, 1), Y(4, 0), Z(1, 1)	1	0	5
Grid 6: A(1, 7), B(5, 7), C(6, 5), D(6, 3) E(3, 0), F(0, 3)	0	1	5

Progress check: Ask: *Which coordinate comes first? What other coordinates are along the same vertical/horizontal line as this point?*

Review

Compare answers and discuss any differences of opinion on them.

Curriculum objectives

● To describe movements between positions as translations of a given unit to the left/right and up/down.

Success criteria

● I can translate shapes up/down and left/right.

You will need

General resources

'Coordinate grid'; 'Coordinate grids'

Equipment

Squared paper; coloured pencils; rulers

Differentiation

Less confident learners

Enlarge the coordinate grids sheet to A3 for these children to work with.

More confident learners

Encourage children to predict the new coordinates of the translated shapes before plotting them.

Lesson 4

Oral and mental starter 34

Main teaching activities

Whole-class work: Explain that today's lesson is about moving shapes across, up or down, or diagonally. Remind children that this is known as *translation*, meaning moving without turning. Display photocopiable page 'Coordinate grid' from the CD-ROM and plot the point (1, 2) on the grid. Give each child a piece of squared paper and ask them to sketch their set of axes, copying the one displayed, and to mark the point (1, 2) on their grid. When they are ready, tell them to follow this set of instructions as you read them out:

- *An ant is at the point (1, 2). He crawls four squares to the right. Mark his new position. What is the coordinate of this point? (5, 1)*
- *He now crawls two squares left and two squares up. Mark his new position. What are the coordinates of this point? (3, 4)*
- *From here he crawls three squares up. Mark his new position. What are the coordinates of this point? (3, 7)*
- *Then he crawls two squares left. Mark the new point. Where is he now? (1, 7)*
- *How many squares down must he crawl to get back to his starting position? (Five squares)*

Discuss that children have been *translating* or sliding a point (the ant) around the grid. Display the correct solution on the board and ask children to describe the shape of the ant's trail. For example: *It looks a bit like a boot.*

Next ask children to move every one of the marks they have made, the vertices (corners) of the boot, *three squares to the right* and *one square down*. Allow time for them to do this and to join the new points, then demonstrate it yourself on the board. Finally discuss the coordinates of the new boot and check that children have correctly drawn an identical boot in a new position that is three squares to the right and one square down.

Independent work: Give each child photocopiable page 'Coordinate grids' from the CD-ROM. They must begin by drawing a boot shape on a grid using one colour (say, red). (The boots do not have to look exactly the same as the one in the whole-class part of the lesson but the vertices must lie at points where grid lines cross.) They should then translate the boot some squares along and some squares up or down and draw a new boot in a different colour. Remind them that each vertex should travel the same distance and direction. They should write the translation they have chosen beside the grid (for example, four squares right, three squares up). Ask them to plot similar shapes and translations on each of the grids on the sheet.

Progress check: While children are translating the shapes ask: *How many across to the left or right are you translating the shape? How many up or down?*

Review

Choose one of the grids from the children's sheet. Ask them to give the coordinates of the vertices of the original shape and then to give them for the translated shape. *What do you notice about the coordinates? Which numbers have changed? By how many?* Invite children to describe the patterns they notice in the coordinate pairs.

Curriculum objectives

- To plot specified points and draw sides to complete a given polygon.
- To compare geometric shapes, including quadrilaterals and triangles, based on their properties and sizes.

Success criteria

- I can plot points on a grid to draw polygons.
- I can recognise and describe the properties of polygons.

You will need

Photocopiable sheets

'Shape explorers'

Equipment

Squared paper; rulers

Differentiation

Less confident learners

If necessary, provide children with pre-drawn coordinate grids so that the focus can be on plotting points and drawing polygons.

More confident learners

Encourage these children to write further questions about the shapes they have drawn.

Lesson 5 Oral and mental starter 34

Main teaching activities

Whole-class work: Discuss some of the aspects of the work the children have been doing this week, including drawing coordinate grids, plotting points to draw polygons, describing their features including references to lines of symmetry, the types of angles inside and whether or not the polygon is regular. Explain that in this lesson they will be doing an activity which draws many of those aspects together.

Independent work: Provide each child with a piece of squared paper and a copy of photocopiable page 'Shape explorers' from the CD-ROM to complete.

Progress check: As the children are working, ask questions such as: *Do any of the shapes have horizontal and vertical sides? Are the angles of shape D all acute, all obtuse or does it have both? What do you notice about those angles?*

Review

Display or draw a coordinate grid in the first quadrant from 0 to 12 as the children have done in the Independent work. Invite different children to read out the coordinates of the extra shape that they drew as per the instructions on the photocopiable sheet (shape G). Ask the rest of the class to plot the positions on your grid. Ask further questions about the shapes such as: *How many sides has it? Is it a quadrilateral? Are the angles acute, right or obtuse? Is the shape regular or irregular? How many lines of symmetry has it?*

Statistics

Expected prior learning

Children should be able to:

- count forward and backwards in steps of 2, 5, 10, 25, 50, 100
- read simple scales (such as 2, 5, 10 units) in pictograms and bar charts.

Topic	Curriculum objectives	Expected outcomes
Statistics	**Lesson 1**	
	To interpret and present discrete and continuous data using appropriate graphical methods, including bar charts and time graphs. To solve comparison, sum and difference problems using information presented in bar charts, pictograms, tables and other graphs.	Interpret information shown in a bar chart with horizontal bars.
	Lesson 2	
	To interpret and present discrete and continuous data using appropriate graphical methods, including bar charts and time graphs.	Collect data and display it in a bar chart.
	Lesson 3	
	To solve comparison, sum and difference problems using information presented in bar charts, pictograms, tables and other graphs.	Solve problems about data in bar charts.
	Lesson 4	
	To interpret and present discrete and continuous data using appropriate graphical methods, including bar charts and time graphs.	Organise data and display it in a line graph.
	Lesson 5	
	To interpret and present discrete and continuous data using appropriate graphical methods, including bar charts and time graphs.	Organise data and display it in a line graph.

Preparation

Lesson 1: copy 'Cube count' sheet, one per child

Lesson 4: copy 'Line graph template', one per child

Lesson 5: copy 'Line graph template', one per child

You will need

Photocopiable sheets
'Cube count'

General resources
'Line graph template'; interactive activity 'Birthday seasons'; interactive teaching resource 'Data handling'; interactive activity 'Comparing data'

Equipment
Individual whiteboards; plastic cubes; rulers; squared paper

Further practice

Photocopiable sheets
'Pictogram puzzle'

Oral and mental starters for week 6

See bank of starters on pages 208 and 251. Oral and mental starters are also on the CD-ROM.

30 Counting on and back

41 Fifths of a metre

33 What's the time, Mr Wolf?

Overview of progression

In lessons 1 and 2 of this week the children will revise, consolidate and extend their knowledge of frequency tables, bar charts and line graphs and will collect data and represent them in different forms. In the early part of the week the focus will be on bar charts, including drawing and interpreting them and answering questions about them involving sums and differences. In lessons 4 and 5 children will work with line graphs, including interpreting them and beginning to draw them.

Watch out for
The most common error in interpreting charts such as bar charts and line graphs is that children fail to notice and use the scales on the axes appropriately.

Creative context

Link this time work to science activities, cooking, athletics and other sporting activities and draw attention to bar charts and pictograms used in real-life situations.

Vocabulary

bar chart, line graph, interpret, scale, axis, data, key, pictogram, frequency, tally

30

Curriculum objectives
- To interpret and present discrete and continuous data using bar charts.
- To solve comparison, sum and difference problems using information presented in bar charts.

Success criteria
- I can interpret information shown in a bar chart with horizontal bars.

You will need
Photocopiable sheets
'Cube count'
Equipment
Plastic cubes

Differentiation
Less confident learners
Let children work in pairs to answer the questions.
More confident learners
Ask children to draw their own bar chart for the data collected in the whole-class part of the lesson.

Lesson I
Oral and mental starter 30

Main teaching activities

Whole-class work: Explain that the focus of today's lesson is bar charts. Choose five children to come to the front. Hold out a large tray of small plastic cubes and, one at a time, ask each of the five children to grab as many cubes as they can in one hand. Ask other children to help them count the cubes and record the information in a frequency table on the board. For example:

Name	Frequency
James	14
Kiera	12
Jack	18
Sarah	9
Mark	11

How could we show this information in a bar chart? Invite children to describe what could be put on each axis of a bar chart and how it could be presented. Draw a vertical line and write the five children's names, down the line. Explain that you want the bar chart to have horizontal rather than vertical bars. Draw an appropriate scale for the horizontal axis (say, going up in 2s), and invite children to draw the bars for each child. Ask a range of questions about the data, including sum and difference questions, such as:
- *How many cubes can Kiera hold in one hand?*
- *How many more cubes can Jack hold than Sarah?*
- *How many fewer cubes can Sarah hold than James?*
- *Who can hold two more cubes than Kiera?*

Independent work: Give each child photocopiable page 'Cube count' from the CD-ROM. Explain that five other children have tried the same experiment as the one just completed in the whole-class activity, and their data is shown in the bar chart on the sheet. Ask children to answer the questions about the bar chart shown.

Progress check: Ask: *How many cubes can each child hold? How does that compare with how many James held?*

Review

Discuss the scale used on the bar chart (going up in 2s). Remind children that the scales on chart and graphs go in in equal steps, usually from zero, but that the steps might be in 1s, 2s, 5s, 10s, 20s, 50s, 100s and so on. The choice of scale, when drawing a bar chart, is made depending on the largest frequency. Discuss what the largest frequency was for the data you collected earlier (the largest number of cubes held by any of the five children). *If our highest frequency was 50, what might be a better step-size on a scale for a bar chart?* Remind children of the importance of looking carefully at scales and reading them correctly.

Curriculum objectives
- To interpret and present discrete and continuous data in a bar chart.

Success criteria
- I can collect data and display it in a bar chart.

You will need

General resources

Interactive activity 'Birthday seasons'

Equipment

Squared paper; rulers

Differentiation

Less confident learners

Provide children with a set of axes already drawn and give support in helping them to choose an appropriate scale.

More confident learners

Ask children to collect data from another class and combine it with the data from your own class, thus enabling them to use a larger scale for their bar charts.

Lesson 2   Oral and mental starter 30

Main teaching activities

Whole-class work: Display the interactive activity 'Birthday seasons' on the CD-ROM on the interactive whiteboard and go through each screen together. Discuss the questions on the second screen. Then explain to the children that you want to find out in which seasons their birthdays are. Revise which months are spring, summer, autumn or winter (spring being March/April/May, and so on). Ensure that each child knows in which season they were born and collect the data for the whole-class on the board.

Independent work: Provide each child with squared paper. Ask them to draw a bar chart (with vertical bars) of the information on their birthday seasons and to choose an appropriate scale for the vertical axis. Remind them to give their charts a title and label the axes correctly.

Progress check: Ask children to describe the information in their bar chart: *How did you decide what scale to use?*

Review

Invite children to make statements about the information in their bar charts. Ask further questions, such as: *How many more children in our class were born in summer than spring?*

Curriculum objectives
- To solve comparison, sum and difference problems using information presented in bar charts.

Success criteria
- I can solve problems about data in bar charts.

You will need

General resources

Interactive teaching resource 'Data handling'

Equipment

Individual whiteboards; rulers

Differentiation

Less confident learners

Pair less confident learners with more confident ones.

More confident learners

Challenge this group to write a report about the data (for example: *People often think that Tyrannosaurus was one of the largest dinosaurs, but it was 36m shorter than the Seismosaurus...*).

Lesson 3   Oral and mental starter 41

Main teaching activities

Whole-class work: Display the final screen of interactive teaching resource 'Data handling' on the CD-ROM. Use the tools to hide the numbers of the y-axis. Talk about the scale and discuss the interval sizes. Ask questions about the data: *What do you think this chart is showing? (Population in a village) How many people in this village are under 20? Over 70? How many more people are aged between 51 and 70 than are over 70? Can you work out the number of people in this village altogether?* Explain that a new baby has been born since the data was collected. Invite a child to change the bar chart to show this. Ask similar questions and also show the bar chart presented with horizontal rather than vertical bars by pressing the second graph button.

Paired work: Write on the board the following information (the heights of six dinosaurs). Children can use the initial letter of each, rather than worrying about each spelling, if preferred! Ask pairs to draw a bar chart of this data (perhaps using ICT tools) and then jointly write five questions about it.

Brachiosaurus	30m	Diplodocus	27m
Pisanosaurus	1m	Argentinosaurus	36m
Tyrannosaurus	12m	Seismosaurus	48m

Progress check: *What scale did you choose to use on the bar chart? Is it the same scale that your friend chose? What questions could you ask about the data?*

Review

Invite each group to discuss their charts and read their questions for others to answer.

Curriculum objectives
● To interpret and present continuous data using line graphs.

Success criteria
● I can organise data and display it in a line graph.

You will need

General resources
'Line graph template'; interactive activity 'Comparing data'

Equipment
Rulers

Differentiation

Less confident learners
Support children in writing the scale and plotting points, by pairing them with a more confident learner.

More confident learners
Once the graph is completed, ask children to estimate Sandeep's height at other ages (for example, at his third, fourth, eighth or ninth birthdays).

Lesson 4

Main teaching activities

Whole-class work: Display the interactive activity 'Comparing data' on the CD-ROM. Go through all the screens together, discussing the way that the data is shown in a line graph. Explain that line graphs are used when the data is continuous – in other words, when something like temperature changes over time, when it goes up and down during the day or in a month.

Introduce the following activity: *When Sandeep was younger his mum kept some notes of his height at certain times in his life.* Display her notes:

At birth 50cm.

On his 1st birthday 75cm.

On his 2nd birthday 88cm.

He was 1 metre when he was 3½ years old.

On his 5th birthday 110cm.

On his 6th birthday 112cm.

Between age 6 and age 10 he grew about the same amount each year.

On his 10th birthday 137cm.

Independent work: Provide children with photocopiable page 'Line graph template' from the CD-ROM and ask them to draw a line graph of the data presented above. Ask them to write Sandeep's age along the horizontal axis from 0 to 10 (under the end of each vertical line rather than in the spaces between them, as you do with bar charts). Assist them in deciding the scale for the vertical axis (for example, going up in steps of 10cm). Remind children that we plot the data and then draw lines linking the points.

Progress check: Ask: *Which part of drawing the line graph did you find most difficult? Why do you think that was?*

Review

Invite children to show their line graphs and discuss any difficulties. Ask further questions about the data such as: *Can you estimate how tall Sandeep was on his ninth birthday?*

Curriculum objectives
● To interpret and present continuous data using line graphs.

Success criteria
● I can organise data and display it in a line graph.

You will need

General resources
'Line graph template'

Equipment
Rulers

Differentiation

Less confident learners
Support children in writing the scale and plotting points, by asking them to work in pairs with a more confident learner.

More confident learners
Once completed, ask children to write statements about the information in the graph they have drawn.

Lesson 5

Oral and mental starter 33

Main teaching activities

Whole-class work: Display one of the completed line graph from lesson 4. Remind children that the line graph shows Sandeep's height from birth to 10 years old. *We didn't have data about his height at every birthday, and yet we can make some judgements about how tall he must have been from this line graph. Why is that?* Help children to see that line graphs are useful as they give you an idea of additional information when the data changes over time. Although you can't be certain about it, you can have a guess at how tall he must have been on his fourth, seventh, eighth or ninth birthdays. Invite children to make estimates of his height by reading up from the age to the line and then across to read his height.

Independent work: Provide children with photocopiable page 'Line graph template' from the CD-ROM and display the following table. Explain that a skyscraper is being built (which takes several years) and that this table shows its height so far as measured on 1 January over several years.

Year	2004	2005	2008	2009	2011	2013	2014
Height on 1 January	0m	50m	200m	300m	550m	675m	750m

Ask the children to write all the years from 2004 to 2014 along the horizontal axis at the end of each vertical line rather than in the spaces (as you do with bar charts). Assist them in deciding the scale for the vertical axis (such as going up in steps of 50m). Remind them that we plot the data and then draw lines linking the points.

Progress check: Ask: *What do you notice about this line graph? What would you estimate the skyscraper's height might have been on 1 January 2012?*

Review

Invite children to show their line graphs and discuss any difficulties. Ask further questions about the data such as: *Can you estimate how tall the skyscraper was in 2006? 2010?*

Two-step problems using addition and subtraction

Most children should be able to solve problems involving more than one step, deciding which methods and operations to use.

Some children will be more confident with one-step problems than two-step ones and may require further support in reading, interpreting and solving such problems.

1. Check

9 Story time

Choose an addition question such as 486 + 725. Encourage the children to think of an appropriate number story for the question. Extend to include two-step questions such as 68 + 17 − 34.

- *What story matches this addition?*
- *Write a two-step story for this fact: 375 + 29 − 146. How can you answer it?*

2. Assess

Provide photocopiable page 253 'Two-step problems'. Observe the children at work, and note those who select appropriate operations and methods of calculation. For the more confident, when they have finished the activity ask them to write their own two-step word problem. Record the outcomes.

3. Further practice

The recommended oral and mental starter and photocopiable activities provide further practice in solving and writing their own word problems.

Short multiplication

Most children should be able to set out the multiplication vertically and multiply, using carrying.

Some children will not have made such progress and will require further practice in recalling multiplication facts and using the carrying process.

1. Check

8 Function machine

Write a function such as ×6, ×7, ×8 or ×9 and list some three-digit numbers as input numbers. Ask children to use a written method to find each output. Observe which children are confident and which need further practice. Extend to four-digit numbers. Ask questions such as:

- *How could you find 357 × 6?*
- *Can you set it out vertically using a written method?*
- *Which digit do you carry?*

2. Assess

Children turn over four 2–9 digit cards to make a three-digit number by a one-digit multiplication and solve each using a written method. Observe the children at work, and note those who work quickly and accurately and whether they set questions out correctly. Children lacking confidence could select two or three number cards and roll a dice to create a two- or three-digit by one-digit multiplication, which would involve recall of simpler times tables facts. Observe when carrying is carried out correctly. Record the outcomes.

Further practice

The recommended oral and mental starter and photocopiable page 252 'Short multiplication' provide further practice in the written method of short multiplication.

Curriculum objectives
● To read, write and convert time between analogue and digital 12- and 24-hour clocks.

You will need
1. Check
Oral and mental starter
32 Time trials

2. Assess
'Time dominoes'; small clock-faces with moving hands

3. Further practice
Oral and mental starters
33 What's the time, Mr Wolf?
Photocopiable sheets
'Time after time cards'
General resources
Interactive activity 'Time pairs'

24-hour time

Most children should be able to read times on both analogue and digital 24-hour clocks and be able to convert between them.

Some children may still need to develop an understanding of how digital time relates to a clock-face.

1. Check
32 Time trials

Ask questions involving both analogue times in the morning, afternoon, evening and night and 24-hour digital time. Observe whether children can recognise the relationship between digital and analogue time and whether they are able to read 24-hour digital times and relate it to 12-hour times.

- *What time is 17:15?*
- *How would you write ten past one in the afternoon in 24-hour digital time?*
- *At what time of day is 20:20? How do you know?*

2. Assess
Provide the cards cut out from photocopiable page 'Time dominoes' from the CD-ROM. Ask children to copy onto paper the digital times from the clocks shown and to write the time in words, using morning, afternoon, evening or night in their descriptions. Note which children work confidently on this task. Children lacking confidence could be shown a clock-face with the multiples of 5 written around at each five-minute interval to make linking digital times with analogue ones easier. Record the outcomes.

3. Further practice
The recommended OMS photocopiable and interactive activities provide further practice in exploring the link between analogue and digital 24-hour times.

Curriculum objectives
● To find the effect of dividing a one- or two-digit number by 10 and 100, identifying the value of the digits in the answer as ones, tenths and hundredths.

You will need
1. Check
Oral and mental starter
39 Divide by 10 and 100

2. Assess
'Dividing by 10 and 100'; place value chart;

3. Further practice
Oral and mental starters
16 Multiply by 10 and 100
38 Decimal divisions
Photocopiable sheets
'Tenths maths'; 'Hundredths maths'

Dividing numbers by 10 and 100

Most children should be able to describe the movement of digits to the right when dividing by 10 and 100. They should also be able to say the value of the two digits after the decimal point.

Some children may need more experience of dividing multiples of 10 and 100 by 10 or 100 first.

1. Check
39 Divide by 10 and 100

Work through the OMS as described. Observe whether children can identify the tenths and hundredths digits to the right of the decimal point and understand that dividing numbers by 10 and 100 can result in a decimal. Note whether children are able to read each decimal aloud correctly.

- *What is the digit 6 worth in the number 0.63?*
- *How can you work out 345 divided by 100?*

2. Assess
Provide photocopiable page 254 'Dividing by 10 and 100'. Give less confident children a place value grid showing the headings H T U . t h to refer to. For the more confident, when they have finished the activity ask them to try dividing numbers by 1000 in the same way. Record the outcomes.

3. Further practice
The recommended oral and mental starter activities provide further practice in multiplying and dividing whole numbers by 10 and 100. The photocopiable sheets can be used to reinforce the value of tenths and hundredths.

Oral and mental starters

Geometry

36 Time for conversion

List the following relationships and ask children to say what number you would multiply each by to convert from one unit to another.

years ⟶ × ? ⟶ months   weeks ⟶ × ? ⟶ days   days ⟶ × ? ⟶ hours

hours ⟶ × ? ⟶ minutes   minutes ⟶ × ? ⟶ seconds

500g	250g	1.7kg	1.2kg	2500g
6.4kg	3250g	1200g	200g	7200g
7.2m	6400g	0.2kg	750g	3¼kg
2½kg	1700g	½kg	0.75kg	¼kg

Then call out a whole number of years, weeks, days, hours or minutes for conversion to the smaller unit. In pairs children write answers on their whiteboards and hold them up.

Extension
Give lengths of time in the smaller units (24 months, 49 days...) and ask children to divide to convert to the larger unit.

Addition, subtraction, multiplication and division

37 Inverses

Write three numbers from a multiplication statement (for example, 4, 7 and 28) and ask children to give you two multiplications that can be made with these numbers. Then ask them to give you two related divisions. Repeat for several sets of numbers, asking for divisions first in the last two questions.

Fraction

38 Decimal divisions

Display a shape divided into ten and highlight several sections (for example, four tenths). Ask children to write this as a fraction and as a decimal on their whiteboards and hold it up. Award points for correct answers. Explain that you will award extra marks if an equivalent fraction is shown (for example, two fifths). Highlight other numbers of tenths (including ten tenths) and discuss equivalences.

Number and place value

39 Divide by 10 and 100

Ask five children to stand at the board and face the rest of the class. Behind them on the board write H T and U and t and h, so that one child is under each letter. Clearly mark a decimal point on the board between the units and tenths. Give the H child a digit card(say, 6), and the T and U children each get the digit zero. *What number is this?* (600) *How do we divide by 10?* The H child passes the card to the T child and the T child passes theirs to the U child. The U child passes their card to the t child. *What number is this now?* (60.0) Repeat again, but this time use digits other than zero (for example, 423 divided by 10). Repeat also for dividing by 100 in the same way.

40 7-times table revision

Draw a snake with 12 sections on the board and in each section write a multiple of 7 from 7 to 84. Explain that these are the answers to the 7-times table. Ask children to say the numbers in order. Call out a series of questions such as *What is 7 times 6?* and gradually begin to rub out the multiples they seem confident with. Continue to ask the children to say the multiples in order, including those that have been rubbed out. Try to reach a position where the children can say all the multiples in order and answer any tables question with all of the numbers rubbed out.

Measurement

41 Fifths of a metre

Hold up a metre stick and point to different positions on it (say, 20cm or 80cm). Ask the children to say what fraction of a metre each is, such as ²⁄₁₀ or ⅕, ⁸⁄₁₀ or ⅘. Discuss equivalents (for example, ²⁄₁₀ being the same as ⅕). Invite the children to use their individual whiteboards to record their answers in words and using fraction notation.

Short multiplication

1.

```
    2 1 5
×       4
  _____

  _____
```

2.

```
    2 1 7
×       3
  _____

  _____
```

3.

```
    1 1 9
×       5
  _____

  _____
```

4.

```
    2 7 2
×       3
  _____

  _____
```

5.

```
    1 4 1
×       7
  _____

  _____
```

6.

```
    1 5 1
×       6
  _____

  _____
```

7.

```
    2 4 7
×       4
  _____

  _____
```

8.

```
    1 3 7
×       6
  _____

  _____
```

9.

```
    1 1 9
×       8
  _____

  _____
```

10.

```
    7 1 2
×       5
  _____

  _____
```

11.

```
    3 4 1
×       7
  _____

  _____
```

12.

```
    7 0 6
×       8
  _____

  _____
```

I can multiply a three-digit number by a one-digit number using formal written layout.

Two-step problems

■ Solve these problems.

1. There are 243 children in a school. 98 of them are boys. How many more girls are there than boys in the school?

_____

2. 127 people are on a Big Wheel. When it stops 36 people get off and 42 people get on. How many people are on the Big Wheel now?

_____

3. A car-park has 2400 parking spaces. On Monday part of the car-park closed for repair so 1800 of the spaces are not in use. If 800 cars arrive, how many cars will not be able to find spaces?

_____

4. A train has two carriages. There are 64 seats in each carriage. How many people are sitting on the train if there are 17 empty seats altogether?

_____

5. Jack has a pedometer that counts the number of steps he takes each day. On Monday he took 4567 steps. On Tuesday he took 1163 more steps than on Monday. How many steps did he take on Monday and Tuesday in total?

_____

6. A cinema has 284 seats. 87 women, 93 men and 77 children go into the cinema and sit down. How many seats are empty?

_____

7. Kim's mum is 173cm tall. Kim's dad is 17cm taller than her mum and Kim is 55cm shorter than her dad. How tall is Kim?

_____

8. Mrs Jones put 850g of flour, 275g of sugar and 215g of butter into a bowl. She puts the bowl with the mixture onto the weighing scales. The reading shows 1500g. How heavy is the bowl, if it was empty?

_____

I can solve two-step problems in context.

How did you do?

Dividing by 10 and 100

■ Write your answers to the questions in the spaces provided.

1. $20 \div 10 =$ _____

2. $46 \div 10 =$ _____

3. $3 \div 10 =$ _____

4. $17 \div 10 =$ _____

5. $500 \div 100 =$ _____

6. $450 \div 100 =$ _____

7. $123 \div 100 =$ _____

8. $28 \div 100 =$ _____

9. $32 \div 100 =$ _____

10. $7 \div 100 =$ _____

11. $6 \div 10 =$ _____

12. $99 \div 100 =$ _____

13. $200 \div 10 =$ _____

14. $5200 \div 100 =$ _____

15. $2 \div 10 =$ _____

16. $18 \div 100 =$ _____

17. $0.1 \div 10 =$ _____

18. $0.8 \div 10 =$ _____

I can divide by 10 and 100.

How did you do?

Equipment list

Number and place value

0–9 number cards, counters, individual whiteboards, large sheets of paper, number fans, place value arrow cards, place value charts, scissors

Addition and subtraction

Dice, digit cards, individual whiteboards, number fans, place value cards, squared paper

Multiplication and division

0–9 number cards, counters, counting stick, dice, individual whiteboards, interlinking cubes, large dice, large sheets of paper, logi-blocks (or a structured set of shapes), long thin strips of card, number fans, small blank cards, squared paper

Fractions

0–10 number cards, an arrow or triangle as a pointer, coloured pencils, counters, counting stick, dice, individual whiteboards, large clock face, large sheets of paper, metre stick, number fans, paper fasteners, place value chart, rulers, scissors

Measurement

0–9 digit cards, clock-faces with moving hands, height measurer, individual whiteboards, metre stick, one-litre measuring cylinder, place value chart, rulers, scissors, squared paper, string, tape measures, trundle wheels, variety of measuring cylinders and containers with different scales

Geometry: properties of shapes

Blank cards, coloured pencils, counters, counting stick, dice, geostrips, glue, individual whiteboards, large sheets of paper, metre stick, mirrors or semi-transparent reflective materials, number fans, paper fasteners, rulers, scissors, squared paper, tracing paper

Geometry: position and direction

Coloured pencils, individual whiteboards, rulers, squared paper

Statistics

Clock faces with moving hands, individual whiteboards, magazines, other spring balance scales (if available), plastic cubes, range of empty drinks containers, range of light and heavy objects to weigh, rulers, several sets of kitchen/bathroom scales (ones with arrows and electronic ones), squared paper

Vocabulary list

Number and place value

Compare, digit, estimate, figure, hundreds, multiples, negative numbers, ones, order, **place value**, rounding, sequences, tens, thousands, units

Addition and subtraction

Add, altogether, borrow, carry, column, difference, digit, equals, exchange, fewer, **inverse**, leave, less, make, minus, more, partition, plus, problem, sign, strategy, subtract, sum, take away, total

Multiplication and division

Array, brackets, column method, common factor, condensed method, divide, divisible, divisor, equivalent, expanded method, expression, **factor**, facts, groups of, inverse, lots of, multiple, multiply, **product,** share, short division, short multiplication, tables, times

Fractions

Convert, decimal, decimal place, decimal point, denominator, equal parts, **equivalent fraction**, factor, fraction, hundredth, integer, numerator, set, simplify, tenth

Measurement

12-hour time, **24-hour clock**, 24-hour time, analogue, **area**, capacity, centimetres (cm), century, clock, cm2, day, digital, gram (g), hour, kilogram (kg), kilometre (km), length, length, litre (l), mass, measurement, measuring equipment, metre (m), millilitre (ml), millimetre (mm), minute, month, pence, perimeter, pounds, rectangle, rectilinear, second, side, time, unit, week, width, year

Geometry: properties of shapes

Acute, angles, decagon, equal, **equilateral triangle**, heptagon, horizontal, irregular, **isosceles triangle**, **line of symmetry**, names of quadrilaterals, obtuse, octagon, **pair of coordinates**, parallel, pentagon, perpendicular, rectangle, reflection, **regular polygon**, right, **scalene triangle**, shape, sides, square, translate, triangle, vertex, vertical, vertices

Geometry: position and direction

Acute, angles, equal, equilateral, horizontal, irregular, isosceles, line of symmetry, names of quadrilaterals, **obtuse**, pair of coordinates, parallel, perpendicular, regular polygon, right, scalene, shape, sides, translate, triangle, vertex, vertical, vertices

Statistics

Axis, bar chart, chart, data, frequency, interpret, key, line graph, pictogram, scale, tally, Venn diagram